TWENTY-FIVE PLAYS
for
HOLIDAYS

Twenty-Five

Plays for Holidays

A collection of non-royalty, one-act plays
for special days the year round

by

MILDRED HARK and NOEL McQUEEN

Publishers   PLAYS, INC.   *Boston*

PN
6120
.H7
H32

Introduction

The success of our previous holiday collection, *Special Plays for Special Days,* has encouraged us to prepare this second volume of holiday plays. The present collection contains new plays for all our major holidays, as well as other special occasions like Election Day, Book Week, Commencement, etc. And since tradition and fun go hand-in-hand when we celebrate holidays, these plays are designed primarily for entertainment, yet traditional themes are used.

The characters in these plays are modern teen-agers, their younger brothers and sisters, and their parents and friends; members of the cast will find that they know these people well. The sets and costumes suggested in the production notes at the back of the book may be as simple or as elaborate as desired, but excellent effects can be achieved with a minimum of effort.

We hope you will enjoy producing these plays. Happy Holidays!

MILDRED HARK
NOEL McQUEEN

Contents

Lincoln's Birthday

Valentine's Day

Washington's Birthday

Easter

Mother's Day

Memorial Day

Commencement

TWENTY-FIVE PLAYS
for
HOLIDAYS

New Worlds to Find

JOHN, *age 13*
ANNE, *age 15*
CARETAKER
CHRISTOPHER COLUMBUS
FATHER JUAN PEREZ

TIME: *The present. Late afternoon.*
SETTING: *A room in a museum.*
AT RISE: JOHN *and* ANNE *are looking about the room excitedly.*
ANNE *is upstage left looking at the glass case when* JOHN *discovers the anchor at stage center.*

ANNE: John, there are a lot of interesting things in this case.

JOHN: Anne, look, here's the anchor from the Santa Maria!

ANNE *(Crossing quickly)*: Not—not really, John?

JOHN: Yes. Listen to this: "Lost at the time of the wreck of the Santa Maria off the shores of Haiti on Christmas Eve, 1492."

ANNE *(Breathlessly)*: Christmas Eve, 1492.

JOHN: "And recovered by the Spanish Government, and presented to this American Historical Society—" *(Breaking off)* Just imagine, Anne, how old it is!

ANNE: Why, I never dreamed you could see things like this. Things that Columbus actually used and—and touched.

JOHN: It—it gives you kind of a funny feeling. Look, here's this anchor lying here. Can't you just see it on the deck of the

3

Santa Maria, and Columbus telling the sailors to drop it over-
board when they sighted land?

ANNE: Yes. . . .

JOHN: Lost in 1492—that's over four hundred and fifty years
ago, and I can reach out and touch it. (*He reaches out and
touches the anchor.*) It's almost like—like shaking hands with
Columbus. You kind of feel maybe he might be around here
somewhere.

ANNE: Oh, John, you're always imagining things! Look over
here, in this case. I want to show you—(*She goes over to the
case and* JOHN *follows.*) There's a key from the house Columbus lived in on the Madeira Islands, and a document signed
by the King and Queen.

JOHN: Look—their signatures! "King Ferdinand and Queen
Isabella," and the royal seal! Let's see if we can read some of
this, Anne.

ANNE: Oh, John, you know we can't. It's in Spanish and the
writing's so faded. Besides, we've got to meet the others soon,
and we'll have to hurry if we're going to see everything. (*She
starts to move upstage.*)

JOHN: But wait, Anne, look at this picture. (*He indicates the
picture above the case.*) The harbor at Palos, and Columbus
saying goodbye. See, there are the three ships. I'll bet that
was an exciting day in his life! He'd waited so long—

ANNE: Exciting maybe, but I wouldn't want to have made that
trip.

JOHN: Why not?

ANNE: We know all about the Atlantic Ocean—how wide it is
and what's on the other side. But they didn't know anything.
They thought maybe it boiled after a certain point, or you
just dropped off the edge of the world, or huge sea monsters
ate you up.

JOHN: Columbus didn't think that.

ANNE: Well, he had to prove it. He didn't know when he started out.

JOHN: It's the "not knowing" that made it exciting. Anne, I'd like to have lived in those days—when men were discovering new worlds, starting out on adventures—

ANNE: Oh, John, all you think about is adventures. You know what Mother says. If you'd study more and dream less . . . I'll bet Columbus had to study—maps and charts and all kinds of things!

JOHN: Yes, but he had something to study for. Something big.

ANNE: Well, so do we. You'd think there wasn't anything left to do in the world the way you talk. (*Crossing and looking up at picture of* COLUMBUS *upstage left*) Look, John, a painting of him. See what it says underneath: "Circa 1451 to 1506."

JOHN: Circa? What does that mean?

ANNE: Well, it means about or around those dates. I guess they aren't exactly sure when Columbus was born.

JOHN: Let's see—1451 to 1506. He lived about 55 years then . . . He—he looks like a great man, doesn't he, Anne?

ANNE: He looks strong—as though he wouldn't be afraid of anything.

JOHN: I guess he wasn't. He had to have enough courage for everybody on that first voyage. The sailors were all scared stiff.

ANNE: I don't know if I blame them. 71 days on the water and not sure if they'd ever reach land—(*Moving toward the alcove and looking up*) Oh, John! Those lanterns and the cross—(*Reading a small tag on door*) John, do you know what that is? It's the cross from the Monastery of La Rabida in Spain.

JOHN (*Who has been reading, too, and looking at the doors*): Yes, and these doors are from there, too. La Rabida—that's where he stayed so long with Father Juan Perez. Don't you remember?

ANNE: Yes, and Father Perez helped him—got him another audience with Queen Isabella. My, these doors must be old.

JOHN: I'll say. See, Anne, parts of them are covered over with glass because they're almost worn away. Think how many times Columbus must have gone in and out of these doors with Father Perez—talking to him and . . .

ANNE (*Getting into the spirit of it too*): And dreaming his dream! . . . Oh, but John, imagine, he never knew he discovered a new world.

JOHN: No, and just think, because he crossed the Atlantic and started people coming over here, he made the United States possible, didn't he? I'll bet he'd like it here, too, Anne, if he could see us now.

ANNE: Sure he would. Americans are all kind of like Columbus.

JOHN: What do you mean?

ANNE: Oh, I don't know. We're way ahead of the rest of the world when it comes to inventions and new ideas. You know, Americans are always trying something new.

JOHN: Yeah, but there aren't any more new worlds to discover.

ANNE: Oh, but there are, John.

JOHN: There are not! Anybody knows they've found all the land there is.

ANNE: Oh, but I mean—you don't have to discover lands or continents in order to find a new world.

JOHN (*Incredulously. Not understanding her*): Hey!

ANNE: Well, you know, John, what Father was talking about the other evening. The new world that everyone is hoping for, where all men can live in peace and help one another and— (*Breaking off*) I guess the people who bring that about will be doing something big!

JOHN: Yeah, maybe—

ANNE: And we'll all have our chance to play a part in that. That's what Father said. (*An elderly caretaker, carrying a large bunch of keys, enters left.*)

CARETAKER: Five o'clock, young folks! I've got to close up.

JOHN (*Disappointed*): Oh . . .

CARETAKER (*As he crosses toward right*): Sorry, but you'll have to say goodbye to Columbus until another day.

ANNE: Yes, sir, we've got to go anyway. We're supposed to meet some other boys and girls.

CARETAKER (*As he is going out right he indicates the door at left*): Well, you can go out that way. I'm going to lock this door as I go through.

ANNE: Yes, sir, we'll go right away. (*The CARETAKER closes door at right and you hear him lock it. JOHN is looking at the anchor again.*) I didn't realize it was so late. Come on, John.

JOHN: O.K. I just want to look at this anchor a minute.

ANNE: But John, the others won't wait for us. We're supposed to meet them by the statue in the park at five.

JOHN: Well, you go on—I'll be right there.

ANNE (*She is turning to go out left*): All right, John, but you hurry now. The man said they're closing right away.

JOHN: I'll be there in a second. (ANNE *goes out and* JOHN *stands looking down at the anchor. He touches it almost caressingly, and then looks dreamily off into space. He has forgotten now about hurrying and wanders upstage again to the alcove. He glances around the room to make sure he is alone, and then steps into the alcove to get a closer look. He stands staring up at the cross, and after a moment, the CARE-TAKER pokes his head in at door left. He glances around and seeing no one, closes the door, and you hear him lock it from the outside. At the sound of the lock, JOHN turns quickly. He looks worried and hurries to the door left and tries it, then across stage and tries the other one. Then he turns facing the*

audience, looking frightened.) Gosh, I—I guess I'm locked in.
(*Before he can think of anything else to do, the lights go
down.*)

JOHN (*His voice still more frightened*): Now, he—he's turned
off the lights. It's—it's kind of scary . . . (*He paces about
a little, talking to himself, to give himself courage.*) Well, why
should I be afraid—just to be caught in the dark in a museum?
Columbus wouldn't have been afraid. It's no worse than the
sea of darkness. . . . (*Suddenly dim lights appear in the
Spanish lanterns in the alcove. JOHN, at right, turns toward
them wonderingly. As the lights get brighter and brighter,
they disclose two figures, COLUMBUS and FATHER JUAN
PEREZ, standing in the alcove. When JOHN sees the two figures, he backs downstage in amazement, finally bumping into
the Spanish chest. He sits on it and watches, as the two figures step from the alcove.*)

PEREZ: Well, Columbus, 'tis a long time since we have passed
through these doors together.

COLUMBUS: Aye, Father, centuries. 'Tis a wonderful thing that
they have brought these doors to this new land to preserve
them.

PEREZ: They did it in honor of you, Columbus. 'Tis a token of
their regard for you. Ah, my son, they appreciate you now.
They realize the greatness of your deed.

COLUMBUS: I am glad, Father, but had it not been for your help,
sustaining me when I was discouraged, going to court in my
behalf—

PEREZ: Ah, my son, that was but a little thing. 'Twas your
great courage made all this possible. Many before you had
thought the world was round, but you alone had the courage
to prove it.

COLUMBUS: 'Tis strange indeed, Father, how I was searching
for India—and found a new world instead.

Perez: And this country you discovered, Columbus. To me, it seems to be so strong. Hardy, unconquerable, like your spirit, my son. The people we've seen—have you noticed them?

Columbus: Aye, Father. A fine people, made up of many strains and come from many lands. 'Tis wonderful to behold. But you know, I often think, they do me so much honor and I—well, I never really touched the United States.

Perez: Ah, my son, but you really did discover America because had you not shown the way, had you not landed on the Islands, others might never have dared to try it. Why, perhaps, none of these people would ever have lived over here. You can be proud of what you started! 'Tis a great country—a land of freedom and liberty.

Columbus: I never dreamed my expedition would have such far-reaching effects. I never dreamed I would find this—land of light. Imagine it, Father, I set sail on what men called the sea of darkness—

Perez: Aye, the Atlantic.

Columbus: And is it not remarkable? Now men sail across it in three or four days. They fly over it in hours.

Perez: Aye, my son. So many remarkable things—and who knows what this fine new generation of Americans growing up now will accomplish?

Columbus: Who knows indeed?

Perez: A very inventive people, Columbus, always discovering things. A people who dream great dreams, Americans. They are always looking for new worlds.

Columbus (*Turning to him*): New worlds? But Father, I thought our globe—have not all the continents been found long ago?

Perez: Oh, surely, my son. When I say new worlds, I am speaking in the larger sense. A new world, for instance, where liberty and freedom can be the lot of all men. That is what

America works toward now. These people here hope to carry their ideals to the four corners of the earth, so that all men may share in what they have found to be good.

COLUMBUS: Ah, Father, 'tis so wonderful to think on. What ignorance we lived in, in our time. I cannot believe it—men are so enlightened now.

PEREZ: But men must guard that enlightenment. There's work to do still, my son. There's always progress to be made, always work to do. That flame of liberty—they must keep it glowing—glowing—until it spreads o'er all the world. (*There is a pause. You hear off the voice of* ANNE *calling.*)

ANNE (*Off*): John, oh John! . . . John! (*At the sound of* ANNE'S *voice,* FATHER PEREZ *and* COLUMBUS *both look toward the door left. The lights of the Spanish lanterns start to dim, and* COLUMBUS *and* FATHER PEREZ *move back and disappear through the alcove as the lights go out entirely.*)

CARETAKER (*Off*): He'll be right in here, miss. I'm sure of it.

ANNE: Oh, I hope so.

CARETAKER: Sure, now, don't you worry. (*The lights come on full.* JOHN *is still seated on the chest. He rises, rubs his eyes a little and walks upstage center peering into the alcove. You hear the sound of the door being unlocked at left. Then it opens and* ANNE *rushes in, followed by the* CARETAKER.)

ANNE (*Excitedly*): John—John—are you all right?

JOHN (*Turning*): All right? Of—of course I'm all right!

ANNE: When you didn't meet us in the park, I didn't know what to think!

CARETAKER: You've certainly caused us a lot of trouble, young man. We were all locked up. Your sister had to ring the night bell.

JOHN: I—I'm sorry, sir.

CARETAKER: It's just lucky I heard her. I was way down in the basement. You might have been in here all night.

ANNE: Oh, John, whatever made you do such a thing? I told you to come right away.

CARETAKER: Well, you'd both better go on home to your folks. They'll be worried, and I reckon there's no use our scolding him any more, miss. He's probably been punished enough— here all alone in the dark.

JOHN: Yeah, I—I guess we'd better go. But sir, it—it really wasn't punishment. I learned something.

CARETAKER: You did?

JOHN: Yes, sir. Most people think that museums are full of old dead things, but they're not. Why, I saw Columbus himself and Father Perez, and heard them talking together—

ANNE: Oh, John! He's always imagining things, sir. I'll bet he went to sleep and was dreaming.

CARETAKER: Dreaming—maybe. But maybe not. Walking these dark corridors at night, I often think I almost see some of the great men of the past.

JOHN: And sir, another thing. You know when you come to a place like this and learn about all of the big things that men have accomplished, you feel, sometimes—well—that there isn't anything more to be done, but that isn't so.

CARETAKER: It isn't, huh?

JOHN: No, sir. There's lots more to do.

ANNE: Why, that's what I told you, John.

JOHN: I know—and it's right. Seeing what men *have* accomplished should make us feel that we won't fail them—the ones who have gone before. We'll keep on discovering things. I guess there are always new worlds to find, if we'll just look for them.

THE END

Happy Haunts

Characters

MR. GHOST

MRS. GHOST

GREAT GHOST

LADY GHOST

OLD MAN GHOST

BOY ⎫
GIRL ⎭ *a newly married couple*

VOICE FROM TELEVISION SET

TIME: *Late evening of Halloween.*

SETTING: *The living room of a new and modern home.*

AT RISE: MR. *and* MRS. GHOST *appear in archway upstage right. She is pulling him by the hand. The hoods of their costumes are pushed back.*

MRS. GHOST (*Leading him downstage center*): Come in, dear, this is the house I want us to haunt.

MR. GHOST: What? But this is a new house.

MRS. GHOST: Of course—isn't it lovely? (*Clasping her hands and looking around*) Not a cobweb in the place.

MR. GHOST (*Looking around too*): And not a spider or a bat or a beetle. My dear Mrs. Ghost, I could never be comfortable here.

MRS. GHOST: Oh, don't be ridiculous—and must you call me Mrs. Ghost? It's so old-fashioned.

MR. GHOST: Old-fashioned? I was always taught to refer to my wife as Mrs. And after all, my dear, you're no spring chicken.

MRS. GHOST: Spring chicken, humph. As ghosts go, I'm practically a fresh egg.

MR. GHOST: You're three hundred and fourteen.

12

Mrs. Ghost: Three hundred and thirteen. You needn't make it any worse than it is. (*Then smiling at him*) But Ghostie dear, please don't be difficult. I've had such a time finding this adorable place. You must try to like it.

Mr. Ghost: You mean you've been here before?

Mrs. Ghost: Oh, yes. While you men ghosts have your lodge meetings in that filthy old attic, I get around. I've been here several times, visiting the young couple who live here. Of course they didn't see me— (*She giggles*) because I'm a ghost, but I've grown so fond of them. They haven't been married very long. They're still a honeymoon couple.

Mr. Ghost: Honeymoon?

Mrs. Ghost: Yes, Ghostie dear, and we never had a honeymoon.

Mr. Ghost: Didn't we? I'd forgotten. It was so long ago.

Mrs. Ghost: Don't you remember? We'd just decided to go to Niagara Falls when we were sent to haunt that old castle in Austria.

Mr. Ghost: Ah, yes.

Mrs. Ghost: And now if we could move in with this nice young couple, why, it would be like kind of a—well, a delayed honeymoon.

Mr. Ghost: But we can't do it. It's unheard of. Whoever heard of a ghost haunting a new house? What would the other ghosts say?

Mrs. Ghost: Well, we've got to move somewhere. That old house we've been living in is being torn down. The men are coming to wreck it in the morning.

Mr. Ghost: But there must be other old houses.

Mrs. Ghost: My dear, you know as well as I do that they're *all* being torn down. There's going to be a terrific housing shortage for ghosts.

MR. GHOST: Then we'll have to go somewhere else—a larger city.

MRS. GHOST: Haven't you ever heard of slum clearance? No, Ghostie, the world is changing and we ghosts have got to change with it. We've got to start haunting new houses. (*She goes to sofa and is about to sit down.*) And this is my choice. I like it here.

MR. GHOST: My dear, don't sit down. (*But she does.*) What if the great high mogul of all the ghosts should find us here?

MRS. GHOST: Pooh—old Ghouly? I'm not afraid of him.

MR. GHOST: Old Ghouly. How can you be so disrespectful? He's been running the affairs of the ghosts for hundreds of years.

MRS. GHOST: That's just the trouble. He's an old dodo.

MR. GHOST: Old dodo?

MRS. GHOST: Yes, an old fogey. He doesn't know what's going on in the world.

MR. GHOST: He knows what's going on in the *ghost* world, and I'm getting very nervous. If he finds us here, he might do anything. He might even banish us to the graveyard. Then we'd have to live on a tombstone.

MRS. GHOST: Well, I'd just as soon if I can't live here. I'd just as soon be dead. (*She giggles.*) Oh dear, I forgot for a minute I was.

MR. GHOST: My dear, I beg you, give up this nonsense at once. Now, we'd better put on our hoods and be about our business. (*He starts to pull up his hood.*) It's Halloween. Tonight of all nights we ought to be out—a-ghosting and a-ghouling.

MRS. GHOST: I think it's silly to go around scaring people.

MR. GHOST: Mrs. Ghost, I command you to get up from that sofa.

MRS. GHOST (*Laughing*): Oh, Ghostie, you wouldn't scare any-one—not even me. (*He sighs and lets his hood drop to his shoulders. She rises and goes to him.*) Now, if you'd just relax and let me show you this darling new house—I know you'll grow to like it. And you'll love the young couple who live here.

MR. GHOST: Where are they?

MRS. GHOST: They're at a Halloween party but when they come home you'll see how sweet they are.

MR. GHOST: My dear, I don't understand you. You keep saying how sweet they are and still you want to live in their house and haunt them.

MRS. GHOST: But not in the way you think. I've got the most wonderful idea. If you'd just say we could move in—

MR. GHOST: Even if the other ghosts would permit it, and I'm sure they wouldn't, I just could never feel at home here.

MRS. GHOST: But why not?

MR. GHOST (*Waving his arms and pointing about*): Well, look at the place. No gingerbread in the decorations—no elaborate cornices to hide behind—no high ceilings. I like to hover about above people's heads.

MRS. GHOST: What's stopping you? You're a ghost, aren't you? Just pop through the ceiling and hover about upstairs. You can watch just as well from there.

MR. GHOST: Oh, yes, I hadn't thought of that.

MRS. GHOST: You don't think of anything. (*Moving upstage from sofa*) Look at these nice plain walls. They're not nearly so solid and troublesome as some we've had. Why, look. They're just lovely to disappear into. (*She slips through opening in upstage wall.* MR. GHOST *smiles and she pops out again.*) See what I mean?

MR. GHOST: Yes, but the whole appearance of the place—it's not —not ghostly.

MRS. GHOST: Not ghostly? Humph. You like tricky things, don't you? Disappearing doors and sliding panels—

MR. GHOST: Ah, yes, that's one thing I liked about the old castle.

MRS. GHOST: Well, the old castle had nothing on this place. You never saw such wonderful gadgets as they have here. (*She goes left to television set and turns it on.*) Look.

VOICE (*From television*): Stand right where you are or I'll shoot! (*There is the sound of "Bang, Bang, Bang."*)

MR. GHOST (*Frightened, backing toward right*): What is that thing? I—I'm getting out of here.

MRS. GHOST: Don't be silly. It's just a television set.

MR. GHOST (*Pointing*): But those figures moving about in there—they must be ghosts!

MRS. GHOST: Ghosts? My dear, you *are* being silly.

MR. GHOST (*Calming*): Oh—er—that's right. We're ghosts, aren't we? But it's very upsetting. Voices coming out of a box and people—

MRS. GHOST: It's wonderful. I'll turn it off now but you'll like it. (*She turns it off and they both move downstage again.*) Sometimes they have a dance band and beautiful music. Why, the other night the young folks had some music on and I danced on the peak of the roof in the moonlight. It was lovely, Ghostie, and I kept wishing you were there too.

MR. GHOST: Did you, my dear?

MRS. GHOST: Yes. And there's something else I want to show you. Just make yourself comfortable while I get it. (*She goes out left.*)

MR. GHOST (*He sits on sofa, picks up newspaper and starts looking at front page. He frowns as he reads, shaking his head*): Atom bombs—flying saucers. (*He shudders and puts the paper down.*) What's the world coming to? (*He notices large cigarette lighter on table right and picks it up and examines it. He pushes button until lighter lights, jumps a little and then smiles. He relights it two or three times, looking more pleased each time.* MRS. GHOST *re-enters with a vacuum cleaner. It is the tank type.* MR. GHOST *lights lighter again.*) My dear, look what I've found. No rubbing sticks together, no flint stones. No matches even.

MRS. GHOST: Oh, that's nothing. Just wait until you see this. (*She sets cleaner on floor, takes cord and plugs it in outlet near door left.*)

MR. GHOST: Whatever is that contraption?

MRS. GHOST: It's a vacuum cleaner. Modern housewives don't have to sweep any more.

MR. GHOST (*He rises and goes toward vacuum cleaner but jumps back as* MRS. GHOST *switches it on.*): What's that noise?

MRS. GHOST: Why, I—I don't know. It's just the thing working. (*She pushes sweeper back and forth on floor.*) But isn't it a lovely sound? A sort of wail.

MR. GHOST: But what's it doing? I don't see anything.

MRS. GHOST: Of course not. It simply sucks up the dirt.

MR. GHOST: But—but isn't it dangerous?

MRS. GHOST: No—not a bit. (*She waves the sweeper toward him. It starts to pull the corner of his robe in. He jumps away.*)

MR. GHOST: Be careful. Don't do that.

MRS. GHOST (*Laughing*): Oh, it won't hurt you. I got caught in it the other day and whizz, I went right in and flopping through the hose and came flying out the other end.

MR. GHOST: You—you did?

MRS. GHOST: Certainly—I had a wonderful ride! It's much better than those roller coasters at the amusement park. Why don't you try it? (*She waves it at him again.*)

MR. GHOST: No—no, please. I'll take your word for it. Some other time.

MRS. GHOST: Very well. But you'll love it after your first trip through. (*She switches it off, pushes it near door left and pulls out the plug.*) And it's really wonderful the way it cleans. It doesn't leave one speck of dirt, not even a cobweb. (*Then remembering*) Oh, but you like cobwebs, don't you?

MR. GHOST: I—I'm not sure, my dear. This is all so new but I'm beginning to think perhaps I could get along without cobwebs. (*He walks right looking all about.*) In fact, I'm beginning to like it here. (*He notices jacket on chair near fireplace and picks it up.*) What's this?

MRS. GHOST: That's the young husband's smoking jacket. It's so bright and nice, isn't it?

MR. GHOST: Do you think I—I might try it on?

MRS. GHOST: Why, of course, Ghostie dear. (*He puts jacket on and struts about a little.*) Oh, you look wonderful in it. So young—and so much at home.

MR. GHOST (*He smiles and shoves his hands in pockets, rocking back and forth on his toes, very pleased with himself. Then pulling his hand out he holds up a twenty-dollar bill*): Look, money—a twenty-dollar bill.

MRS. GHOST: Well, it won't do you any good. Put it back. (*He puts bill back in pocket and she takes him by the hand.*) Now, come on, I want to show you the rest of our new house.

MR. GHOST: Very well, my dear.

MRS. GHOST (*Pulling him toward left*): We'll look at the kitchen first. It's full of the loveliest gadgets. A dishwashing machine and a clock that rings a bell when your eggs are done. (*She starts leading him off left. There is a loud wail off right. They stop and turn.*) My goodness, what was that?

MR. GHOST: It—it might be ghosts. (A LADY GHOST appears *from behind fireplace right and an* OLD MAN GHOST *from the wall upstage left. They wear robes similar to* MR. *and* MRS. GHOST'S *but on their entrance their hoods are over their heads.*)

MRS. GHOST: It *is* ghosts! (*The* GREAT GHOST *appears in archway upstage right. His costume is the same as the others.*)

MR. GHOST: We're lost—it's the great mogul himself!

MRS. GHOST: Old Ghouly! (*The* GREAT GHOST *comes downstage and throws back his hood. He has a large ghoulish nose.*)

GREAT GHOST (*In deep tones*): I, the Great Ghoulish Ghost of all the ghosts, am indeed shocked and surprised to find you here.

MR. GHOST: I—I'm sorry, Great Ghoulish One. I don't know what to say.

GREAT GHOST: Say nothing. Let me speak. We have known for some time about this—this insubordination of your wife's. When she should have been behaving herself properly with the other lady ghosts, she has whisked herself away to this—this place.

MRS. GHOST: It's a nice place.

GREAT GHOST: Silence, woman. (*To* MR. GHOST) That was bad enough but now she has enticed you to come here, to a new house. I can't believe it. Ghosts in a new house.

MR. GHOST: I told Mrs. Ghost you wouldn't like it.

GREAT GHOST: You'll have to be punished. I have brought with me a committee of two to decide what shall be done with you. (*The* LADY GHOST *steps forward to one side of* GREAT GHOST *and throws back her hood. She has a pile of gray hair.*)

LADY GHOST: You're a disgrace to respectable ghosts—and on Halloween, too. (OLD MAN GHOST *steps to other side of* GREAT GHOST *and pushes back his hood. He has a long white beard.*)

OLD MAN GHOST: Yep. I had to give up important work to come after you two. I was out having myself a time a-chilling folks' blood and spooking around.

MRS. GHOST: I'll bet no one was frightened by you.

OLD MAN GHOST: Young woman, what do you mean by that?

MRS. GHOST: Just that a ghost wouldn't scare anybody these days.

GREAT GHOST: Have you ever heard such libel against the great and honorable profession of ghosts?

OLD MAN GHOST: Well, excuse me, Great Ghoulish One, but I did notice that no one bothered much about my weird wails tonight.

MRS. GHOST: I'm not surprised.

MR. GHOST: Please, Mrs. Ghost.

MRS. GHOST: No, you can't shush me. People aren't frightened of ghosts these days and why should they be? They're frightened about too many other things. Horror on the radio, horror in the movies. Why, I saw a billboard the other day: Double feature— A murder a minute—

GREAT GHOST (*Shaking his head*): A murder a minute—why, that's shocking, and certainly not the sort of thing a ghost would go in for.

OLD MAN GHOST: Of course not. You take tonight. Some kids were having a Halloween party and someone was reading them a ghost story. Well, I just popped in and out and rattled a door here and a window there to help the mood along. Just good clean ghost fun.

GREAT GHOST: Perfectly proper, perfectly proper. But we wouldn't stoop to anything like that—that murder a minute.

MRS. GHOST: Of course we wouldn't. And even if we did, no one would pay any attention. There's too much competition.

MR. GHOST: Pardon me, Great Ghoulish One, but there's something to what my wife says. (*He picks up paper from sofa.*) Look at this. Atom bombs, hydrogen bombs, flying saucers— all these things. They've got everyone so frightened that every day is like Halloween. (*He puts paper down on table right of sofa.*)

GREAT GHOST (*Shaking his head*) : It's a terrible state of affairs.

LADY GHOST: Oh dear, oh dear, I'm afraid our days are numbered.

GREAT GHOST: Don't be silly. Ghosts' days are never numbered.

LADY GHOST: But what can we do if we're being out-ghosted at every turn?

GREAT GHOST: I don't know. I just don't know.

MRS. GHOST: Well, I know. If we're being out-ghosted it's because we're not doing the right kind of ghosting. We'll have to change our ways. We'll have to start haunting people in a happy way.

LADY GHOST: Happy haunting? I never heard of such a thing.

GREAT GHOST: Neither have I.

OLD MAN GHOST: Wait a minute. It rings a bell somewhere in my mind. Maybe Mrs. Ghost has got something. Yes, yes, it's beginning to come to me. Way, way back when I was young I heard tales of some ghosts who never tried to scare people at all. Instead they tried to help them.

GREAT GHOST: But I don't remember any such tales.

OLD MAN GHOST: Naturally you don't. You're just a young whipper-snapper compared to me.

LADY GHOST: But he's the great mogul of all the ghosts. He's been running our affairs for hundreds of years.

OLD MAN GHOST: But I've been around for thousands.

MRS. GHOST: My, you're a great-great-grandfather ghost!

OLD MAN GHOST: I sure am. And yes, sir, there was a time when ghosts didn't live in old musty houses. They just moved in with certain families and tried to help them. Happy haunts, folks used to call 'em.

MRS. GHOST: Happy haunts—isn't that lovely? And it's just what I want to do. Haunt people in a happy way. Why, who knows? Maybe we'll start a trend. Maybe the whole world will start being constructive. Now, I thought if Mr. Ghost

and I could move into this house and help the young couple
who live here—

GREAT GHOST: But what could you do? How could you help
them?

MRS. GHOST: There must be a great many ways. Mr. Ghost and
I have been married for some time and we know all the pitfalls
of marriage.

MR. GHOST: Pitfalls, my dear?

MRS. GHOST: Oh, you know, Ghostie. We often disagree or get
angry with one another, but we don't take it seriously any
more. Now, if this young couple should quarrel we can step
in and help them.

MR. GHOST: I'd like to do that.

OLD MAN GHOST: Say, it sounds fine to me, too. Maybe I ought
to find me some happy haunting grounds.

GREAT GHOST: Just a moment, please.

LADY GHOST: But it would be nice if all the ghosts could do
something like that.

GREAT GHOST: Silence. We've got to be practical. You've had
no experience in this sort of thing—happy haunting—it's out
of your line.

MRS. GHOST: Just let us try, please. (*The sound of a car is
heard off.*) Oh, there's the car now. The young couple are
coming home from their Halloween party. Do give us a
chance!

MR. GHOST: Yes, please let us try. What harm can come of it?

GREAT GHOST: I don't know but it's against all tradition. At
least this happy haunt business is all new to me. (*Turning to*
OLD MAN GHOST *and* LADY GHOST) How about you two?
You're the committee. What do you think?

LADY GHOST: It's such a lovely idea.

OLD MAN GHOST: Well, I vote to give 'em a chance.

GREAT GHOST: Very well, then. (*To* MR. *and* MRS. GHOST) The committee has voted to give you a chance.

MR. GHOST: Oh, thank you, sir.

GREAT GHOST: Now, wait a minute. This is a serious thing and if you fail you will have to take the consequences.

MRS. GHOST: Oh, we will. We'll do anything you say.

GREAT GHOST: Good. If you succeed you may remain here in this new house. But if you fail—well, you will be banished to the graveyard!

MR. GHOST (*Frightened*): The graveyard—if we fail?

MRS. GHOST (*Taking his hand*): Never mind, Ghostie. I'm not afraid. (*Voices of the young couple are heard off upstage right.*)

GREAT GHOST: Well, here come your friends. We'll leave you now. (GREAT GHOST, OLD MAN GHOST *and* LADY GHOST *go quickly to fireplace and disappear behind it.* MRS. GHOST *takes vacuum cleaner and rushes off left.* MR. GHOST *rushes to wall upstage left and bumps into it but cannot get through.* MRS. GHOST *runs in left and starts for wall upstage left and sees* MR. GHOST.

MR. GHOST: I can't get through—I can't get through.

MRS. GHOST: It's the coat, silly. Take it off. (MR. GHOST *quickly takes off coat and drops it to floor and they both disappear through wall just as the young couple enter through archway upstage right.*)

BOY (*As they enter*): It was a good party, wasn't it?

GIRL: Wonderful, but I'm tired. (*Yawning*) I'm glad to be home.

BOY: And to our own home, too. It's a great feeling. (*He puts his arm around her and motions around the room.*) Our very own living room. Everything just the way we want it.

GIRL (*Frowning a little*): Well, almost everything.

Boy: What do you mean, *almost?*

Girl (*Pointing to coat on floor*): Oh, nothing much except it won't be a nice living room very long if we just throw our clothes on the floor.

Boy (*Going and picking up coat*): Oh, for gosh sakes, my coat. But I left it on the back of that chair.

Girl: I suppose it jumped off and ran over there all by itself.

Boy (*Angry now*): No, it didn't. (*He puts coat over middle of back of sofa.*) I left it on the chair and someone moved it. And you're the only one who—

Girl: Oh, so you're accusing me of throwing your clothes on the floor?

Boy: No, I'm not. I'm just agreeing with you that it couldn't get there by itself.

Girl: You might at least admit it when you do something. (*She slumps down on left end of sofa.* Boy *slumps down on right end of sofa and sits scowling.* Mr. *and* Mrs. Ghost *appear from wall upstage left looking worried. The three other* Ghosts, *now wearing their hoods, come from behind fireplace and stand shaking their heads sadly at* Mr. *and* Mrs. Ghost.)

Mrs. Ghost (*To* Mr. Ghost): Now look what you've done.

Boy (*Angrily without looking up*): Well, what have I done now?

Girl: What do you mean?

Boy: You said, now look what you've done.

Girl: But I haven't said a word.

Boy: But I heard you—oh, what's the use?

Mr. Ghost: Now see what *you've* done. (Mrs. Ghost *puts her finger to her lips and they slip quickly through wall. The other* Ghosts *go back of fireplace.*)

Boy (*Rising*): Well?

Girl (*Rising and facing him*): Well, yourself.

Boy: I suppose you didn't say anything.

GIRL: I heard *you* say something.

BOY: But I didn't. Are you deliberately trying to make me lose my temper?

GIRL: No, I'm not and if I were it wouldn't take much trying.

BOY: Ohhh! (*He waves his arms and sits down again on sofa.*)

GIRL: What's the matter with you? You're acting like a spoiled child. Did you eat something that didn't agree with you?

BOY: If I did it was that apple pie we had for supper tonight.

GIRL (*Angry*): What was the matter with that pie?

BOY: You should ask. It was more like apple goulash. There was more stuck to the plate than there was to eat.

GIRL (*Starting to cry*): I—I never made one before. I don't know why it stuck. The juice all leaked through and it stuck, that's all.

BOY (*Scowling*): The ones my mother made didn't stick.

GIRL: Well, if all life means to you is apple pies, why don't you go back to your mother? (*She flops down on left end of sofa. There is a pause. MR. and MRS. GHOST enter again and stand near wall upstage. Three GHOSTS appear again and line up against wall right, watching.*)

BOY (*After pause*): Well, there's no use having all this fuss about an apple pie. Next time just go out and buy one.

GIRL: Buy one. What with?

BOY: With money, of course. Your food allowance. I gave you twenty dollars last Tuesday.

GIRL: It was the Tuesday before last—you're always forgetting.

BOY: I am not. Besides, you could ask me.

GIRL: I don't like to keep asking you for money. Before we were married I was working and I had my own money. Now it seems I never have a cent in my purse.

BOY: Then it's because you're extravagant. Not every wife gets twenty dollars every week for food.

GIRL: Every week. I tell you, you didn't give me any this week.

Boy: And I tell you I did. I can remember. (*He pulls out wallet and looks in it.*) It was a twenty-dollar bill. I took it out and —well, it's not here so I must have given it to you.

Girl (*Angrily*): Ohhh! (*She turns away from him and he glares off in the opposte direction.* Mr. Ghost *steps downstage behind them, picks up the coat, takes out the twenty-dollar bill, holds it up and smiles at* Mrs. Ghost. *Then he puts bill back, leaving one end sticking out of pocket. He carefully replaces the coat on back of sofa between them, making sure that the money is in plain view. He steps back near* Mrs. Ghost.)

Boy (*Changing his position to look toward* Girl, *he notices money*): Say, how did that get here?

Girl (*Turning*): Your coat? You put it there.

Boy: I don't mean the coat. Look. Twenty dollars. (*He takes bill from pocket and holds it up.*) Why, it's your allowance.

Girl: My allowance?

Boy: It must be. You weren't here when I took it out of my wallet and I just shoved it in this pocket and forgot it. (*Handing her bill.*) Here. I'm sorry.

Girl: Thank you. (*She places bill on table left and leaves her her hand over arm of sofa and resting on table.*) And I'm sorry about the apple pie. (Mrs. Ghost *goes to bookcase, pulls out a book, opens it to a certain place and quietly puts it on table left of* Girl. *The* Girl *sighs.*) I wish I knew what I did wrong with that old pie.

Boy: Never mind. Now you can buy one.

Girl: But I don't want to buy one. I want to make one—and a good one. (Mrs. Ghost *pushes book across table so it touches* Girl's *hand.* Girl *pulls her hand away and* Mrs. Ghost *moves quickly upstage and stands near* Mr. Ghost *watching.* Girl, *realizing she has felt something, turns and sees book. She picks it up.*) Why, how did this cookbook get here?

BOY: You're not accusing me of buying you a cookbook?

GIRL: No—this is an old one of Mother's. I remember she put it in with my things when I moved, but it's been in that bookcase over there.

BOY: You must have taken it out. You're getting absent-minded.

GIRL: Well, absent-minded or not, look—it's open at apple pie. And here's the very thing we were talking about. It says: Does your pie leak?

BOY: And if it does?

GIRL: You juice-proof the bottom crust with a little flour and sugar. Why, that's wonderful. I'll bet my next pie won't leak. (*She puts book down on table left. MR. and MRS. GHOST look happy. The three GHOSTS nod their heads up and down approvingly.*)

BOY: Well, that's settled. At least we're going to have good apple pies.

GIRL (*Rising, angry again*): What do you mean, at least? We'll have more than good apple pies if you don't forget to give me my allowance.

BOY (*Rising too*): You talk as though I'm the one who forgets things. Who forgot to put the sugar under the apple pie?

GIRL: I didn't forget. I didn't even know about it. And if you're just going to argue I'm going to bed. It's almost midnight. (*She starts left but he doesn't follow. She stops with her back toward him, tapping her foot. MR. and MRS. GHOST look very worried, throw up their hands in despair. Other three GHOSTS shake their heads at MR. and MRS. GHOST. MR. GHOST runs out upstage right and returns brandishing a big umbrella. MRS. GHOST grabs at umbrella but MR. GHOST waves her away and ducks down behind sofa. GIRL turns angrily.*) I said I was going to bed!

Boy: Go ahead. It's all right with me. But don't get mad all over again.

Girl (*Starting toward him*): Who's getting mad?

Boy: You're mad—mad as a wet hen.

Girl (*Shaking finger at him as she goes closer*): I'm no hen. (Mr. Ghost *crawls out left of sofa and just as* Girl *passes, pokes umbrella out near* Girl's *feet and she appears to trip over it. She falls into* Boy's *arms.* Mr. Ghost *rises quickly and moves back.*) My goodness, I—I tripped over something.

Boy: You tripped over your own feet.

Girl: I did not.

Boy: Well, never mind. You tripped into a good place. (*Holding her closer*) You're in my arms. That's where you should have been all along.

Girl: Darling. (*They stand for a moment as* Mr. Ghost, *grinning and waving umbrella, runs off upstage right. As he goes, three* Ghosts *at right smile and nod and make gestures of approval at him.* Lady *and* Old Man Ghost *exit behind fireplace.* Great Ghost *turns toward* Mrs. Ghost *who is all smiles and makes her a deep bow, then exits behind fireplace.* Mr. Ghost *re-enters through wall and stands beside* Mrs. Ghost.) Oh, why do we fight about such silly things?

Boy: I don't know. Let's sit down. (*He pulls her toward sofa and they sit.*) Here, put your head on my shoulder. (*She does.*) Happy?

Girl (*Smiling*): Of course. (*Then laughing a little*) Darling, do you know something? If this wasn't a brand new house, I —I'd think it was haunted.

Boy (*Laughing*): A new house haunted? Whatever put that into your head?

Girl: Well, after all, it *is* Halloween. You'll think I'm silly but I just know something tripped me when I fell into your arms.

Boy: Oh, a ghost, huh? Well, in that case, all I can say is thank you, Mr. Ghost. (MR. *and* MRS. GHOST *hold hands and dance around happily.*)

GIRL (*Laughing*) : How do you know it was a Mr. Ghost?

BOY : I don't. But Mr. or Mrs., I thank them just the same, and one thing we know for sure—if there are any ghosts around here, they must be happy ones. (MR. *and* MRS. GHOST *nod their heads up and down happily as the curtain falls.*)

THE END

Hometown Halloween

Characters

MOTHER, *Vera Brown*
FATHER, *Tom Brown*
JOHNNIE BROWN, *about seventeen*
SUE BROWN, *about sixteen*
LUCY BROWN, *aged nine*
MARY FISHER, *about seventeen*

TIME: *Halloween. Late afternoon.*
SETTING: *The Brown living room.*
AT RISE: MOTHER, *Vera Brown, enters left carrying a small newspaper, and humming as* SUE *enters upstage right.* SUE *wears a jacket which she takes off and tosses over a chair as she talks.*

SUE: Mom, I've just come from downtown and you ought to see Main Street. All the children standing in front of the store windows and painting away for dear life—and the pictures are wonderful! There are owls and witches and big orange moons.

MOTHER: I'll see them tonight. I can hardly wait.

SUE: It's a sight all right. The town looks like fairyland or something out of Mother Goose.

MOTHER: Oh, Sue, it's a wonderful way for the children to spend Halloween! And to think it was all our Johnnie's idea.

SUE: It's not original, Mom. Lots of other cities have done it before this.

MOTHER: Yes, but we haven't and it took Johnnie to get it started. Oh, I'm so proud I could burst. I don't know where that boy gets his ideas and he's still just in high school. Why, if he keeps on, he may even be president some day.

SUE: Now, Mom, don't get carried away. Of course he is pretty smart, but don't tell him I said so. I don't want to add to his swelled head.

MOTHER: Swelled head, indeed. Johnnie's as modest as can be. (*Holding up paper*) Did you see what it says about him in the school paper?

SUE (*Looking over* MOTHER's *shoulder*): No.

MOTHER: Well, listen to this. (*Reading*) Johnnie Brown saves Halloween from becoming Horror Night. Lawlessness stopped. Johnnie Brown goes to mayor with new idea. Persuades merchants to loan display windows for children to paint Halloween pictures. Johnnie Brown lifts Halloween to higher level with a safe and happy Halloween for the children. Johnnie Brown's ingenious idea— (*Breaking off*) Well, you see what a wonderful write-up it is for Johnnie.

SUE: Naturally. He wrote it himself.

MOTHER: What's that?

SUE: Of course. He's the editor of the paper, isn't he?

MOTHER: My, I'd forgotten that for a minute. Well, just the same, it is wonderful. A really worthwhile civic project and Johnnie got the idea and went to the mayor himself.

SUE: Oh, Johnnie has the nerve all right. Of course, Dad being head of the merchants' association helped too. He got the other storekeepers to say they'd put up the prize money.

MOTHER (*Sitting down in easy chair left and placing paper on table next to her*): My, I wonder what child will win the prize. Did you see Lucy? Was she painting a picture?

SUE: Yes, she was doing one on Dad's store window.

MOTHER: Of course, Lucy's only nine and some of the children are older but I did think maybe she'd have a chance at the prize. After all, Johnnie is one of the judges—

SUE: Mom, you don't give prizes to members of your own family, not to your own sister. That wouldn't be fair.

MOTHER: It would be if Lucy's picture was the best.

SUE: Well, it won't be. I'm sure Johnnie wouldn't do that. Besides, there are other judges.

MOTHER: Who are they?

SUE: The mayor and then that portrait painter, Mr. Whitacre.

MOTHER: Well, I still think Lucy may have a chance. She has a lot of creative instinct for a child of nine. She's very talented.

SUE (*Laughing*): Oh, Mom, you think all your children are talented. (*Patting* MOTHER's *shoulder*) But you're an old dear. (LUCY *runs in upstage right. She has paint on her blouse and carries some brushes. She is excited.*)

LUCY: Mom—Mom, I finished my picture! It's right on Dad's store window. It's beautiful.

MOTHER: Is it, Lucy?

LUCY: I'll say. It's a pumpkin and a black cat.

SUE (*Sitting down right*): Look at your dress. I'll bet you put more paint on you than you did on the window.

LUCY: I did not. I've got lots of paint on the window—orange and black and all colors.

MOTHER: Did you see your brother, Lucy?

LUCY: Yes, he was kind of taking charge of everything and watching us all. But most of the kids are finished with their pictures now. My, it was fun. All the boys and girls say so. The most fun we've ever had on Halloween—even that little Carl Meyer painted a picture—on the drugstore window.

MOTHER: Is that the new little boy? The one that doesn't speak English very well?

LUCY: Yes.

SUE: I saw Carl, too, and I've never seen him look so happy. He usually seems so lonesome and sort of out of things.

MOTHER: I suppose it's hard for him at school. The other children probably don't understand him.

LUCY: He's so different, Mom.

MOTHER: Now, Lucy, you must try to help him feel at home.

LUCY: His picture was good, but not as good as mine, I guess. I think maybe I'll win the prize.

SUE: Now, Lucy, don't get that idea into your head—

LUCY: I don't see why not. My picture *is* good. (*She puts her brushes on a table and goes and sits on sofa.* JOHNNIE, *likable and full of enthusiasm, enters upstage right.*)

JOHNNIE: Hi ya, folks!

MOTHER: Johnnie, my boy, I wondered when you'd be home. How's everything going?

JOHNNIE: Fine, Mom. Everything's perfect. Our town's never seen a Halloween like this, and are the kids enjoying it. They're having a lot more fun than they ever had chalking up windows or tearing down fences. The pictures are all finished now.

MOTHER: And Sue says they're wonderful.

JOHNNIE: Wonderful? They're out of this world. Who'd ever have thought our boys and girls had so much talent? There are goblins, ghosts and witches parading along all the windows on Main Street.

LUCY: Did you see my picture, Johnnie, on Dad's store?

JOHNNIE: Sure, it was fine, Lucy.

MOTHER: I do think Lucy has a lot of talent.

JOHNNIE: All the kids seem to have, Mom. You ought to see some of the ideas they've dreamed up. Jack-o-lanterns dancing, owls wearing glasses—

SUE: And Johnnie, the one of the witch riding over the moon and the moon winking—that was little Carl Meyer's, wasn't it?

JOHNNIE: Yeah, and before he finished it, he added a black cat, hanging to a star by his tail. Well, I tell you, when I saw those finished pictures, I made up my mind—we've got to have more prizes.

MOTHER: More prizes?

JOHNNIE: Sure. There are too many good pictures to give just one prize. We've got to have a second and third prize too. I stopped in at the mayor's office on the way home and he agrees with me.

SUE: But Johnnie, that'll mean more money out of the merchants' pockets. After all, they put up the prize money.

JOHNNIE: Sure, and they ought to be glad to do it.

SUE: But now each storekeeper will have to pay more.

JOHNNIE: Oh, that's all right. Dad can O.K. it. Isn't he home yet, Mom?

MOTHER: No, dear, but he should be here soon.

JOHNNIE: I haven't too much time. I'll have to talk to Dad, have some supper and then get back downtown to manage the parade.

LUCY: Goody-goody, I can hardly wait for the parade.

MOTHER: We'll all be there watching, Johnnie.

JOHNNIE: All the boys and girls are going to march right down Main Street past all the display windows to the park, and then I'm going to give out the prizes.

MOTHER: *You're* going to give them out?

JOHNNIE: Sure. The mayor asked me if I would. After all, the whole thing was my idea. I have to make a speech too.

MOTHER: A speech? Oh, Johnnie, we're so proud of you. How you accomplish all these things, I don't know.

JOHNNIE: Oh, well, Mom, you just have to use your brains a little.

SUE: Listen, Johnnie, it sounds as though you're going to be awfully busy tonight. What about the dance at the high school gym?

JOHNNIE: I'll make it there eventually. After I make the speech and maybe confer a little with the mayor about next year's celebration.

SUE: But don't you have a date with Mary Fisher? Didn't you promise to pick her up?

JOHNNIE: Yes, but I've got that all fixed. I asked Chuck Evans to look out for her until I get there.

SUE (*Rising*): You asked *who*?

JOHNNIE: Chuck. He's going to call for her—gee, Sue, what's the matter?

SUE: You know very well what's the matter. Chuck Evans is taking me to the dance.

JOHNNIE: Of course he is, but is there any law against his having two girls for a while?

SUE: There certainly is—especially when one of them is Mary Fisher!

JOHNNIE: Now, listen, what's wrong with Mary?

SUE: Nothing except she's always playing up to all the fellows.

JOHNNIE: She is not. Mary can't see anyone but me!

SUE: That's what you think. You're so conceited—

MOTHER: Sue, such a way to talk to your brother.

SUE (*Almost crying*): But Mom, he's ruined my whole evening. For weeks I've been hoping that Chuck Evans would ask me for a date, and now that he has, Johnnie has to spoil it all.

JOHNNIE: Who's spoiled anything? The three of you can have a good time at the dance until I get there.

SUE: Three's a crowd and I'll be the one that's crowded out. Mary will wiggle her eyelashes at Chuck a couple of times, and he won't know I'm alive.

JOHNNIE: Oh, for gosh sakes. Just because Mary's full of pep and friendly to everyone you have to talk about her like that. I tell you, she doesn't go for Chuck.

SUE: Oh, she doesn't? All right. Then why was she handing him a note after class the other day?

JOHNNIE: A note? But she couldn't have—

SUE: I saw her—a note in an envelope—and after that they were talking together.

JOHNNIE: Now, listen, Sue, you must be mistaken. Besides, what do you want to worry me for at a time like this, when I've got important things on my mind?

SUE (*Starting to cry*): Important? Well, this dance was important to me. It was the most important thing in my life.

MOTHER (*Rising and going to her*): Now, Sue, don't cry.

JOHNNIE: Gosh, Sue, what's a dance compared to the future of our children?

SUE: What children?

JOHNNIE: The children of our town. Last year what happened? Half the kids spent Halloween in acts of destruction. This year they're doing something constructive and loving it. Just think, there'll be no windows broken, no fences down, no acts of lawlessness—

SUE: Oh, why don't you get a soapbox? (SUE *sits down disgustedly in chair left and dabs at her eyes.*)

JOHNNIE: Gee, maybe I will. Why, sure, maybe I can use some of these ideas in my speech tonight. (*Gesticulating*) The destructive force, I'll say, that's what's wrong with the world. Today our boys and girls have learned that's it's better to be *con*structive than destructive, and those boys and girls are going to be our citizens of tomorrow. (FATHER TOM BROWN, *enters upstage right, smiling. He puts his hat on a table.*)

FATHER: Well—well—well, someone making a speech?

JOHNNIE: Kind of, Dad. Practicing for tonight. (*He sits down at right.*)

MOTHER (*Going to* FATHER *and kissing him*) : Tom, my dear.

FATHER: Hello, Vera. You ought to see the picture Lucy painted on my store window. There's certainly a holiday spirit downtown. Never saw so many people on Main Street.

LUCY: Are they looking at my pumpkin and black cat, Dad?

FATHER: Sure are. Haven't had so many people standing in front of my window since I had that big sale last spring. Of course there are crowds in front of all the windows, but I think I've got the biggest one. (*He clears his throat.*) And that reminds me, Johnnie. Have you—uh—that is, have you decided which picture is to win the prize?

JOHNNIE (*Remembering*) : Prizes, Dad. (*He rises.*) Gosh, I've got to talk to you about that.

FATHER (*Pleased*) : You have? Well, in my opinion, son—

JOHNNIE: Listen, Dad, we've got to have more prizes. A second and third as well as a first.

FATHER: What's that? But there was to be just one prize—twenty-five dollars.

JOHNNIE: I know, Dad, but now we're going to have a second prize of fifteen dollars and a third prize of ten.

FATHER: But that makes twenty-five dollars more.

JOHNNIE: Sure. The mayor and I decided it.

FATHER: The mayor and you? But you're not the ones who put up the money.

SUE: That won't bother Johnnie. He can make all kinds of plans for other people.

JOHNNIE: Now, listen, Sue—

FATHER: Johnnie, I can't spring this on the merchants at the last minute like this. There isn't time for a meeting.

JOHNNIE: But you're the head of the association, Dad. You can O.K. it.

FATHER: I don't like to do it without their consent. They may be angry.

JOHNNIE: Angry? Why, it'll only be a dollar or so more when it's split up among them. Gee, you don't mean to tell me that the storekeepers of this town are going to be small about a big thing like this, do you?

FATHER: Small? Now, wait a minute, young man—

MOTHER: Tom, don't lose your temper. I'm sure it will be all right if you O.K. it. As long as Johnnie and the mayor think it's a good idea—

JOHNNIE (*Grinning*): Johnnie and the mayor. That sounds good, doesn't it? Boy, I'm glad somebody's on my side, Mom. Thanks.

FATHER (*Sighing*): Oh, very well, I'll O.K. it then. (*He sits down in easy chair right.*)

JOHNNIE: Fine, Dad. Fine. And now if you'll just give me the twenty-five dollars—

FATHER: *I* should give it to you?

JOHNNIE: Why, sure. You said yourself there wasn't time for a meeting. We've got to get the money somewhere.

FATHER: Oh, is that so?

JOHNNIE: If you'll just write one check for fifteen and another for ten, so I can hand out the prizes—

FATHER: And what if I never get the money back? What if I don't collect from the other fellows?

JOHNNIE: You will, Dad, you will. What are you worried about?

FATHER: Johnnie Brown, your ideas are all very well but sometimes you go too far. I thought I was going to enjoy this evening—the parade and the prize giving—but when it's my own money being handed out. Twenty-five dollars—that's an expensive evening. Too expensive to enjoy.

SUE: Johnnie's spoiled my evening too, Dad, but he doesn't care. (MOTHER *looks upset.*)

JOHNNIE: Oh, for gosh sakes! A fellow tries to do something

worthwhile and what happens? No one cooperates. All they do is heap recriminations. (*The phone rings.*)

MOTHER: Oh dear . . . (*Going upstage left*) I'll get the phone.

JOHNNIE: If it's the mayor, Mom, I'll speak to him.

MOTHER (*Into phone*): Hello? Oh, hello. . . . Why—why, yes he is. Just a minute . . . (*To* JOHNNIE) It isn't the mayor, dear. It's Mrs. Henderson.

JOHNNIE: Mrs. Henderson next door?

MOTHER: Yes, she wants to speak to you.

JOHNNIE: To me? But Mom, she always talks to you. About recipes and knitting and stuff.

MOTHER: Well, now she wants to talk to you.

JOHNNIE: But what for?

MOTHER: I don't know, dear. Come on. Maybe she wants to congratulate you on your idea. (JOHNNIE *takes phone.*)

JOHNNIE: Hello, Mrs. Henderson . . . Gee, thanks . . . What? . . . Oh, sure I saw your little Jimmy's picture. I saw all the pictures . . . Oh, sure, I remember it. It was a goblin, wasn't it? Huh? Oh, not a goblin—a gremlin. Oh . . . Yes —yes, they're all good . . . The best? Oh—er—well, I guess it's natural for a mother to think her own offspring's picture is the best, Mrs. Henderson.

MOTHER: Johnnie, be careful what you say.

JOHNNIE: But, Mrs. Henderson! . . . Well, sure I'm glad you called it to my attention but I'm only one of the judges, Mrs. Henderson—and besides—well, this may sound funny, Mrs. Henderson, but it's up to me to make up my own mind which picture is the best. (*He hangs up.*)

MOTHER: Johnnie, what on earth was that all about?

JOHNNIE: Can you imagine? She wanted to tell me her little Jimmy had done the best picture. She wanted me to cast my vote for it. She practically said so.

FATHER: Well, of all the nerve. I tell you when it comes to

prizes people lose all sense of values. Why, I saw Jimmy's picture. It can't compare with Lucy's.

LUCY: No, Jimmy's was kind of blotchy.

MOTHER: Well, I haven't seen Lucy's yet but I've seen some of the scrawling Jimmy's done when he's been over here playing with Lucy. Why, he hasn't a bit of originality. Oh dear, now I suppose Mrs. Henderson is going to be terribly offended if Lucy wins the prize.

JOHNNIE (*Shocked*): If what, Mom?

MOTHER: If Lucy wins the prize, dear.

JOHNNIE: Mom, you—you haven't been thinking—

FATHER: Lucy's picture is certainly good all right. But, of course, Johnnie will have to decide for himself.

JOHNNIE: Of course, it's good, Dad, but there are lots of pictures. Lucy has a good enough cat and a pumpkin but there's no story to her picture.

LUCY (*Her face puckering*): You mean I'm not going to win the prize?

JOHNNIE: Well, I don't know how the other two judges are voting, but I'm pretty sure they won't think your picture is the best either.

MOTHER: Oh, dear! But then, Lucy, second or third prize is nice too.

LUCY: Not as nice as first.

JOHNNIE: I already cast my votes when I stopped in at the mayor's office.

MOTHER: Did you give Lucy second or third?

JOHNNIE: Mom, I didn't give Lucy any vote. Her picture wasn't even in the running—I know that.

MOTHER: Not even in the running?

SUE: Well, Dad, it looks as though you're not going to get any of your money back tonight. (LUCY *rolls over on sofa, crying and kicking her legs.*)

LUCY: I didn't win the prize. I didn't win the prize! (JOHNNIE *goes to her.*)

JOHNNIE: Lucy, don't cry. You've got to be a good sport.

LUCY: I don't want to be a good sport. I want to win the prize.

MOTHER: Oh, Johnnie, I wish we'd never had the contest.

JOHNNIE: Mom, you too? You mean you're going back on me? Gee, don't you see how unfair it is for you all to feel this way? What's the matter with everyone?

MOTHER: Oh, I don't know. I'm so upset. I just don't like to see Lucy's feelings hurt—(*The doorbell rings.*) Who can that be? (MOTHER *goes off upstage right.*)

JOHNNIE: Listen, Lucy, you've got to learn to enjoy competition whether you win or not. Everybody can't win.

LUCY: But I could have. My picture was good. (*She cries harder.* MOTHER *re-enters with* MARY FISHER, *an attractive girl.* MARY *wears a jacket over her dress.*)

MOTHER: Come in, Mary. Johnnie, it's Mary.

JOHNNIE (*Surprised*): Why—hi, Mary.

MARY (*Smiling*): Hi, Johnnie . . . Hello, everyone.

JOHNNIE: Gee, Mary, I didn't expect to see you until the dance tonight.

MARY: I know, but I was on my way home from downtown and —(*She stops, looking at* LUCY *who is still crying.*) My goodness, what's the matter with Lucy?

MOTHER: Oh—uh—just a little family crisis—they happen, you know. I suppose they happen at your house too, Mary.

MARY: Of course they do.

FATHER (*Rising and pointing to a chair*): Sit down, young lady, sit down.

MARY: No, I can't stay but a minute and I—I'm sorry if I've interrupted anything. (FATHER *sits again, and* MOTHER *sits near him at right.*) You don't look too happy either, Sue. Aren't you looking forward to the dance tonight?

SUE: I *was*.

MARY: Was?

JOHNNIE (*Quickly*): Sue just means she—she was—she is—yes, that's it, of course she is.

MARY: *I* certainly am. Chuck's coming for me at eight and then we'll be right over and pick you up, Sue.

SUE (*Too sweetly*): Well, isn't that nice? Just lovely.

MARY: And the thing I wanted now, Johnnie—well, I was so excited after I saw all the pictures downtown that I just had to stop in and talk to you about them.

JOHNNIE: They *are* good, aren't they?

LUCY (*Sitting up and gulping*): Mine was good.

MARY: They're all just wonderful. The whole idea's terrific for Halloween and we owe it all to you, Johnnie. My, I'm so proud of you.

JOHNNIE: Well, gee, thanks.

MARY: And I'm so proud of all the kids! Why, I never dreamed they'd be able to paint such cute pictures. I was so surprised —especially at Dora.

JOHNNIE: Dora?

MARY: You know—my little sister, Dora. I never knew she had a bit of talent and her picture is—well, it's really outstanding.

FATHER (*Apprehensively*): Oh-oh.

JOHNNIE: Oh, yeah, I remember. Hers is the one on the bakery window—with the witches.

MARY: And the witches are wearing the cutest pointed hats.

FATHER: My dear young lady, all witches wear pointed hats.

MARY (*Smiling*): But not like these. There was just something about them—well, I do think it's a prize picture.

MOTHER: A prize picture?

MARY: Yes. Of course, I know it's up to you, Johnnie, and I don't want to influence you—

SUE (*Sarcastically*) : Oh, no, of course not.

JOHNNIE: It's not up to me alone, Mary. There are other judges.

MARY: Well, just the same, you're one of them and when something is as good as Dora's picture, I do think it deserves consideration.

LUCY (*Starting to cry again*) : Don't you dare give Dora Fisher's picture the prize, Johnnie. It isn't as good as mine!

JOHNNIE (*Getting mad*) : Lucy, be quiet. . . . Listen, Mary, is that why you stopped in here, just to ask me to vote for your little sister's picture?

MARY: Well—uh—no, of course not. Not exactly. Not unless you really think it's the best—

JOHNNIE: Well, I don't, and that *is* the reason you stopped in, and your pulling a thing like this is the last straw!

MARY: I haven't pulled anything.

JOHNNIE: Oh, yes, you have. You stopped in here expecting I'd vote for your sister's picture just because you and I are friends. And why, why, that's terrible. It's just like crooked politics. If you're honest, you don't vote for people just because they're your friends, you vote for the best man.

MARY (*Mad now too*) : Well, I certainly don't have to stand here and listen to you making insinuations. I've had just about enough.

JOHNNIE: So have I.

MARY: And you needn't bother coming to the dance at all tonight. I'll spend the evening with Chuck—and enjoy it, too.

SUE (*Rising*) : There, you see, Johnnie? I knew something like this would happen. Where does that leave me?

JOHNNIE: Never mind, Sue—

SUE: Never mind? When you've ruined everything. It's all your fault. (*She slumps in chair again.*)

MARY (*Starting upstage*): Well, I'm going.

JOHNNIE (*Grabbing her arm*): Mary, wait.

MARY: Let me go—and you don't ever need to speak to me again!

JOHNNIE: All right, I won't. (*Dropping her arm*) And see if I care. (MARY *stops and stares at him as he turns and speaks to all of them.*) Boy, that's gratitude, isn't it? A fellow tries to do his best, and what does he get? A kick in the pants. A kick in the pants all the way around. Boy, I'll bet the president of the United States feels the way I do—a lot of times.

MOTHER (*Rising and half going toward* JOHNNIE): Johnnie—

JOHNNIE: It's all right, Mom, I can take it. I spent all my spare time for months working on this idea—just because I felt it was something worthwhile for the town, and I thought until a while ago it was all going to be a great success. But now— well, it's funny how unappreciative people can be.

FATHER: Now, son—

JOHNNIE (*Going right on*): Just because they're inconvenienced or have to fork out a little more money or don't get their own way.

FATHER: Son, there's something I want to say—

JOHNNIE: Never mind, Dad. It's too late now. I'm through. Never again. The kids can tear up the town next year if they want to. A fellow has a good idea, and what happens? He loses his best girl, his whole family gets mad at him, Lucy bawls her head off because she thinks she ought to win the prize—(*They are all staring at him. The phone rings, and* MOTHER *starts toward it.*) And she isn't the only one. Everyone in town thinks he knows who ought to win. No one's satisfied just to let the judges pick the best picture.

MOTHER (*Into phone*): Hello? Oh, Mayor Stanton. Why, yes, just a minute. (*Turning*) It's for you, Johnnie—the mayor.

JOHNNIE: O.K., Mom. I guess I'll have to talk to him. (*They all watch* JOHNNIE *as he goes to phone.*) Hello, Mayor Stanton . . . Yes, sir . . . I see, sir . . . Unanimous? Well, that's the way I thought it would be. I was sure of it . . . O.K., Mayor Stanton. Thanks for calling. Goodbye. (*He hangs up.*)

MOTHER: Johnnie, was that—have they decided about the prizes?

JOHNNIE: Yes. The judges were unanimous in their decision. The first prize will go to little Carl Meyer.

FATHER: Little Carl Meyer? Well.

JOHNNIE: And second and third prizes to a fourth-grader and a seventh-grader, Sally Cole and Freddie Johnson. But I thought, and so did the mayor and Mr. Whitacre, that the picture little Carl painted was by far the best of them all.

SUE: Why, I—I just never would have thought of Carl Meyer winning the prize. But his picture was unusual. I remember thinking when I looked at it that it showed so much imagination.

MOTHER: Carl Meyer, the new little foreign boy. My goodness!

FATHER: You know we—we really shouldn't be surprised. It just goes to show that in America anybody can do anything!

LUCY: Oh, Johnnie, if I couldn't win, I'm glad Carl did!

JOHNNIE: Why, Lucy!

MARY: Oh, Johnnie, I feel just the way Lucy does. I mean— well, if my little sister Dora couldn't have a prize, there's no one I'd rather see have it than little Carl Meyer.

JOHNNIE: Well—gee—gee whiz—you mean you're all glad about it? All of you?

MOTHER: Johnnie, of course we are. My, I don't know what got into us—we've all been acting so foolish.

LUCY: I'm not going to cry any more. I'm going to cheer for Carl.

MOTHER: Of course you are, dear.

LUCY: Maybe I might win some other year. I can practice up—
I can try anyhow.

JOHNNIE: Sure, Lucy, that's half the fun. It's the doing it that
counts—not who wins the prize.

MOTHER: It's just perfect—Carl's winning. It's the perfect finish to your Halloween celebration, Johnnie. First prize to
little Carl Meyer—new to our town, new to our country even.
Why, it's the way we do things in America.

FATHER: Not always, Vera, but it's the way things should be
done. (*Rising and gesturing*) Why, just think—Carl had no
friends in high places, he didn't know anyone, neither did his
parents—but he won, and why? For one reason only—because
he had the best picture.

JOHNNIE: Gosh, Dad.

FATHER: Johnnie, I don't mind telling you I feel ashamed for
grumbling about the extra money—and for trying to tell you
which picture was best. When a man's so loyal to his own
family that he doesn't want to cooperate—

JOHNNIE: Gee, Dad, I don't know. Maybe that's the way we are
here in America. Everybody grumbles and pulls for his side,
but once the decision is made, we all—well, we all abide by
the decision and pull together. You're all glad now that little
Carl won.

MARY: And the whole town will be, Johnnie. You'll see. They'll
all be tickled about it. It's just the kind of thing that will
please everyone. Oh, I can hardly wait to see little Carl's face
when you hand him the prize tonight.

MOTHER: And his parents will be so proud of him. This will
help them so much. It will make them feel at home—a part of
our town—a part of America.

MARY: Oh, Johnnie, I'm not going to the dance before you do.
I want to stay right with you and not miss a thing.

JOHNNIE: Gee, Mary, do you mean that? That'll be fine.

MARY: And Sue, Chuck can pick you up, and we can see you two at the dance.

SUE (*Rising*): Mary, you mean—well, I thought you wanted to go with Chuck.

MARY: Go with Chuck? He's your guy—not mine. (*The doorbell rings, and* LUCY *rises and runs off upstage right.*)

SUE: But—well, I did see you handing him a note the other day.

MARY (*Laughing*): Oh, but that wasn't a note. That was my best picture of Johnnie.

JOHNNIE: My picture? But why did Chuck want it? (LUCY *runs in waving a newspaper.*)

LUCY: Look—look, everyone—the evening paper!

FATHER: So we see. What about it?

LUCY: Johnnie's picture is on the front page!

MARY: Well, Johnnie, now you see why Chuck wanted your picture.

JOHNNIE: Sure, now I get it. Chuck's Dad is the editor of the *Evening Gazette*. (*He takes the newspaper.*)

MARY: Of course. He wanted the story to be a surprise, and he knew I'd have a picture to go with it. Look at the headline— Johnnie Brown, Boy Hero of Halloween! (JOHNNIE *holds newspaper and they all crowd around looking at it.*)

MOTHER: My goodness—a whole column about Johnnie—right in the *Evening Gazette*. Now, Sue, you can't say Johnnie wrote this about himself.

SUE: He certainly didn't. Look what it says. (*Reading*) Johnnie worked on the theory that a little good American common sense could save Halloween.

FATHER: I guess a little good American common sense can save anything. Son, I'm proud of you.

JOHNNIE: Oh, it was nothing, Dad. I just figured that if Halloween was going to the dogs, we'd better find some way to give it back to the goblins and the black cats. (*Then with a big grin.*) Happy Halloween, everyone!

THE END

The Great Gift

Characters

HERR GUSTAV, *a patrician*   HERR DIETZ, *a scribe*
ELSA, *his daughter*   HANS, *a gem cutter*
PETER, *a servant*

TIME: *The fifteenth century. About 1457.*
PLACE: *A town in Germany.*
SETTING: *The great hall in the house of* HERR GUSTAV, *a patrician.*
AT RISE: *It is evening and the candles are lighted. A fire is burning in the fireplace.* ELSA *is sitting on the stool near the fireplace with her face buried in her hands. She is crying.* HERR GUSTAV, *her father, stands downstage from the table. At the moment he is very angry as he speaks to his daughter.*

HERR GUSTAV: Elsa, stop crying!

ELSA (*Looking up*): I cannot help it, Father. You shouted at Peter so angrily. He's been such a faithful servant and I have told you it was my fault.

HERR GUSTAV: Whose fault it was I care not. A valuable manuscript has been burned.

ELSA: You have others, Father. No house in this part of Germany has as many. Only the monasteries have more manuscripts on their shelves.

HERR GUSTAV: But this was the Bible, Elsa—a labor of years to copy it. (*The heavy door at left opens and* PETER, *an elderly servant enters. He is out of breath and hurrying.*)

49

PETER: Herr Gustav, sir, I ran as fast as I could to the house of the scribe—

HERR GUSTAV: Stop stuttering, Peter. Did you find him?

PETER: Yes, here he is, sir. Come in, HERR DIETZ. Come in. (PETER *steps aside and* HERR DIETZ, *the scribe, enters.*)

HERR DIETZ (*Removing hat*): Good evening to you, Herr Gustav. I have heard of your misfortune.

HERR GUSTAV: Yes—yes—the whole volume charred—the pages burned beyond recognition. The book fell into the fireplace— an accident—

PETER (*Wringing his hands*): Oh, sir, I am so sorry. I bumped the table as I was attending to the fire—

HERR GUSTAV: Be still, Peter. Your whimperings will not mend the book. Well, Herr Dietz, well? How soon can you copy another one for me? A few months perhaps?

HERR DIETZ: A few months? Herr Gustav does but joke. So many pages of fine writing—the illuminators, the artists must do their part. 'Tis a labor of years, you know that.

HERR GUSTAV (*Impatiently*): Years? I cannot wait.

HERR DIETZ: What else *can* you do?

HERR GUSTAV: Perhaps the monastery may have a Bible they wish to part with.

HERR DIETZ: I happen to know they have not. There are so few. Why, Herr Gustav, you are a man who knows the work that must go into each volume.

HERR GUSTAV: Yes—yes—all right. That's enough. You may go.

HERR DIETZ: But do you wish me to begin the work?

HERR GUSTAV: I will let you know. When could you begin if I desire it?

HERR DIETZ: In a week or two, perhaps. I am finishing a Latin grammar, a Donatus.

HERR GUSTAV: Very well. (*He turns away.*)

HERR DIETZ (*Bowing as he turns to leave*): Good evening to you, Herr Gustav. (GUSTAV *dismisses him with a wave of the hand and* PETER *leads him out.* ELSA, *who has been listening, rises and goes to her father. He is pacing about.*)

ELSA (*Putting her hand on his arm*): Father, please, I beg of you not to be so upset.

HERR GUSTAV: Elsa, it is monstrous. When I think of such carelessness—(PETER *re-enters, closing the door behind him.*)

PETER: Herr Gustav, sir, is there anything I can do for you? I am so distressed.

HERR GUSTAV: Out of my sight, Peter. That is all I ask.

PETER: Oh, sir. . . . (*He shakes his head sadly and wringing his hands crosses upstage right. He opens the door and exits, closing door behind him.*)

ELSA: Father, how can you speak to Peter so? I have told you it was my fault. I was reading and left the volume on the table. It was my carelessness, not Peter's.

HERR GUSTAV (*Upset to the point of shouting*): Elsa—quiet—quiet your tongue—(*He stops, and then more quietly*) I am sorry, my dear. A man should not speak to his daughter so. But I am distraught—the loss of the book. And then there are other matters on my mind. Weighty matters. Affairs in the town are not going well. Trouble with the guilds.

ELSA: With the guilds, Father?

HERR GUSTAV: Yes—yes. It happens periodically. We've got to expect it, I suppose. They want more voice in the town council. They want their sons to go to school.

ELSA: And why should they not?

HERR GUSTAV: Elsa, you don't understand these matters. The craftsmen keep their place, and we keep ours. It is where we are born.

ELSA (*Lifting her head*): I cannot agree with that, Father. And there's something I must tell you. I've been wanting to tell you all evening. I've been upset, too. That's why I was reading the Great Book—I needed guidance—then in my anxiety I left the Book on the table.

HERR GUSTAV: The book—the book—must we keep talking about the book?

ELSA: No, Father, but I must tell you the truth. I had a note from Hans today.

HERR GUSTAV: Hans? Hans, the gem cutter?

ELSA: Yes, Father. He has come back.

HERR GUSTAV: I thought we had seen the last of him in this town. How dare he send notes to my daughter, a patrician? How dare he? I'll have him—

ELSA: John, the shoemaker, brought me the note, Father. But I need not have told you. We could have deceived you. We could have met somewhere outside the city gates, but Hans suggested in the note that he come here.

HERR GUSTAV (*Very angry again*): He shall not come to this house. I'll have him before the magistrate. I'll bar him from his guild!

ELSA: Father, please, if you would only listen to reason!

HERR GUSTAV: Reason? (*Softening*) Ah, you are young, my Elsa. Let me do the reasoning. You will forget this Hans—you will meet someone else.

ELSA: But Father—

HERR GUSTAV (*Turning and calling*): Peter! Peter!

ELSA: Father, if you would only listen. (*The door right rear opens and* PETER *enters.*)

PETER: Yes, sir. Yes, Herr Gustav. Oh, sir, I know not what to do about the book. I have been trying to think—

HERR GUSTAV: Enough of that. It is not your place to think. Just do as you are told. And now, see to the great door yonder—(*Nodding toward door left*) and the outer gates. Lock them both—lock them securely. Let no one in or out.

PETER: Yes, sir—at once, sir. (*He goes out the door at left leaving it partly open.*)

HERR GUSTAV (*With a deep sigh*): I am weary. I am going up to bed. Are you coming soon, my Elsa?

ELSA (*Sadly*): Soon, Father. (*She crosses right*) I thought I would sit by the fire for a moment.

HERR GUSTAV: Well, do not dream. Sleep would be to better purpose. (*He goes right.*) Ah, yes, there's nothing like a good night's sleep to clear the cobwebs from a young girl's head. (*He picks up candle from table near fireplace, pats ELSA's cheek.*) Goodnight, my dear.

ELSA: Goodnight. (HERR GUSTAV *exits up right, closing the door behind him.* ELSA *sighs and sits down on stool near fire.* PETER *re-enters, shuts the great door and slides the bolt into place.*)

PETER: 'Tis all securely locked. Has the master gone to his bed?

ELSA: Yes, Peter, and you had best do the same. It has been a trying day.

PETER: Ah, Fraulein, it has been a *sad* day—the Great Book destroyed and now this extra locking up. Does the master fear thieves will steal his precious manuscripts?

ELSA: No, Peter, 'tis not the manuscripts he fears for—

PETER: But it seems they are all he thinks of. (*Gesturing toward shelves*) All those great volumes—what can be in them that they are worth so much?

ELSA: They contain ideas, Peter, the thoughts of learned men. If more people could have books and read them, this world might be a better place.

PETER: But Fraulein, only a man of means, a patrician like your father, could own a book—(*There is the sound of quiet knocking.*)

ELSA: Peter, the great door. Someone is knocking.

PETER: It cannot be. I have just now locked the outer gates. No one could get in to knock.

ELSA: But I am certain I heard—listen. (*The knock is repeated.*)

PETER: Fraulein, our ears deceive us, or else it is spirits come to haunt us.

ELSA: No. Spirits do not knock. They come straight through barred doors. I'll go. (*She crosses left and starts to unbolt the door.*)

PETER (*Frightened*): You must not. We know not who it is.

ELSA: Perhaps I do know, Peter.

PETER: But the master's orders—(ELSA *pulls back the bolt and opens the door far enough so that* HANS *is seen standing outside. He has a leather bag slung over one shoulder.*)

ELSA: Hans—Hans, is it you? I was afraid—

HANS: Elsa—Elsa, let me come in.

ELSA (*Still holding the door*): I cannot. My father has forbidden it.

HANS: Then I'll let myself in. I must see you, Elsa. (*With one arm he gently pushes* ELSA *in and enters, shutting the door behind him with the other arm.*)

PETER: So? It is young Hans.

HANS: Good evening to you, Peter.

PETER: But how—how did you enter the grounds? I locked the gate securely.

HANS: So I discovered, but I scaled the garden wall. (*He strides to stage center and deposits his bag on the table.*)

PETER: But the master said—let no one in—

ELSA: He is in now, Peter—don't fret. I'll be responsible for this.

PETER: But, Fraulein—

ELSA: Please, Peter. Go to bed. (PETER *shakes his head and starts for door upstage right*) And try to rest well. (PETER

goes out still shaking his head and closes the door behind him.
ELSA *turns to* HANS) Hans, you can only stay a moment—
HANS (*Taking her hands*): Elsa, your eyes are as blue as ever.
    Ah, you cannot look angry. You are pleased to see me again.
ELSA: I thought you had forgotten me until today when I got
    your note. For months you have been away. I have enquired
    in the village of Karl, the woodcarver, and John, the shoe-
    maker, but no one knew where you were.
HANS: I have been in Mainz, my Elsa, learning a very wonder-
    ful art—something that is going to change the face of the
    world.
ELSA: Hans, what do you mean? You speak so strangely.
HANS: And your father will be most interested.
ELSA: Father? Hans, you dare not speak to Father about any-
    thing. I told him about your note. I had hoped he might have
    changed but he is still set against you. He forbade me to see
    you. If he finds you here—
HANS: Elsa, do not tremble so. (*Softly*) Do you remember
    how we used to meet secretly in the garden? You were like
    one of the flowers with your yellow hair shining in the sun-
    light—
ELSA: Hans—
HANS: We were so happy. We are meant to be together. We'll
    find a way.
ELSA: Hans, how can you speak so? There is no way for us.
    I have lost all hope since I talked to Father tonight. He says
    we must stay in the position to which we were born.
HANS: And I am a poor craftsman and you are a patrician, is
    that what you mean?
ELSA: Oh, Hans, you twist my words. You are a fine work-
    man. How many times I have stolen into your shop and
    watched you cutting and polishing the precious stones and
    making the moulds for some beautiful brooch—

HANS: I am polishing gems no longer for fine ladies to adorn themselves with, unless perhaps one for you, my Elsa—a ruby brooch for your pretty neck—(*He comes nearer.*)

ELSA: Hans, let go of my hand—

HANS: I am opening a new shop. I will make—ah, Elsa, you cannot dream what I am going to do. My work will enlighten men's minds. It will help bring truth to the world.

ELSA: Truth to the world? Hans, what are you saying?

HANS: But I should not say *my* work. It is the work of one man and he has spent his life perfecting it. Now he has taught others, young men like myself, and we will carry it on. Already we are beginning in cities all over Germany—

ELSA: Hans, I know not what you talk of, but I believe in you. Only Father—

HANS (*Enthusiastically. Starting to lead her towards the fire*): Elsa, come, let us sit by the fire and I'll tell you all about it. I have some examples of this wonderful new work in my bag—

ELSA (*Pulling away*): No, Hans, no, we dare not. I am so afraid that Father may hear us. He has threatened terrible things against you—

HANS: Elsa, I am not afraid of your father.

ELSA: Hans, I don't know what he might do. Tonight of all nights. He is especially angry. A valuable manuscript was burned—his Bible—

HANS: (*Starting*): What's that you say, Elsa? The Bible?

ELSA: Yes.

HANS: Elsa, Providence is with me. I told you there would be a way. I must speak to your father tonight.

ELSA (*Frightened. Trying to lead him to great door left*): No —no, I have told you—you dare not.

HANS (*Raising his voice*): But Elsa, this is our chance—

ELSA (*Pushing at him*): No—no—you must go at once—go at once!

HERR GUSTAV (*Off. Loudly calling*) : Elsa—Elsa—did I hear voices?

ELSA (*More frightened*) : Hans, it's too late. Father is coming.

HANS (*Confidently*) : Do not worry, Elsa. Let him come. (*The door up right opens and* HERR GUSTAV *stands there a moment, staring angrily.* HANS *and* ELSA *watch him in silence. There is a pause.*) Good evening to you, Herr Gustav. (HERR GUSTAV *strides downstage to right end of table.* HANS *moves to left end of table facing* GUSTAV *and* ELSA *backs upstage center watching fearfully.*)

HERR GUSTAV: How dare you enter this house? Elsa, what's the meaning of this?

ELSA: Hans was just going, Father. I have told him what you—

HERR GUSTAV: You dare to come here. Hans, the gem cutter!

HANS: Yes, Herr Gustav, Hans, the gem cutter. A very fine craft, sir, and it has helped me in learning a finer one.

HERR GUSTAV: I care not. A craft is a craft and a craftsman should keep his place.

HANS: Even a craftsman who makes books?

HERR GUSTAV (*Sarcastically*) : Ah—so now you are going to tell me you have become a scribe—

HANS: No, not a scribe, sir. A printer.

HERR GUSTAV: A printer? (HANS *reaches for his bag and pulls it toward him on the table. He unloosens the cords at its mouth.*)

HANS: I have learned the art of printing books, and I hear you have lost a Bible, sir. I can replace it.

HERR GUSTAV (*So astonished that he speaks less angrily*) : What's that? Replace, you say? (HANS *takes out one large volume and pushes it along the table toward* HERR GUSTAV. *Then he takes out another and lays it on the table.*)

HANS: A gift for you, sir, with my compliments. It's the Gutenberg Bible—in two volumes. Printed on the finest water-marked paper—

HERR GUSTAV (*Opening one volume and examining it eagerly*) : A beautiful piece of work. But you, a poor guildsman, how came you by this? (ELSA *has come near and is looking too.*)

HANS : I did not steal it, Herr Gustav. I worked in the shop where it was printed, and paid for this copy with my wages. (*Turning to* ELSA *who is looking at the book*) See, Elsa, is it not remarkable?

ELSA : It is beautiful—but *printed,* you say, Hans?

HERR GUSTAV : Printed—this is the work of a scribe—a very fine scribe. We have none so fine in this part of Germany.

HANS : I tell you this is not the work of a scribe. This book has been printed, Herr Gustav. 210 copies were made.

HERR GUSTAV : Printed? I know not what you talk of. Playing cards have been printed from woodblocks and I know single letters have been inscribed—but a whole book—it's impossible. It cannot be done.

HANS : It has been done. By the master, Johannes Gutenberg. You are holding in your hands the very first printed book in the world.

ELSA : Hans!

HERR GUSTAV : But I cannot believe it—

HANS (*Going quickly to shelf and bringing back a large volume*) : Then let me prove it. (*He opens volume on the table*) For instance, in this hand-scribed volume—(*He points to a spot on the page*) The F—see, it slants so—now further down—the position of the scribe's arm changed—it slants not so much.

HERR GUSTAV (*Nodding his head*) : Yes, of course.

HANS : (*He turns over a few pages*) : And here, a different style still—

HERR GUSTAV : Yes—yes, 'tis the same in all books.

HANS: No, Herr Gustav, not in this one. (*Pointing to page in Bible*) These letters are made from metal types. These same types set and reset and they print always the same. (*Pointing down the page of the Bible*) F—F—another F. They are identical.

HERR GUSTAV (*Examining the page for a moment*): Yes—yes. You are right. I can see it is so. All the letters even. Beautiful. But how it is done I cannot understand.

HANS: It is no miracle. It is the life's work of one man—Johannes Gutenberg. And now it is no secret. It can be told. Why, this Great Book was finished in a shop no longer owned by Gutenberg.

HERR GUSTAV: What's that?

HANS: Yes. Herr Fust, a money lender of Mainz, has taken the shop over because the master could not pay his debts. But nothing can discourage him. Now he carries on in a smaller shop, using his old type to print another Bible. It will be of fewer lines to the page because his type is larger.

HERR GUSTAV: Type—type—what mean you by this type?

HANS: Of course, you know not. I will show you. (*From his bag he takes a piece of brass and a lead type. He fits the end of the lead type into a marking on the brass*) See—the brass contains the matrix—the form of the letter in reverse—and types like this (*Holding up the small piece*) are moulded from it so they are all the same.

HERR GUSTAV: Ah, I see. They can be set up row by row—the words spelled out and then reassembled for other pages.

HANS: Exactly, Herr Gustav. That is printing from movable type. Gutenberg's great gift to mankind.

ELSA: And you can do this—this printing, Hans?

HANS: Yes, Elsa, my shop is ready. I have bought an old wine press and built in a frame for printing and I have already made my types. (*To* GUSTAV) You see, Herr Gustav, my work as gem cutter made it easy for me to learn this art. (*Fishing out a page of print from his bag*) And here—my first work. I have an order from the Monastery for 300 of these religious calendars. They are to be ready by Easter.

HERR GUSTAV: 300 by Easter? So short a time?

HANS: That is printing, Herr Gustav. This is but a page, but I have many ideas—to print books of all sorts on all subjects —the lectures of learned men from the universities. They can be set in type for all to read and profit by.

ELSA: Hans, now I understand what you meant. Your work— it will enlighten men's minds—help bring truth to the world.

HANS: Yes, and I can also make a good living, Elsa, so that if your father will consent, you and I can be married.

ELSA (*Turning to* FATHER *almost fearfully*) : Father, what say you?

HERR GUSTAV (*Shaking his head and sinking down on bench in back of table, almost bewildered*): I know not what to say. When you came here, Hans, I ordered you out of the house. Now, you show me this wonderful work you can do. But between you and Elsa, there is still a great difference—a difference in station—in birth—

HANS: The world is changing, Herr Gustav. Perhaps this invention of printing will bring a rebirth. Are not these differences in station artificial? Have they not come about because only a few have had the privilege of learning? Now, if books can be brought to everyone—

HERR GUSTAV: But will not this be dangerous? Already the guildsmen, your class, are rising up against us. There will be war—

HANS: If all men knew the truth, they would understand one another. They could learn to live together peacefully. There need be no wars.

ELSA: You make it sound so wonderful, Hans. A better world for everyone.

HERR GUSTAV: I do not know. I am an old man. Perhaps I have been wrong—harsh—not understanding—but all this change—it. frightens me.

HANS: It need not. (*He picks up the Bible.*) The Great Book. It is the will of God that His Word should have been printed before any other books—the Book which contains all truth. You love this Book—you revere it—and yet if we do not live its truth, what good is it doing us?

HERR GUSTAV: Live its truth?

HANS: Does it not say that all men should have an equal chance? The Golden Rule, Herr Gustav. "Do unto others as ye would have them do unto you."

HERR GUSTAV: "Do unto others as ye would have them do unto you." You argue strongly. You quote the words of the Great Book to me. Almost taking the judgment out of my hands. (*With a little sigh and a smile*) I'll take it completely out of my hands. Elsa, you shall decide.

ELSA (*Kissing HERR GUSTAV*): Oh, Father. (*Laughingly*) I do not need to ponder long. There has never been anyone for me but Hans. There never could be. And believe me, you'll not be sorry. (*Going to HANS*) Will he, Hans? (HANS *puts his arm around her.*)

HERR GUSTAV (*Slowly. Looking at them*): No, I can see. I shall not be sorry. You will be happy. My blessings on you both.

HANS: Thank you, sir. Thank you.

HERR GUSTAV: And this great new work, Hans. May it prosper.

HANS: I have much confidence, sir, that what has been accomplished so far is just a beginning. The books of tomorrow will bring changes beyond our comprehension.

HERR GUSTAV: Changes. Well, see to it that they are changes for the better.

HANS: Yes, it is a great responsibility. May the books of tomorrow help to spread only truth, that they may lead all men to good.

THE END

Ghosts in the Library

Characters

LOUISE	BECKY SHARP
DON	D'ARTAGNAN
MARY	DAVID COPPERFIELD
FREDDIE	JO MARCH
GRANDPA	CAREER GIRL
GRANDMA	BASEBALL PLAYER
SHERLOCK HOLMES	VOICE FROM RADIO

TIME: *The present. Early evening.*

SETTING: *The library of Grandpa's and Grandma's house.*

AT RISE: LOUISE, *a girl of sixteen, is seated in chair left with a pad of paper on her lap and a pencil in her hand. She is studying and her book is open on small table near chair.* DON, *a boy of fifteen, is seated in straight chair at right end of table. His books and papers are spread around him on the table.* MARY, *about fourteen, is seated on the upstage side of table. She is writing on a sheet of paper. The radio is set on table in front of her.* FREDDIE, *twelve years old, sits next to* MARY. *He is studying geography, but next to his geography book is a comic book. Dance music is blaring from the radio.*

LOUISE (*Looking up*): Mary, turn that radio down.

MARY: But Louise, we always have the radio on when we're studying.

LOUISE: At home, yes. But we're at Grandma's and Grandpa's now, remember? (MARY *turns radio down.*)

FREDDIE: So what? They said we could use the library for anything we wanted, didn't they?

DON: Sure they did, Freddie, but Louise is right. We've got to use some sense. They're, listening to a symphony concert in the other room.

FREDDIE: Symphony music. Is that what you listen to when you get old?

LOUISE: Freddie, that's no way to talk. It's wonderful of Grandma and Gramp to have us here so Mom and Dad could take a trip.

DON: And they're trying to do everything to please us. This library is their favorite room and they're letting us use it to study in.

FREDDIE: My, this must be an old house. Look at those old candlesticks on the wall. (*He points toward rear wall.*)

MARY: I guess this is a nice room all right, but it's awfully full of books.

FREDDIE: Yeah, we get enough of books at school and doing all this homework. (*He steals a look at his comic book.*)

LOUISE: You'd better do your homework instead of looking at that comic book.

FREDDIE (*Disgustedly going back to his geography*): O.K.—but this geography is so dry.

DON: How are you coming, Louise? I've almost finished with my math.

LOUISE: I'm practically finished too, Don. Maybe we can go to a movie.

FREDDIE (*Slamming his book shut*): Now, you're talking! Let's go. (*He stands up.*)

LOUISE: Not so fast, Freddie. We've got to ask Grandma and Grandpa.

MARY: But I don't know if I want to go to a movie. I hate to miss the Voice, and he comes on at eight-thirty.

FREDDIE: Oh, you and your crooner. (*Imitating singing*) I love you—I love you! He's terrible.

MARY (*Looking soulful*): Freddie, you're just too young to understand.

DON: Well, I'd just as soon stay home and listen to the radio myself. My mystery program is on tonight.

LOUISE: But the movie should be good. It's Lena Ruben, that new glamour gal.

MARY: Lena Ruben! For her I might even miss the Voice. She's super.

FREDDIE: Oh, who wants to see *her?* (*He sits down again.*)

LOUISE: But Freddie, it's a double feature—

DON (*Laughing*): There seems to be a difference of opinion. As long as we can't make up our minds, we might stay home and read.

LOUISE (*Shocked*): Read!

MARY: But we've been reading ever since supper.

DON: But that's different. You know how Mom and Dad have always been trying to get us to read books and here we are in a library full of them.

FREDDIE: It's all right with me to stay home and read.

DON (*Surprised*): Well, since when has our young brother turned literary?

FREDDIE: I've got a whole suitcase of comic books upstairs.

MARY: So that's what made it so heavy. I knew you didn't bring that many clothes.

LOUISE: Freddie, comic books aren't reading. That's just looking at pictures, like three-year-olds.

FREDDIE: Is that so? Well, I notice you look at them and so does Don.

DON: Maybe we do but that's not what Mom and Dad mean by reading. Reading takes brains.

MARY: It sounds like hard work.

LOUISE: I still vote for the movie.

FREDDIE: If only it was a *good* movie.

LOUISE: But you didn't let me finish before. It's a double feature, and the other half is a Western.

FREDDIE: A Western, that's different.

MARY: My, I guess there's no accounting for some people's tastes. But if we can sit through a Western, you boys ought to be able to stand Lena Ruben. (GRANDPA *and* GRANDMA *enter downstage right. They are a lovable old couple and are both smiling as they come in.*)

GRANDMA: Well, children. (*The children all rise.*)

GRANDPA: Now, now, sit down, children—don't let us disturb you. This is your home while your mother and father are away. You don't have to be so formal. (MARY, DON *and* LOUISE *sit down again.*)

GRANDMA: No, indeed. How are you getting along with your studying?

FREDDIE: I'm all through, Grandma.

LOUISE (*Closing her book*): I guess we all are.

DON: Is the concert over?

GRANDPA: No, they're having a ten-minute intermission. Mr. Parker is explaining about the symphony.

GRANDMA: And tonight it's Beethoven's Fourth and we've heard him explain it so many times over the years.

FREDDIE: Gee, Grandma, you mean you've been listening to the same one for years?

MARY: My, if you hear the same popular song even for a few months you get tired of it.

GRANDPA: Of course you do, Mary, but a good symphony is

different. A good piece of music is like a good book—you never get tired of it.

GRANDMA: Books—that reminds me—that's one reason we came in. We want you to feel free to use this library just as though it were your own. We do want you to be happy here.

GRANDPA: Sure—just pick out any book you want. (*Pointing toward right wall*) Over here are the encyclopedias and dictionaries and Gibbon's *Decline and Fall of the Roman Empire—*

LOUISE: Oh my!

GRANDMA: Now, Father, stop your fooling. You know those aren't the things the children will want. See these shelves over here? (*She crosses upstage to a shelf of books near the alcove.*) Here are the books we enjoyed when we were your age. And your father enjoyed them too.

GRANDPA (*Crossing and pushing back one of the curtains a little and looking into alcove*): Have you explored the alcove off here, children?

FREDDIE: We—we kind of peeked in. But we thought maybe it was your private study or something.

GRANDPA: No, nothing private about that. (*Little chuckle*) Fact is, that place is full of people all the time.

FREDDIE: It is?

GRANDMA: It seems to us that it is, Freddie. You see, it's in that alcove that we used to read stories to your father and the other children. And we read some of the books so often that actually some of the characters seemed to come alive.

GRANDPA: Children, I remember when your father took *The Three Musketeers* off the shelf here and went in there and sat on that cushioned seat near the window and started to read. We couldn't get him to stop. All he could talk about was D'Artagnan and the Musketeers. Wouldn't be surprised if their ghosts are still in there.

FREDDIE: Ghosts?

GRANDMA: Now, Grandpa, don't frighten the children. They're all nice ghosts. (*Half pulling out a book from shelf*) Yes, *The Three Musketeers* is one you boys will like; (*Indicating other titles*) and then there's *Little Women*—you'll love that, Mary, and Louise too. And *Vanity Fair*—the story of Becky Sharp.

GRANDPA: And don't forget David Copperfield, Mother.

GRANDMA (*Half pulling out book*): No, he's here too.

GRANDPA: And you like mystery stories, don't you, Don?

DON: You bet I do.

GRANDPA: Have you ever read *Sherlock Holmes?*

DON: No, but I think I've heard a couple on the radio.

GRANDPA (*Indicating book on shelf*): Well, his adventures are right here in this book.

GRANDMA: And next to these old books that people have loved for so long are some new books.

GRANDPA: New books, Mother?

GRANDMA: Yes, Father. When I knew the children were coming I went out and bought some of the best new things.

GRANDPA: But Mother, they can't stand up to the old classics.

GRANDMA: Now Father, how do you know? That's what some people said about Dickens' works when he first wrote them. Don't be so old-fashioned. Some of the modern authors are doing very fine things.

GRANDPA: Humph.

GRANDMA: But they are. Now, there's a career book or two here and some sports stories. Here's a good one about baseball . . . (*Turning to the children*) Well, I guess there's enough to keep you children busy.

GRANDPA: Sure. Just pick out whatever book you want and start enjoying yourself. You can take it into the alcove there or up to your room.

LOUISE: Thanks, Grandpa, but—

FREDDIE: Do we have to do it right now?

GRANDMA: Why—why, no. You don't have to do it at all. But we thought—

DON: You see, Grandma, we planned to go to a movie tonight.

GRANDPA: A movie? Oh, I—I see. Well, if that's what you want to do, perhaps your grandmother and I ought to go with you.

LOUISE: But we don't want to take you away from your concert—

DON: It isn't necessary, Grandpa. After all, I'm fifteen and Louise is sixteen.

GRANDPA: Sure—sure, you're old enough and it isn't far. (GRANDPA *and* GRANDMA *start right.*) Well, it's certainly nice to have you children here—and maybe you can start on those books some other night.

GRANDMA: Of course they can, Father. After all, they're going to be here two weeks. (*They go out. There is a pause.*)

LOUISE: Oh, me. . . . Do you think we ought to go, Don?

DON: I don't know.

MARY: Why not go?

LOUISE: Well, Grandma and Grandpa were rather disappointed that we weren't more interested in their books.

MARY: But *Little Women*—isn't that awfully old-fashioned?

LOUISE: And I wanted to see Lena Ruben—she's so glamorous. . . . Oh, come on, let's go to the movie! (*She rises, leaving her book and papers on small table.*)

MARY: I'm ready. (*She rises, turns off radio and straightens her papers.* DON *and* FREDDIE *straighten theirs too so that center of table is clear. There is the sound of thunder off.*)

FREDDIE: Was that thunder?

DON: We'd better hurry if there's going to be a shower.

LOUISE: All right. Tomorrow night I suppose we'll have to look at some of those books.

MARY: Oh, maybe not. Maybe Grandpa and Grandma will forget all about it. Mom and Dad have given up trying to make us read.

DON: Yes, I've got to really *see* or *hear* my characters. That's what the older generation never seems to understand about us. Characters in books are just dead as far as I'm concerned.

LOUISE: And I guess they're going to stay dead—and buried— what with movies and radio and television. Turn off the light, Freddie. (*The children exit right,* FREDDIE *last. He presses a switch near door and the lights go off. There must be enough light left so that objects upstage may be seen. There is a pause. Then there is a slight sound upstage left, the curtain moves and a figure appears in the doorway of the alcove. The figure strikes a match, holds it up, illuminating his face. It is Sherlock Holmes with his calibash pipe in his mouth. He crosses toward right lighting first one candle and then the other. If more than one match is necessary he uses it. As he lights the candles, the stage is illuminated by a yellow light.*)

SHERLOCK (*As he lights last candle*): There, that's better. Hmmm, dead and buried, are we? We shall see . . . (*He goes upstage, takes book off shelf and walks downstage to table, looking at book as he walks.*) The Adventures of Sherlock Holmes. (*He tosses book open onto table*) Why, they don't know what they're missing! (*BECKY SHARP appears in alcove door.*)

BECKY: Oh, hello, Sherlock, how are you?

SHERLOCK (*Turning with a formal bow*): Detective Sherlock Holmes at your service, Miss Sharp.

BECKY: Can't you ever get in the habit of calling me Becky? Why must you always be so formal?

SHERLOCK: Perhaps because I was brought up that way.

BECKY: Well, I was not. I had to scheme and fight for everything I got—and I'm in a fighting spirit right this minute. Those children— (*There is more thunder off.* BECKY *jumps a little.*) My, what was that?

SHERLOCK: Thunder. There's going to be a storm.

BECKY: There, you see? A perfect night to stay home with a good book, and instead of that, those children all run off. (*She runs to shelf and takes book off, bringing it back to table.*) *Vanity Fair*—this is the whole story of my life and what a life I had! (*She puts book open on table. The curtains are thrown open and* D'ARTAGNAN *strides in left.*)

D'ARTAGNAN (*Waving his rapier*): Where are the rascals? The scoundrels! Let me at them.

SHERLOCK: Ah, if it isn't D'Artagnan, the hot-headed youth from Gascony.

D'ARTAGNAN: Who dares to cast aspersions on the Musketeers? I shall call Athos, Porthos and Aramis. (*He turns toward alcove.*) All for one and one for all!

SHERLOCK: Now, now, not so fast, my dear fellow. We don't need an army. I find that quiet reflection helps to solve problems.

D'ARTAGNAN: Perhaps, sir, but in my day we did things differently. (*He brandishes his rapier.*) The only honorable course is a duel.

BECKY: Oh, fiddlesticks, D'Artagnan, stop waving that overgrown carving knife. Sherlock is right. The mind is mightier than the sword, someone said. Didn't they, Sherlock?

SHERLOCK: The correct quote is: "The pen is mightier than the sword," but it's the same idea.

D'ARTAGNAN (*Frowning and grabbing his book from the shelf and opening it*): Perhaps so, perhaps so. But for that young rapscallion to say (*He points to book.*) that *The Three Mus-*

keteers is not exciting—why—why— (*He puts book open on the table.*) there's excitement in every page!

SHERLOCK: My dear D'Artagnan, we understand just how you feel. We have all been grossly insulted.

D'ARTAGNAN: Why is it that these young rascals don't like us?

SHERLOCK: Now you've hit on something. We must search for the reason.

BECKY: I know the reason. They're just ignorant. (DAVID COPPERFIELD *enters left.*)

DAVID: My dear Miss Sharp, let us not make too hasty a judgment.

BECKY: Well, David Copperfield, I believe.

DAVID: In truth it is, and as I was going to say, in my long and varied career I have known a great many people, and while a few of them, it is true, turned out to be complete rascals—

SHERLOCK: Ah, yes, Uriah Heep for instance.

DAVID: Exactly, but there were so many others who did not. You take Micawber—he had faults aplenty but could anyone help liking him? (*He takes his book from a shelf and leafs through it.*) And then there's Aunt Betsey and Peggotty, Barkis and Steerforth—

BECKY: Steerforth—he didn't treat you very well, I'd say.

DAVID: My dear Miss Sharp, for you to criticize Steerforth after the way you treated some of your friends—

BECKY: Oh, you would bring that up. And I know I'm not your type. But what difference does it make whether we like your friends or not? The point is that these children don't like us. (Jo MARCH *runs in left.*)

JO: Who says they don't like us?

BECKY: Oh, hello, Jo.

SHERLOCK: Why, how do you do, Miss March? Surely you heard what they said about *Little Women?* Old-fashioned, they called you.

Jo: Yes, I heard them. (*Little laugh*) Old-fashioned indeed. Why, I was a lady author at a time when lady authors were something unusual.

D'Artagnan (*Sarcastically*): Lady author. If the pen is mightier than the sword, perhaps Miss Jo can solve our problem for us.

Sherlock: Oh, don't take that trite saying too much to heart, D'Artagnan. (*To* Jo) Our friend is anxious to fight a duel.

Jo: Of course. And I understand, D'Artagnan. I was always a tomboy and wanting to fight duels myself, but in this case it's just that the children don't know us. (*She runs and gets her book from shelf and opens it.*) Why, if they could only spend one evening with the March family, with Meg and Amy and Beth— (*She puts book open on table.*)

David: You do have a wonderful family, Jo.

Jo: Yes, and with these children visiting here I thought we'd have a chance to really come alive again.

D'Artagnan: Alive? Who says I'm not alive?

Jo: Oh, don't be difficult, D'Artagnan. You know what I mean. We're really all just ghosts of the library the way things are now. But if these children would read us, it would be like old times again.

David: You're right. I'm sure we'd enjoy them. They seem like nice children.

Becky: Well, David, if they're such nice children, why don't they like us?

Sherlock: Miss Sharp, as usual you have come to the crux of the matter. Might I offer a few humble deductions?

D'Artagnan: Very well, if we must have words instead of action.

David: By all means, let's hear what you think, Mr. Holmes.

Sherlock: Thank you. The case in a nutshell seems to be that these children are nice people and we are nice people. Why can't we know each other? Now, as I see it, there must be something coming between us. We have to look for clues. (*He goes to table and points to radio.*) Now you take this strange machine over here— (*They all gather near table and look at radio.*)

BECKY: Oh, they call it a radio. All sorts of voices and noises come out. That little knob turns it on. (*She reaches for knob. There is a loud clap of thunder and she pulls her hand away as though afraid.*) My gracious!

SHERLOCK: That was only the storm.

BECKY: Oh, of course. Thunder.

SHERLOCK: But just the same, you must be careful, Miss Sharp.

D'ARTAGNAN: Oh, let me at the thing. (*The rest all stand back. He brandishes his rapier in one hand and turns the knob with the other.*)

VOICE FROM RADIO (*Half singing, half talking*):
How's your stomach? How's your feet?
Do you feel woozy when you eat?
If you want a cure for all your ills,
Take a dose of cure-all pills!

DAVID: Dear me. Let's not have any more of that.

D'ARTAGNAN (*Threatening radio with rapier*): Such vulgar twaddle. I'll run it through.

JO: No—no, it may blow up. Just turn it off.

SHERLOCK (*Turning radio off*): There. My, I've come up against some strange things in my life but I don't know what the children see in that.

JO (*Looking at comic book*): Maybe I've found a clue, Mr. Holmes. Look at this.

SHERLOCK (*Picking up comic book*): A comic book. It must be funny. (*They all look solemnly at book but none of them laughs.*)

D'ARTAGNAN: I see nothing funny. (*Leafing through*) Hairy

Hank, the Ape Man. A vulgar character he seems to me. Always fighting—on every page.

BECKY: Well, after all, D'Artagnan, you're not exactly a peaceful man.

D'ARTAGNAN: But I fight for King and country. This fellow has no honor—you can tell that by the look of him.

JO: The pictures certainly are horrible—and printed on such cheap paper with cheap colors. They make me dizzy.

DAVID: Why, one illustration in my book would be worth a hundred of these.

SHERLOCK: Hmmm, these clues are mystifying to say the least. Why the children should prefer them to us—

BECKY: And now they've gone off to see a glamour girl. I'd like to see any glamour girl who could compare with me.

DAVID: But this one is in the—the movies, as they call it. I don't know exactly what movies are but—

SHERLOCK: As near as I can understand it, they're more pictures. Pictures that move and speak—very wonderful in a way, but they leave nothing to the imagination. I wish I understood more of these things. (*Two characters enter left. One, a boy, is dressed in a baseball uniform with all the paraphernalia of a catcher. The other, a girl, is dressed in a modern business suit.*)

BASEBALL PLAYER: Perhaps we can help you.

CAREER GIRL: Hello, everybody. We know you even if you don't know us.

DAVID (*Bowing a little*): Indeed, and how can that be?

CAREER GIRL: Grandma brought us home with her yesterday. We're characters from the new books. (*Taking two books from shelves and handing one to baseball player, then indicating him*) Here you have a baseball star and I'm a career girl. (*Holding up her book*)

BECKY (*Hostilely*): A career girl? What, might I ask, is a career girl?

JO: I know. She made a career of something, the way I wrote stories.

BASEBALL PLAYER: That's right, and I made a career of sports —playing baseball.

D'ARTAGNAN: Baseball. What is this flimsy armor you're wearing? (*He pokes at chest protector with point of his rapier.*) Why, I could run it through.

BASEBALL PLAYER (*Backing away and laughing*): Say, take it easy. This is part of my uniform. I'm a catcher. (*Opening his book*) See, there's a picture of me in the World Series. (*He puts book open on table.*)

CAREER GIRL (*Opening her book*): And here's a picture of me applying for my first job. (*She puts her book open on table.*)

BECKY: If you're characters from new books I don't think you have any right to be here.

D'ARTAGNAN: No—we've been around this library for a long time. It belongs to us.

BASEBALL PLAYER: But Grandma brought us here.

SHERLOCK: Now—now, just a moment, please. I'm inclined to think these new books may be all right.

CAREER GIRL: Of course we are. There are just as many good new books as there are old.

BASEBALL PLAYER: Fine books are being written today too.

BECKY: But we've lasted for generations.

CAREER GIRL: Grandma wouldn't have brought us here if she hadn't thought we were worthwhile.

DAVID: The young lady is right. And we won't get anywhere by arguing. We must try to cooperate. If we unite, maybe we can solve our problem.

BECKY: Well, I don't know. (*To new characters*) I suppose you think the children like you?

CAREER GIRL: Not at all. We're in the same boat you are.

BASEBALL PLAYER: You saw how it was tonight. They didn't pay any attention to us either.

SHERLOCK: Then it's as I said. These other things are keeping them from us. This terrible machine they call the radio.

BASEBALL PLAYER: Oh, there's nothing wrong with the radio, or the movies either. They've done some fine things. But the point I make is that we ought to be able to stand up against this competition.

DAVID: But how can we if the children just aren't interested in books?

SHERLOCK: You heard what the oldest boy said—that he had to see and hear his characters? It's a mistaken idea of realism.

JO: Of course. Don't the children know that the things of the mind are more real than pictures?

D'ARTAGNAN: Haven't they any imagination?

CAREER GIRL: Yes, they have imaginations, but they don't know how to use them.

SHERLOCK: Then we'll have to find some way to show them how.

JO: If we could just get them interested in us—

DAVID: If they would only look at us. If they would give us half a chance our stories would do the rest.

BECKY: I ought to be able to figure something. I always could.

CAREER GIRL: You're a great little conniver, Becky, but some of the methods you use—

BECKY: But this is in a good cause. (*Getting an idea*) Pictures! They like pictures!

CAREER GIRL: Of course they do. They're trained to them. What with movies, television, and radio I think this must be the pictorial age.

BECKY: Then listen. All our books have illustrations, so let's leave them open on the table where the children will be bound to see them.

DAVID: No—no, we can't do that.

JO: We can't upset the library. After all, Grandpa and Grandma have let us live here a long time.

SHERLOCK: You're right, Jo. They're always so careful to put the books away. It would upset them if they found the place in a muddle. (*There is a loud clap of thunder.*)

D'ARTAGNAN: Hah, the storm is getting worse. (*There is the sound of voices off.*)

SHERLOCK: Shh-h—quiet . . .

FREDDIE'S VOICE (*Off*): Boy, it's raining cats and dogs!

BASEBALL PLAYER: The children! They didn't go to the movie. They're coming back.

JO: We'll have to get to the alcove. We mustn't be caught here. (JO, CAREER GIRL and BASEBALL PLAYER *run off left.*)

DAVID: But how about the books?

BECKY: It's too late. (BECKY *and* DAVID *run off leaving* SHERLOCK *and* D'ARTAGNAN.)

SHERLOCK: Off with you, D'Artagnan.

D'ARTAGNAN (*Starting left, then turning*): What about the candles, Sherlock?

SHERLOCK: Ah—the candles. Very careless of me. But it's too late—too late. (*They go off.* MARY *and* LOUISE *come running in right followed by* DON *and* FREDDIE.)

LOUISE: What a storm! Where's that light switch?

DON: Right here. (*He pushes light switch.*) The lights are off. That last crash must have done it.

FREDDIE: But—but—the candles—look—they're lighted.

MARY: Yes, Grandma and Grandpa must have lit them.

LOUISE: That was nice of them. I guess they knew we'd get stuck and wouldn't be able to go to the movie.

FREDDIE: We could have waited under that awning until it stopped raining.

DON: Ho, it's never going to stop. We were smart to run back that block instead of trying to go on.

LOUISE: Yes, I'm wet enough as it is. (*Shaking her hair*) But what are we going to do now?

DON: At least we can listen to the radio. I'm glad it's a portable. (*He turns radio on and there is a blare of static.*)

LOUISE: What's the matter?

DON (*Disgustedly*): Static—it's all over the dial. (*He switches radio off.*)

MARY: You mean to say we can't listen to the radio? What on earth will we do?

DON (*Sitting down at table*): Search me. (*Noticing books open*) Say, what are all these books?

LOUISE (*Crossing near DON*): I don't know, and they're all open. Do you suppose Grandma and Grandpa put them out?

MARY: They must have. These are the books they mentioned. (*Looking at a book*) Here's *Little Women*. (*She sits down.*)

FREDDIE (*Looking at open book*): Say, here's a picture. The Three Musketeers on horseback—it looks kind of exciting. I wonder if there's a picture on every page. (*He sits down and turns page.*) Oh, no, there's a lot of reading in between, I guess. (*He stops and studies a page.*)

DON (*Looking at a book*): Hmm—here's Sherlock Holmes and Dr. Watson working on a case.

LOUISE: I can't imagine what this picture's all about. There's a girl peering out of a carriage. (*Sitting down and turning to cover of book*) Hmm, *Vanity Fair*. I guess I'll read some and find out what this picture means.

MARY: My, this family in *Little Women* look as though they're having a good time. I wish I knew who they all were. The costumes are old-fashioned all right, but they're kind of cute.

FREDDIE: Quiet.

MARY: What's the matter with you?

FREDDIE: I'm reading.

MARY: No—you don't say so?

FREDDIE: Well, I couldn't find the place where it told about the picture, so I'm starting from the beginning.

LOUISE: Good for you, Freddie. I'm started too. And I think the girl in the carriage is Becky Sharp. She seems like quite a gal.

DON: Boy, this Sherlock Holmes is all right. It has you guessing right at the start.

MARY: I've been skipping. The sisters are Jo and Meg and Beth and Amy—and there's the most wonderful boy next door called Laurie—but I guess I'd better start at the beginning too.

LOUISE (*Rising with her book*): Do you know what I'm going to do? I've often heard Mother say how wonderful it was on a rainy evening to curl up in bed with a good book. I think I'll try it.

MARY: That's a good idea, Louise, but what will we do for light?

DON: Oh, the lights probably won't be off long. Humph, you know this is something. The four of us sitting here reading by candlelight.

MARY: It is funny, isn't it? What happened to us?

LOUISE: Oh, a lot of things I guess. The storm—and then we didn't have anything else to do.

DON: Yes, and Grandpa and Grandma weren't so dumb, leaving these books open at the illustrations.

FREDDIE: Sure. They knew we liked pictures.

DON: I'm beginning to think we've relied too much on pictures. Why, I've only read a few pages here and I can see the characters in my mind just as clearly as if they were on a screen.

LOUISE: I know, and as you read what they say, you can hear them too. (*The lights come on.*)

FREDDIE: Boy, the lights are on. (*Rising with his book*) Come on, Don, let's you and I go upstairs with our books.

DON (*Rising*): O.K. . . . (*Then noticing other books*) Say, what are these other books? Here's *David Copperfield* by Charles Dickens.

LOUISE (*Picking up book*): Why, this is the story of a career girl. It must be a new book.

DON (*Picking up another*): And this is a baseball story.

FREDDIE: Baseball? Oh, give me that. (*He takes book from Don.*) But gee, I don't know—*The Three Musketeers* is so exciting—

DON: Well, Freddie, there's no law against reading two books, you know. I think I'll take both of these.

LOUISE: I'm going to take this modern story. Then when I finish *Vanity Fair,* I can start that.

MARY (*Ruefully*): But I've got only one.

LOUISE: Oh, *Little Women* will keep you busy for a while, and when you've finished that you can have one of mine. We can change around.

DON (*Laughing*): I guess you two needn't fight over books— there's a whole library of them here.

MARY: There certainly is, and it's going to be fun. (*She starts right as* GRANDPA *and* GRANDMA *enter right.*)

GRANDMA: Why, children. I thought we heard voices. You didn't go to the movie after all.

LOUISE: No, the storm chased us back.

DON: We've been looking at the books—the ones you told us about—and if it's all right with you we are going right up to our rooms and read.

GRANDMA (*Surprised*): Why, my goodness! Of course it's all right.

Don: And say, thanks a lot for putting them out.

Louise: Yes. Good night.

All: Good night, Grandpa. Good night, Grandma. (*They go off right.* Grandpa *and* Grandma *look at one another.*)

Grandma: Well! What's happened to those children? They're so enthusiastic about the books.

Grandpa: Yes, and they certainly weren't before. And what did they mean about our putting them out? Did you put some books out for them?

Grandma: No. Didn't you?

Grandpa: No. Well, it's beyond me.

Grandma: And look, the candles are burning. Why, they haven't been lighted for years.

Grandpa: The children must have lit them when the lights went out.

Grandma: Just think, here they were reading by candlelight. Oh, I'm so glad they're going to enjoy the library. (Grandpa *takes her hand. They are both in front of the table now facing downstage.*)

Grandpa: Yes, Mother, it kind of makes the old library come to life again, doesn't it? (Sherlock Holmes *steps quietly out from left holding a candle snuffer in his hand, and starts tiptoeing across backstage. During the next few lines he snuffs out both the candles and tiptoes left again.*)

Grandma (*Smiling*): Yes, it does.

Grandpa: Y'know, I can almost imagine all our different friends in the alcove having a sort of get-together tonight—a celebration. D'Artagnan, Copperfield, Becky Sharp—

Grandma: And Jo and Sherlock Holmes; and then there'll be the characters from those new books—(Holmes *has finished putting out the candles and exits through curtains making a slight noise as he does so.* Grandpa *and* Grandma *turn at*

the sound in time to see the curtain falling back into place.)
What was that? I heard a noise.

GRANDPA: Thought I did too. Must have imagined it.

GRANDMA: No, I'm sure—and look—the candles are out!

GRANDPA: Why, so they are. Now, that's a funny thing.

GRANDMA: But how in the world? (*As they look at alcove corner, the curtain billows out again and then back.*)

GRANDPA (*Chuckling*): So that's it. It's the last breath of the storm, Mother, blowing the curtains, and it blew the candles out for us. Saved us the trouble.

GRANDMA: Well, I never. You know, I was almost frightened for a minute.

GRANDPA (*Taking her arm and turning toward exit at right*): Me, too. You know, Mother, we'd better be getting off to bed before we scare ourselves with our own ghost stories.

GRANDMA (*Smiling as they start right*): Yes, you're right—but still I did hear a noise as though there was someone in that alcove.

GRANDPA: Of course you did, Mother. (*Smiling and patting her arm. Half-jokingly*) And why not? We know it's full of the characters from our books.

THE END

A Book a Day

Characters

FATHER, *Frank Davis*	PETER DAVIS
MOTHER, *Jane Davis*	HILDA, *the maid*
JOHNNIE DAVIS	MARGARET SHELDON
LOUISE DAVIS	PROFESSOR SHELDON

TIME: *Saturday afternoon.*

SETTING: *The Davis living room.*

AT RISE: FATHER, *Frank Davis, is seated in easy chair at right reading a book.* MOTHER, *Jane Davis, sits left, knitting. Upstage from* MOTHER, PETER, *about nine years old, is playing with his electric train.* PETER *gradually makes the train go faster and faster until it falls off the track at one of the curves.*

PETER: Oh, gee whiz.

FATHER (*Looking up from his book*): Trouble, son?

PETER: I'll say. A wreck on the main line. (*He puts the train back on track but doesn't start it immediately.*)

MOTHER: Dear me, and until the train wreck it was such a peaceful Saturday afternoon. (JOHNNIE, *about seventeen, enters from left. He is all cleaned up as though going somewhere. He crosses to his father and clears his throat.*)

JOHNNIE: Listen, Dad, haven't you finished that book yet?

FATHER (*Looking up*): No, I haven't and if you want it, you'll have to wait.

MOTHER: What is the book, Frank?

84

FATHER: It's one of the Trollope novels, Jane—my father used to like them. And I'm certainly enjoying it.

MOTHER: That's nice. (*Then to* JOHNNIE) Johnnie, I'm glad to see you're developing a taste for good books.

JOHNNIE: Who? Me? I haven't read it.

FATHER: Well, you may when I've finished.

JOHNNIE: But I don't want to. I want to return it to Professor Sheldon.

FATHER: What's that? But you only borrowed it day before yesterday.

JOHNNIE: I know, but now I guess I ought to return it—right away. This afternoon.

FATHER: But I don't understand. I must say I thought it was very nice of our new neighbor to loan you some books, but you said he wanted to. Now why the rush to get them back?

JOHNNIE: Well, after all, Dad, he's not the public library. And I feel responsible for the books. Mom, how about the one you had? Maybe I could return that. (FATHER *starts reading again.*)

MOTHER: No, you can't, dear.

JOHNNIE: You mean you haven't finished yours either? I brought that home on Tuesday.

MOTHER: I know you did, but it was so good that I told your Aunt Martha about it. She's reading it now.

JOHNNIE: You mean you loaned a borrowed book?

MOTHER: What's so terrible about that? Aunt Martha's very careful. She'll return it in a day or two.

JOHNNIE: A day or two. That doesn't help. Peter, what about the book I brought home for you?

FATHER (*Looking up*): Well! The professor must have an extensive library. Does he have children's books too?

JOHNNIE: Yes, he does, but he said this one had a lot of authentic information in it. Where is it, Peter? You've had your book almost a week.

PETER: Sure, I have, and I'm using it. (*He starts the train.*)

JOHNNIE (*Going upstage*): What do you mean, you're using it?

PETER: I'm using it under my train tracks for a bridge. (*The book can be out of sight behind* MOTHER'S *chair.*) It's just the right size. (*He stops train.*)

JOHNNIE: Listen to him. I should have known he wouldn't have enough sense to know how to use a book. (*Going to* PETER) You give me that! (*He bends down and picks up the book jogging the tracks as he does so.*)

PETER (*Standing, grabbing book and tugging*): No—you can't do that. Give it back!

FATHER (*Rising and going over*): Now, now, boys, that's enough. Let me see the book. (JOHNNIE *lets go and* PETER *hands book to* FATHER.)

PETER: O.K.

FATHER: Hmm, the Overland Special—why, that's one of our crack trains. (*Opening book*) I've heard about the man that wrote this book. He used to be an engineer.

PETER: You mean a real one?

FATHER: Yes, and this is all about how he operated the Overland Special. I imagine if you'd read it, Peter, you would find that real engineers slow their trains down before they come to curves and maybe you wouldn't have so many wrecks.

PETER: Gee, maybe not. Maybe I ought to read it.

FATHER (*Handing book to* PETER): I think it's a good idea. (PETER *goes and sits on love seat, opens book.*)

JOHNNIE: But Dad, it'll take him forever. (FATHER *settles down in his chair and starts reading again.* JOHNNIE *looks frustrated.*) Oh, me . . . (*Then turning to his mother*) Mom, do you know if Hilda's in the kitchen?

MOTHER: Why, I think so.

JOHNNIE (*Starting left*): Well, maybe she's finished with *her* book. (*He stalks out left.*)

FATHER (*Looking up*): Good gracious, did he borrow a book for Hilda too?

MOTHER (*Shaking her head*): So it seems. I just don't understand it, Frank. I don't understand any of it. Johnnie told me what an interesting library Professor Sheldon had, but Johnnie's never been that interested in books.

FATHER: Nor in professors.

MOTHER: Of course we haven't met the professor yet. He's probably a very interesting gentleman.

FATHER: But not exactly Johnnie's type.

MOTHER: Well, Johnnie *is* in the professor's class at school—ancient history.

FATHER: Since when did Johnnie seek out his teachers with such zeal?

PETER (*Impressively*): He's been going over every single day for a week now and borrowing a book every time.

FATHER: But why the sudden rush to return them all?

MOTHER: It is strange. Obviously he wants some excuse to go there.

PETER: Of course he does. He wants to play football.

FATHER: Peter, aren't you a little confused? Professor Sheldon teaches history—he's not the football coach.

PETER: Oh, I know that. But Johnnie has to keep his grades up if he wants to stay on the squad.

FATHER: Hmmm, what do you think of that theory, Jane?

MOTHER: Not much. I don't think Johnnie would do anything like that.

PETER: Well, just the same, he keeps going over there, doesn't he? (JOHNNIE *enters left.*)

JOHNNIE: Mom, Hilda wasn't in the kitchen. Where's Sis?

MOTHER: Louise went out, dear. To the movies with one of the girls.

FATHER: Johnnie, my boy, there's something I'd like to speak to you about (*But* FATHER *is interrupted by* HILDA, *the maid, who enters left.*)

HILDA: Did you want me, Johnnie? I was down in the basement. I heard you calling.

JOHNNIE: Gosh, yes, Hilda, that book I borrowed for you—

HILDA: Oh, yes. Land sakes, I sure am enjoying it. It's an old cookbook, Mrs. Davis.

MOTHER: Oh, so he borrowed a cookbook for you, Hilda?

HILDA: Yes'm, but it's no ordinary cookbook—it's an antique. It has recipes and stories about the people that first thought 'em up. Land sakes, how those people used to eat. Some of 'em would have as much for breakfast as we have for Thanksgiving dinner.

JOHNNIE: Well, I'm glad you enjoyed it, Hilda, because now I've got to take it back.

HILDA: Oh, but Johnnie, you can't do that. I'm still a-looking for that Dutch apple cake your mother used to make, Mr. Davis.

FATHER: Hilda, you—you think you might find it?

HILDA: There seems to be everything in there. I'll keep a-looking.

FATHER: Say, it would be wonderful to taste that Dutch apple cake again.

HILDA: See? You can't take that book back yet, Johnnie. I need it. (*She starts left.*)

JOHNNIE: But Hilda—

HILDA: I'll let you know when I've finished. (*She exits left.* JOHNNIE *starts after her, then gives up and turns.*)

JOHNNIE: Oh, for gosh sakes! (LOUISE, *about sixteen, enters right. She wears a short jacket.*)

LOUISE: Hi, family.

MOTHER: Hello, dear. Was it a good movie?

LOUISE: Sure—and afterwards we had chocolate sundaes.

JOHNNIE: Listen, Louise, have you finished with that historical novel I borrowed for you?

LOUISE: Of course not. How could I finish it in a movie? (*She tosses coat over chair at right.*)

JOHNNIE: But I just have to take it back.

LOUISE: Well, that's nice, I must say. You practically force a book on me, and now that I'm interested you want to return it.

FATHER: Yes, John, let's get to the bottom of this—the M. O. as they say on the television shows. The motive.

JOHNNIE: The motive? For what? Gosh, can't I do a favor for the family without having a motive?

FATHER: I don't like to seem suspicious, son, but having done the favor you now seem to want to undo it.

LOUISE (*Sitting down right and picking up a magazine*): Dad, he just wants an excuse to go over to the Sheldons.

FATHER: Exactly—but why? It has been insinuated, Johnnie, that you want to be sure of good grades in ancient history.

JOHNNIE: Insinuated? (*He starts toward* PETER) That sounds like you. (PETER *dodges off love seat and to right of* FATHER. JOHNNIE *turns to* FATHER.) Dad, you don't think I'd do a thing like that, do you?

FATHER: No, son, I really don't but—

LOUISE (*Laughing*): You're on the wrong track, Dad. Can't you put two and two together? He goes over to see Margaret.

JOHNNIE: You leave her out of this.

MOTHER: Margaret—why, of course, the professor's daughter.

FATHER: But I didn't even know he had a daughter.

MOTHER: Frank, you never listen to anything I tell you.

LOUISE: She's just darling-looking, Dad—everyone at school

thinks so, but she's kind of hard to get acquainted with. Stand-offish or something.

JOHNNIE: She is not.

LOUISE: Well, you ought to know. You've been walking home from school with her every day, and borrowing a book from her father.

PETER (*Sing-song as he goes back to love seat*): Johnnie's got a girl friend. Johnnie's got a girl friend.

JOHNNIE: You keep out of this.

LOUISE: I'm afraid he hasn't, Peter. You still haven't got a date with her, have you, Johnnie?

JOHNNIE: That's my affair.

LOUISE: Oh, don't be so high and mighty. I know you haven't. And you'd give anything to take her to the big party at school next week. Lots of the fellows would.

MOTHER: Have you asked her to go with you, Johnnie?

JOHNNIE: Well—er—not exactly. I was kind of working up to it.

FATHER: Working up? Excuse me, son, but if I were a young man and had borrowed as many books as you have—what's the matter? Where's your nerve?

JOHNNIE: Dad, you don't understand. A thing like this takes time. Margaret—well, she's different. You can't ask her something all of a sudden.

FATHER: I certainly wouldn't call it sudden.

JOHNNIE: You can't talk about just ordinary things to Margaret. You kind of feel as though you ought to talk about poetry or the moon or—

FATHER: Tsk, tsk. He really has it bad, Jane.

MOTHER: Now, Frank, don't tease him. Johnnie, if I'd known you wanted to get better acquainted with Margaret, I'd have invited her over.

JOHNNIE: Gosh, Mom, you can't do that. She might think I was running after her.

FATHER: You mean she doesn't think that now?

JOHNNIE: Of course not. She just thinks I'm interested in her father's library, but if I could have gone over there this afternoon, I was going to ask her.

MOTHER: My goodness. I tell you, dear, why don't you go over and borrow a book for yourself?

JOHNNIE: I've done that already.

FATHER: Well, then return it.

JOHNNIE: But that's just it, I can't. They're sure to ask me how I liked the one I borrowed for myself and I—I haven't read it yet.

FATHER: Ah, you're in the same boat we are.

JOHNNIE: No, it's worse. I haven't even opened mine. I've been so busy thinking how I could ask Margaret to the party.

LOUISE: Well, if you want my opinion, you're not her type anyhow, Johnnie. She is different, Mom. I think it's the way she's been brought up, just by the professor. Her mother died when she was a little girl. She's—well, sort of shy and she loves books and music.

MOTHER: She sounds sweet.

JOHNNIE: Gosh, she is. I mean—

LOUISE: Bill Foster thinks so too. I saw him talking to her on the porch when I went by.

JOHNNIE: Hey, you didn't.

LOUISE: I certainly did—and he's much more her type. He's read a book.

JOHNNIE: Listen, so have I.

FATHER: Better get busy, son, and read that one you've got so you can hurry over there—

JOHNNIE: But Dad, it's a big thick book. It would take ages.

LOUISE: Well, it looks as though you're out of luck, and Bill's going to be the one who takes Margaret to the party.

JOHNNIE: But he can't—listen, Mom, wouldn't you think just one person in this family could cooperate a little?

MOTHER (*Rising and going to him*): Now, Johnnie—

JOHNNIE: But for something that may affect a fella's whole life? You'd think that was more important than some old book.

FATHER: It seems the book *was* important, Johnnie. If you'd read yours—

MOTHER: Never mind, Frank. Johnnie, if it means so much to you, maybe you *can* return one of the books. Mine's loaned out but how about yours, Peter?

PETER: No, Mom. Now that I've started reading it, I'm learning all about trains.

MOTHER: Frank?

FATHER (*Shutting book resignedly*): Oh, very well. I'll be the martyr. Johnnie, I certainly hate to forego the ending but if you think returning this book will help you ask the girl to the party—

LOUISE: The whole thing's silly. It's too late now anyhow. I'll bet she's going with Bill Foster.

JOHNNIE: Louise, do you have to keep rubbing it in when you know— (*The doorbell rings off right.*)

MOTHER: Oh dear, there's someone at the door.

LOUISE: I'll go, Mom. (*She rises and goes off right.*)

MOTHER: Now, Johnnie, I think you're taking this whole thing too seriously.

JOHNNIE: But Mom, it *is* serious. (LOUISE *re-enters right with* MARGARET SHELDON.)

LOUISE: Mother, it—it's Margaret. Margaret Sheldon.

MOTHER: Why, my goodness—I mean, come in, dear.

MARGARET (*Smiling*): I—I'm sorry to bother you, but I—I wanted to speak to Johnnie about something.

JOHNNIE (*Pleased*) : Gosh. You—you did?

LOUISE : I guess you haven't met my mother and father, Margaret.

MARGARET : How do you do?

FATHER (*Rising*) : We're glad to know you, Margaret. (*He sits again.*)

LOUISE : And this is my little brother, Peter.

PETER (*Nodding*) : H'llo.

MARGARET : Well—uh—I'm awfully sorry, Johnnie, but Father needs one of his books.

JOHNNIE : He—he does?

MARGARET : Yes. He's working on a lecture and he wants to look up something. I—I thought you'd be coming over and I could ask you for it but then when you didn't—

JOHNNIE : I'm sorry, Margaret. Which book does he need? Maybe it's the one my father is reading.

FATHER : I wouldn't be a bit surprised. It seems I am not meant to finish my Trollope novel. (*He holds book out to* MARGARET.)

MARGARET : Oh, it's not that one, Mr. Davis. (FATHER *puts book back on table.*) It's the one you were so interested in reading, Johnnie.

JOHNNIE : The one I—I was so interested in?

MARGARET : The one on logic. I know you'll hate giving it up if you haven't quite finished it yet, but I'm sure Father won't need it for long.

JOHNNIE : Oh, that—that's all right. I—I'll get it for you. (*He goes hurriedly out left.*)

MOTHER (*Sitting down left again*) : Do sit down, Margaret.

MARGARET : Thanks, but I really can't stay. (*Smiling shyly at them all*) It isn't very nice to re-borrow books after you've loaned them, I guess.

LOUISE: Don't worry, Margaret. Johnnie'll never miss that book.

MOTHER: Louise.

FATHER: You needn't apologize, young lady. We're indebted to you and your father. It was very nice of him to loan Johnnie all these books.

MARGARET: Oh, Father loves to loan his books. Some people don't, I know, but he's so fond of his library and he likes to find other people who appreciate the books the way he does. He thinks there aren't enough people who realize the value of books. That's why—well, that's why he was so taken with Johnnie right away.

PETER: See, what did I tell you, Mom?

MOTHER: Peter, just go on reading your book.

MARGARET (*Looking toward* PETER): Oh, he has the one about trains, hasn't he? Father felt it was so thoughtful of Johnnie to borrow one for each member of the family. (JOHNNIE *enters left with a large book.*)

JOHNNIE: Well—uh—here's the book for your father, Margaret. (*He hands book to* MARGARET.)

MARGARET: Did you get a lot out of it, Johnnie, as far as you've gone, I mean?

JOHNNIE: Why, I—

MARGARET: Father had me read it and I found it a little difficult to understand. But I don't suppose you'd have any trouble. I think it's more of a man's book.

JOHNNIE: Gosh—a—a *man's* book?

MARGARET (*Opening book*): How far did you get? As far as chapter— (*She breaks off.*) Why, you haven't read the book! You haven't read any of it.

JOHNNIE: Well, I—

MARGARET: You haven't even opened it.

JOHNNIE: But—but—gee whiz, how did you know?

MARGARET: Because I—(JOHNNIE *reaches for book to look at it and a folded note drops out.*)

JOHNNIE (*Picking note up*): What's this?

MARGARET (*Reaching for it*): It's mine.

JOHNNIE: But it says "To Johnnie." Why, it's a note to me.

MARGARET (*Taking it*): It *was* a note to you, but it isn't any more. You—you've just been pretending to be my friend—and pretending to be interested in the books.

MOTHER: Margaret—Margaret, my dear—perhaps Johnnie isn't as interested in the books as he might be, but he wasn't pretending to be your friend.

MARGARET: But he must have been.

FATHER: And my dear, all the rest of us are enjoying the books.

PETER: I'll say.

LOUISE: Of course we are, Margaret.

MARGARET (*Embarrassed*): Oh, I'm sorry. I apologize, Mrs. Davis. It's terrible of me to be talking like this the first time I come over but—but having friends means so much to me.

MOTHER: Of course it does, dear, when you've just come to live in a new place.

MARGARET: Oh, Mrs. Davis, you do understand. That's what I tried to say in this note.

JOHNNIE: Margaret, please, let me read it.

MARGARET: No, *you* wouldn't understand. Anyway, all I said was that I was so happy to have a real friend. You see, Mrs. Davis, I was so lonesome when I first came here. Daddy and I had always lived in the same town and I'd grown up with all my friends and they liked all the things I liked. And then we came here and I missed them so, but then he—(*Glancing toward* JOHNNIE)—Johnnie came along and he was so friendly and sincere— (*Breaking off and turning to* JOHNNIE) I said that in the note too. But you weren't sincere. (*Angrily*) Coming over and pretending to be interested in

Daddy's books—letting him talk about them and show you each, one!

JOHNNIE: Gee, Margaret, if you'd just give me a chance to explain—

MARGARET: No, I'd better take my book and go home. (*She starts right.*)

MOTHER (*Half rising*): Oh, my dear, I wish you'd stay a little while. (*The doorbell rings.*)

LOUISE: Peter, see who's at the door. (PETER *goes off right.* LOUISE *realizes there's nothing more they can do at the moment. She goes to* MARGARET.) Well, you'll just have to come over again, Margaret, and—and we'll see you at school.

MARGARET: I suppose so.

LOUISE: And the party next week—you'll be there.

MARGARET: I don't know. Bill Foster asked me but—

JOHNNIE: Bill Foster? Listen, Margaret— (PETER *enters right followed by* PROFESSOR SHELDON, *who is a scholarly looking man wearing glasses.*)

PETER: Mom, it's Professor Sheldon.

MARGARET (*Surprised, almost bumping into her father*): Daddy, I was just leaving with your book. What are you doing here?

PROFESSOR: Well, as a matter of fact, Margaret, I just got tired of working on my lecture. I knew you were over here and well, I thought I'd come over too and get acquainted.

JOHNNIE (*Coming forward*): Why—hello, Professor Sheldon.

PROFESSOR (*Heartily*): Hello, Johnnie.

LOUISE: Good afternoon, Professor Sheldon.

JOHNNIE: I guess you haven't met my mother and father.

PROFESSOR: How do you do, Mr. and Mrs. Davis. (FATHER *rises and shakes hands with* PROFESSOR.)

MOTHER: We're so glad to have you come over.

FATHER (*Offering his chair*): Yes—yes, do sit down, Professor Sheldon.

PROFESSOR: Thank you.

MARGARET: But Daddy, I was just leaving. Don't you think we ought to be going?

PROFESSOR: Nonsense. (*He sits in* FATHER's *chair.*) I just got here. Besides, it's high time I called on my neighbors. (FA-THER *sits upstage from* PROFESSOR. PETER *takes his book and returns to floor near train and continues reading.*)

MOTHER: We should have called on you, Professor.

PROFESSOR: Well, your boy has, several times.

FATHER: Yes—uh—so we gather. Seems to have started sort of a book-a-day club. We certainly are enjoying them, Professor.

PROFESSOR: I'm glad. Thought you would. You know, I could tell what kind of a family you were by talking to Johnnie. Knew I'd feel at home with you.

MOTHER: It—it's nice of you to say that, Professor. (JOHNNIE *looks uncomfortable.*)

PROFESSOR: No—not nice at all. Of course, my library is my hobby and I like to show it off, but it's unusual to find a boy like Johnnie these days. So interested in good books.

MARGARET: Daddy, you don't know—

PROFESSOR: What's this, Margaret—insinuating there's something your father doesn't know? (*Laughing*)

MARGARET: It's not funny, Father.

PROFESSOR: Well, what is it?

MARGARET: Uh—nothing.

JOHNNIE (*Making the supreme effort*): Professor Sheldon—sir—I guess there's something I ought to tell you. You see, I—well, I didn't just come over because I was interested in the books.

PROFESSOR: You—you didn't?

JOHNNIE: No, sir. I've never really paid enough attention to books, I guess. Mom and Dad have wanted me to, but—

MARGARET: See, what did I tell you? He wasn't interested in our books at all.

PROFESSOR: Well—now, isn't that strange? Then why on earth did he come over so much?

MARGARET: Oh, Daddy, haven't you ever heard of students trying to get in good with their professors?

PROFESSOR: Hmm. Yes, I have heard of it and I've experienced it. And for some strange reason Johnnie doesn't seem to fit into that category. In the first place he has done quite well in ancient history.

MARGARET: Well, you can't go on saying he was interested in the books.

JOHNNIE: No, that's right. You see, Professor Sheldon, I was interested in—I was interested in—

FATHER: Perhaps I can explain. Professor Sheldon, as one father to another, has it ever occurred to you that you have another attraction in the house besides your books?

PROFESSOR: Another attraction? Dear me. I—

FATHER: Your daughter. (*Nodding toward* MARGARET) A very attractive attraction, I might add.

PROFESSOR (*Looking at* MARGARET) : Why, so she is—so she is —and not a little girl any longer.

MARGARET: Daddy, please.

PROFESSOR (*Starting to laugh*) : Well—well—well. This is very amusing—very amusing indeed. So that's why you've been coming over so much, Johnnie. (*Laughing harder*) Well— well—and I thought it was my books.

MARGARET: Daddy, how can you laugh? I thought Johnnie was sincere.

PROFESSOR: But my dear child, he *was* sincere.

LOUISE: I may as well get in my two cents' worth. Margaret, Johnnie kept borrowing books because he wanted to ask you to go to the party next week.

MARGARET: But he didn't ask me and he didn't read the book. Oh, I'm all mixed up.

PROFESSOR: Let me see that volume. (*He takes book from* MARGARET.) Johnnie, you may as well face it. If you are going to be interested in my daughter you are going to be interested in books. She has been brought up on them. Now, what is this book? (*Looking at cover*) Hmmm—*The Ethics of Logic.* Well, there you are. Let that be a lesson to you.

JOHNNIE: A lesson to me?

PROFESSOR: Of course. If you'd read this book you would have discovered that there are certain mathematical axioms that apply to everything. For instance: The shortest distance between two points is always a straight line.

JOHNNIE: It—it is? O.K., Professor. (*Going to* MARGARET) Margaret, will you go to the party with me next week?

MARGARET: Why, I— (*She starts to smile.*) Oh, Johnnie, of course I will.

JOHNNIE (*All smiles*): Golly, it worked.

PROFESSOR: Naturally. As simple as can be. That, my boy, is what you learn from books. (*He hands book to* MARGARET. *They all laugh.* JOHNNIE *takes* MARGARET'S *hand and leads her upstage. They sit on love seat looking at book. She opens it, points to page and smiles.*)

FATHER: Just the same, Professor Sheldon, in this case, I'm glad Johnnie didn't take the quick way. If he hadn't borrowed so many books, I wouldn't have had a chance to enjoy your Trollope novel. (*He indicates book on table.*)

PETER (*Looking up*): Same here, Professor. I'm learning all about trains.

PROFESSOR: Well, at any rate, I guess it's a good thing I took the shortest distance between our house and yours or we wouldn't have straightened this out. (HILDA *enters left.*)

HILDA: Mrs. Davis, supper's just about ready and we've got a special dessert. (*She stops.*) Oh, excuse me, I didn't know you had guests.

MOTHER: That's all right, Hilda. This is Professor Sheldon and his daughter, Margaret. (HILDA *nods, smiling.*) Professor, won't you both have supper with us?

PROFESSOR: Oh, now, now, you haven't prepared—

HILDA (*Smiling*): Land sakes, Professor, I love to cook and I'm always prepared for extras.

MOTHER: You see, Professor.

HILDA: And besides, Professor, we're having a dessert from your very own book. Dutch apple cake.

FATHER: Hilda, you found it.

HILDA: I sure did and it's just like your ma used to make and from what the professor's book says, like your grandma used to make too. The crust's brown and the apples are juicy. I can hardly wait to serve it.

PROFESSOR: It sounds irresistible. I've always known that books fed the spirit but—

HILDA: A good cookbook's of great benefit to the stomach too, Professor.

PROFESSOR: Yes—yes. To think of the times I've perused that book, my mouth watering, but never expecting to actually taste any of its contents.

LOUISE: Well, now's your chance, Professor.

PROFESSOR: But Hilda, are you sure you're prepared for us?

HILDA: Professor, the supper's practically on the table.

PROFESSOR: Do you think we should, Margaret? (MARGARET *smiles and looks at* JOHNNIE. JOHNNIE *rises.*)

JOHNNIE (*Pointing left*): Professor, there's the way to the dining room and the shortest distance between two points is a straight line. (*They all laugh as the curtain falls.*)

THE END

Voices of America

Characters

SUE   JOHN PAUL JONES
JOHNNIE   ADMIRAL DEWEY
JANE   GENERAL CUSTER
PETE   COMMODORE PERRY
MARY   CAPTAIN JAMES LAWRENCE
SOLDIER   GENERAL GRANT
WAVE   GENERAL LEE
GEORGE WASHINGTON

SETTING: *A city park with a background of trees. There are eight statues in the park, one of George Washington at right, one of John Paul Jones at left, and between them, across the stage there are statues of General Custer, General Grant, General Lee, Captain James Lawrence, Admiral Dewey and Commodore Perry.*

AT RISE: *In the foreground are four young people, two boys and two girls, grouped around a picnic table. They are SUE, JOHNNIE, JANE and PETE. SUE and JOHNNIE wear bright-colored band uniforms; JANE wears the uniform of a Girl Scout and PETE the uniform of a Boy Scout. They are just finishing eating and there is laughter and chatter. MARY, a little girl about eight years old, is upstage looking at the statues.*

SUE: My, I couldn't eat another thing!

JOHNNIE: I could, and I'm going to. (*He reaches for a cookie*

101

from a paper plate.) Just one more of your Mom's cookies, Sue.

JANE: This was certainly a wonderful idea—to have a picnic after the Armistice Day parade.

PETE: I'll say. We'd have been starved before we got home. I think I'll have another hard-boiled egg. (*He reaches for it.*)

JANE: There's still lots of food left. Maybe Mary wants some more.

SUE: Where is she? Mom told me to be sure and look after her. That's what I get for having a little sister. (*Calling*) Mary!

JOHNNIE: She's over there staring at the statues.

PETE: She looks as though she's talking to George Washington.

SUE: Well, she probably is. She has such an imagination! (*Calling again*) Mary!

MARY (*Turning*): What do you want, Sue?

SUE: Would you like another sandwich or a cookie or something?

MARY: No, thanks . . . I'm looking at statues. (*She starts marching across the stage to another statue, saying as she goes*) Left, right. Left, right. Left, right.

JANE (*Laughing*): She's still pretending she's marching in the parade. (MARY *stops marching and stands in front of another statue, looking up at it.*)

JOHNNIE: Those little kids looked cute all right in that United Nations group.

SUE: Yes, wearing the costumes of the different countries . . .

PETE: And carrying United Nations flags.

JANE: The whole parade was wonderful, wasn't it?

SUE: I felt so proud marching with all those veterans.

JOHNNIE: Me, too, and if I do say so, I think our band held up with the best of them.

SUE: We certainly got plenty of applause all along the line.

JOHNNIE: And at the reviewing stand when we played "America" I got the funniest feeling—I felt—well, just kind of glad I was an American.

PETE: I wish I could play in the band.

JOHNNIE: What are you worrying about, Pete? You Scouts did all right, just marching.

JANE: But Johnnie, that's just it. All we did was march. Anyone can do that.

SUE: But Janey, don't forget that the reason your Scout troops had a chance to march in the parade was because you sold the most savings bonds. That's doing something.

JANE: I suppose.

SUE: But I do understand what you mean, Jane. Compared to the real veterans, all of us seemed like—well, sort of decoration.

JOHNNIE: Yes, all those Army and Navy men and the WACS and WAVES—they've really marched for their country.

PETE: I wish I could be a real soldier.

SUE: You'll have to wait a while for that, Pete. (*Yawning*) Oh, but I'm getting sleepy. It must be all those miles we walked.

JOHNNIE: Well, I suppose we really ought to be starting home.

JANE: But our folks said we could stay until it began to get dark.

PETE: It *is* getting dark but maybe we can wait a little while longer.

SUE: No, I'd better round up Mary. (*Looking upstage*) There she is still looking at the statues.

JOHNNIE: You know, in the twilight like this, that statue of Washington almost seems real.

SUE (*Looking at other statues*): They all do. My, there's John Paul Jones and General Grant and General Lee—

PETE: And Custer and Admiral Dewey and Commodore Perry—

JANE: And Captain James Lawrence.

JOHNNIE: Great men all right. I don't know what this country would have done without them.

SUE (*Calling*): Mary, it's almost time to go home! Better come.

MARY (*Turning from statues*): All right, Sue. In a minute.

PETE (*Picking things up from table*): Look at these good sandwiches we have left. I suppose we'd better take them home. (*A* SOLDIER *and a* WAVE, *arm and arm, enter upstage left.*)

JOHNNIE (*Noticing* SOLDIER *and* WAVE): Say, look, a soldier and a Wave. (*The* SOLDIER *and* WAVE *come downstage.*)

JANE: Why, hello. We saw you in the parade today.

SOLDIER: And we saw you, didn't we? You were in that Scout troop that executed all those trick formations.

PETE: Yes, we won first prize in our district.

WAVE (*To* JOHNNIE *and* SUE): And you two were in the band. We certainly enjoyed your music.

JOHNNIE: Sure, but that's just a high school band. You're real veterans.

SOLDIER: Oh, you shouldn't feel that way. You did your part. All of you young people added a lot to the parade.

PETE: But that's not really doing anything for our country, the way you've done.

SUE (*Holding out paper plate to* WAVE): You—you wouldn't like a sandwich, would you? We have some left over, and we —we'd be honored if—

WAVE: Why, it sounds wonderful. (*She takes a sandwich.*) I'm hungry, aren't you, Don?

SOLDIER: I certainly am. (*Taking a sandwich*) Hmm, a real home-made sandwich—looks good.

WAVE (*Taking bite*): And it *is* good.

SOLDIER: But say, getting back to this business of our country, you young people shouldn't feel that there isn't anything you can do.

JOHNNIE: Well, it doesn't seem there is much. We're not old enough to be soldiers. We couldn't even fight for her if she needed us.

SOLDIER: There are lots of ways to fight for your country besides being in the Army and Navy.

WAVE: I should say so. Why, I don't think there's ever been a time in our history when there was a greater opportunity for young people to help.

SOLDIER: There are so many opportunities for you to learn these days. You can learn our country's ideals—what makes her great and how to keep her that way.

PETE: But I still don't see how that helps—

WAVE (*Motioning*): Why, look at those statues. All great men, heroes of our country. Why do you think we have those statues in our parks? It's to remind us of what those men stood for. They're not only remembered for the battles they fought in but for the ideals they upheld.

SUE: I—I never thought of it in that way.

SOLDIER: You see, there are many ways to fight for your country. Learn all you can about her—about her ideals—her great men. Start now. You young people can fight to keep the peace, if it's possible. You can work toward a real armistice, when all men will lay down their arms and live in brotherhood.

JANE (*Impressed*): My, if we could really do that . . . (MARY *walks downstage.*)

MARY: Did you say it was time to go home, Sue?

WAVE: Well, who's this?

SUE: My little sister.

WAVE: She looks like a little French girl.

SUE: She *was* a little French girl in the parade.

WAVE: Oh, the United Nations group.

SUE: She's been looking at the statues, haven't you, Mary?

MARY: I've been talking to them, too.

SOLDIER: Well—well.

SUE: Now, Mary, you were only pretending to talk to them.

MARY (*Wistfully*): I wonder if they were marching too—I mean in the parade today.

PETE: Hey, how could they march today? They're dead.

SOLDIER: I wouldn't be too sure of that.

JOHNNIE: What?

SOLDIER: What I mean is—well, it's just as we were saying, their real selves, the ideals they stood for are still very much alive, and particularly on days like this.

WAVE: Yes, if I close my eyes, in the twilight like this, I can almost hear some of the things they said. Things we learned in our history books—that you boys and girls are learning now. What was that famous saying of Washington's? If we want peace, we must be willing to go to war. (*There is silence for a moment. Then* WASHINGTON'S *statue speaks.*)

WASHINGTON: That's not quite correct. I said we must be *ready* for war.

WAVE: Thanks, Don. You remember better than I do. Thanks for correcting me.

SOLDIER: But I didn't say anything.

WAVE: You didn't? But I was sure I heard a voice.

SOLDIER (*Half laughing*): Maybe it was Washington. Maybe those statues *are* talking.

WAVE (*Laughing a little*): Maybe. Funny things happen in the twilight.

SOLDIER: Well, I suppose we'd better be getting along. Thanks a lot for the sandwiches, kids.

WAVE: And don't forget some of the things we've told you.

JOHNNIE: We won't.

ALL: Goodbye.

WAVE: Goodbye—and Don, let's say goodbye to the statues before we go. (SOLDIER *and* WAVE *walk upstage and stand silently in front of the statues for a moment. Then they both salute statues and go off upstage right.*)

SUE: Did you see that? They saluted those statues just as though they were alive.

PETE: Yes, it gives you a funny feeling. And it really is getting dark. Maybe we ought to be going.

MARY: But if we wait, maybe the statues will talk to us some more.

SUE: Nonsense, Mary. (*All the statues speak quickly, one after the other.*)

WASHINGTON: If we desire to secure peace it must be known that we are at all times ready for war.

JONES: I have not yet begun to fight!

DEWEY: You may fire when ready, Gridley.

CUSTER: I will meet you on your own terms, Sitting Bull.

PERRY: We have met the enemy and they are ours.

LAWRENCE: Don't give up the ship.

GRANT: We will fight it out along this line if it takes all summer.

LEE: I was sent here to do certain work and I shall do it. (*There is silence for just a moment.*)

PETE: Say, I—I'm getting out of here. I know that much.

SUE: No—wait, Pete.

JANE: But the statues, Sue. They're—they're all talking.

MARY: See? I hoped they would.

SUE: Hush, Mary . . . I don't know if it's my imagination but I thought they said some of the things we remember them by. Did you hear John Paul Jones say: "I have not yet begun to fight?"

PETE: I heard all I wanted to. Statues don't talk. They—they must be ghosts.

WASHINGTON: Wait a moment, Pete—we're not really ghosts.

PETE: But you—you must be. You lived a long time ago, and—and well, you know what I mean.

CUSTER: You mean we're dead?

JANE: Are you General Custer—that fought the Indians?

CUSTER: Yes, and I'm not surprised you think I'm dead—that all of us are dead. The strange thing is that we aren't, really.

JOHNNIE: You aren't?

CUSTER: Of course not. Our spirits live on.

WASHINGTON: General Custer is right. For instance, take John Paul Jones. Don't you think his spirit is always with the Navy?

JONES: Yes, sir! Never a ship that sails but what she has my blessing. I remember when I hoisted the first American flag on my good ship, the *Ranger*. And then I remember the *Bon Homme Richard*—how I remember her! Now, there was a ship—

JOHNNIE: I've heard about the *Bon Homme Richard* and her battle with the *Serapis*.

JONES: And have you heard about Captain James Lawrence and how he said: "Don't give up the ship"?

LAWRENCE: Of course they know me. I'll wager they can even tell me the name of my ship.

SUE: The *Chesapeake*. Oh, we've heard all about you, Captain Lawrence.

JANE: And you, too, Admiral Dewey. We've read all about the way you led your squadron into Manila Bay. We could never forget you.

DEWEY: I am glad to be remembered. Do you know this other old sea dog, Commodore Perry?

SUE: Commodore Perry, what you said always thrills me—"We have met the enemy and they are ours."

PERRY: I hear the boys in the last war made history by some of their remarks. Didn't one of them say: "Saw sub—sank same."

PETE: Sure—a Navy flier.

PERRY: Well, I don't understand it exactly, but it has a ring to it that I like. Typical Navy.

GRANT: Well, of course the Navy is all right—

PERRY: Ah, General Grant has been heard from.

GRANT: But there's a great deal to be said for the Army. Now, you take my friend, General Lee—

JANE: Your friend? Are you two *friends?*

GRANT: Of course we are. Once we fought on different sides, but because we fought, America was welded together stronger than ever. Am I correct, General Lee?

LEE: Of course you are, sir. You're an officer and a gentleman, General Grant.

PETE: Gee, you know, I always thought you fellows who won great battles or fought for America would be kind of—well, what I mean is—that you'd be different from other folks.

WASHINGTON: Not at all. We were just ordinary people. Of course we like to think we did our part to make our country great, to establish traditions just as you boys and girls can do some day, but we wish you'd think of us not as heroes whom they made statues of but as real people whom you can feel you know.

JOHNNIE: I do—now. But if America is in trouble or has a fight on her hands, can you fellows help any?

CUSTER: Certainly we can help.

WASHINGTON: Whenever our country needs us, we're right on hand—somewhere in the background, of course, but we're always there. You wondered a while ago if we were marching today. Well, we were. Whenever America marches, we march with her.

JONES: Just because you see us in stone like this doesn't mean we're dead. Our spirits live on.

DEWEY: Our spirit is the spirit of America.

PERRY: We march with America—

LAWRENCE: Helping to make her brave, giving her courage.

JANE: We wish that we could do more for our country.

JOHNNIE: We marched in the parade today but we'd like to do more—help our country fight if she needs us.

PETE: Be a soldier—

SUE: Or a Wave.

GRANT: You can help your country without going to war.

LEE: Yes—by helping to keep up the ideals we fought for—bravery and courage—

WASHINGTON: And freedom—and the blessings of liberty. It depends on you—each one of you. For America is only as strong, remember, as we, her people, make her.

THE END

Vote for Uncle Sam

Characters

UNCLE SAM
MR. WORLD
MISS JUSTICE
MISS LIBERTY
MR. TOO LAZY TO VOTE
MRS. TOO BUSY TO VOTE
MR. TOO DUMB TO VOTE
MR. NO USE TO VOTE
MR. SHILLY SHALLY
TEN CITIZENS WHO DID VOTE

TIME: *Shortly after Election Day.*
SETTING: *Uncle Sam's office.*
AT RISE: UNCLE SAM, *dressed in his traditional costume, is seated at the desk talking on the telephone.*

UNCLE SAM: Uncle Sam speaking. Yeah. Sure—sure, the election's all over. No—no, I feel fine. Elections don't bother me. I'm used to 'em, you know. We've been having them for a long time in this country. It's the only way to decide things. Well, maybe I will take a little rest from politics now—hope I can anyway. Yeah—yeah. So long. (*He hangs up, leans back in the chair, stretches and yawns. There is a knock at the door downstage right. UNCLE SAM sits up straight again.*) Come in. (*The door opens and MR. WORLD enters. UNCLE*

111

SAM *rises*.) Well, well, Mr. World—hello! Come on in. Glad to see you.

MR. WORLD: Hello, Uncle Sam. Just dropped around to see how the election went.

UNCLE SAM: Oh, fine, fine, never better. We had some pretty good scraps during the campaign, but once the voters went to the polls and made their choice, that was that. Everybody's friends again now—working together. Free elections, they're wonderful.

MR. WORLD: Yes, yes, the voice of the people—it's the only way to decide things. I wish all my countries could be like you, Uncle Sam—strong and free.

UNCLE SAM: Well, they could be if they wanted to be. All they've got to do is let the people vote.

MR. WORLD: Yes, but it's funny how hard it is to get that idea across.

UNCLE SAM (*Swelling out his chest*): I don't know why. We've been doing it here for over 150 years and getting bigger and stronger and healthier all the time. (*He pounds his chest.*)

MR. WORLD: You'd better not boast so much, Sam. You're all right now, but no matter how strong a country is, if the people forget their responsibilities—get careless—

UNCLE SAM: Who says my people are getting careless?

MR. WORLD: I don't know, but if they do, it's bad. Some sort of "ism" bug bites them and they get sick as a dog.

UNCLE SAM (*Laughing*): Oh, you're just pessimistic today, Mr. World. What's the trouble? Things not going so well?

MR. WORLD: I don't know. I just keep going around—in circles —doing the best I can.

UNCLE SAM: Hmmm-m.

MR. WORLD (*Putting his hand to his head*): Makes me a little dizzy sometimes.

UNCLE SAM (*Sympathetically*): No wonder.

MR. WORLD: I've got aches and pains. (*He feels his back, then his stomach.*) And there's a sore spot here (*He touches one spot*) and a sore spot there. (*He touches another.*) But I suppose everything will come out all right eventually.

UNCLE SAM: Sure, sure, it will. Just give it time, Mr. World.

MR. WORLD: Well, I feel better now that I've seen you. You're the brightest spot I've got. But for goodness' sakes, don't let anything happen to you. I couldn't stand it.

UNCLE SAM: No, no, nothing will happen to the good old U.S.A. Our people are too smart for that. The election we just had proves it.

MR. WORLD: Yes, yes. Well, guess I'd better be going. (*He starts for door.*) It's good to see you feeling so well, but keep in mind what I said. Don't let your people forget their responsibilities.

UNCLE SAM: Don't worry, they'll never do that, not the citizens of the good old U.S.A. They're for Uncle Sam every time. Goodbye, Mr. World.

MR. WORLD: Goodbye. (MR. WORLD *exits.* UNCLE SAM *returns to chair behind desk, sits down and stretches again comfortably. He smiles.*)

UNCLE SAM: Humph. "Isms"—responsibilities—what's he worrying about? (*There is a pause. Then a clamor is heard off right.* UNCLE SAM *looks surprised. The clamor grows louder. Then voices are heard:* "Let us go." "Oh, no, you don't." "Bring 'em along." "This way—this way.") Oh, oh, now what? (*The door at right opens and a group of* CITIZENS, *both men and women, enter. There are fifteen in all. Five of them are in the custody of the ten others, each one of the five being held by two persons.* UNCLE SAM *rises.*) What's this? What's going on?

1ST CITIZEN: Uncle Sam, these people have committed a crime against you.

2ND CITIZEN: They've committed a crime against their country.

3RD CITIZEN (*A woman*): We demand that they be punished.

MR. TOO LAZY (*One of those being held*): We haven't done anything.

MRS. TOO BUSY: We're innocent.

1ST CITIZEN: Oh, no, you're not.

UNCLE SAM: Now, now, wait a minute. What's the argument all about?

ALL CITIZENS (*Babble of voices*): Not good citizens! Yes, we are. No, you're not. Let us go! (*Etc.*)

UNCLE SAM (*Stepping downstage toward them*): Quiet—quiet! We'll never get anywhere this way. (*The shouting stops.*) Let go of those people. (*As the* CITIZENS *holding the other five hesitate.*) Do as I say now. And you five come over to this side of the room. (*The five being held are set free.*) Come on now. You're safe in here. (*The five cross to left.*) And the rest of you stay where you are. (*Somewhat sternly*) And now, all of you will kindly be seated. (*The ten* CITIZENS *sit down on chairs against right wall, and the other five sit at left.* MR. TOO LAZY *sits on chair furthest upstage. He moves very slowly and when he speaks he drawls.* MRS. TOO BUSY *sits next to him. She is fidgety and tries to knit and read a magazine at the same time. Next to her sits* MR. TOO DUMB *who lets his mouth hang open and looks blank. Then comes* MR. NO USE *who keeps shrugging his shoulders, and last comes* MR. SHILLY SHALLY *who keeps turning his head one way and then another with a perplexed look on his face.*)

1ST CITIZEN: But they've got to be punished.

UNCLE SAM: Well, we'll see about that. No one gets punished in this country without a fair trial.

2ND CITIZEN: Let's have a trial then.

UNCLE SAM: Hold your horses now. That's just what we're going to do. We'll have a trial all right—and a fair one. But we'll need a little help. We don't do anything in this country without Liberty and Justice. (*He goes to door upstage right and knocks.*)

JUSTICE (*Off*): Yes.?

UNCLE SAM (*Opening the door*): Miss Justice, we need your help here. Could you come out? (JUSTICE *enters, closing the door behind her.*)

JUSTICE: I heard all the noise, Uncle. What's it all about?

UNCLE SAM: I don't know yet but you'll have to be the judge. (*Pointing to large chair behind desk*) Won't you sit down?

JUSTICE: Thank you. (*She sits.*)

UNCLE SAM (*Starting left, nodding at the five*): There are the alleged culprits.

JUSTICE: Oh? Have they anyone to represent them?

UNCLE SAM: No, but I'm going to call in Miss Liberty.

JUSTICE: A very good idea.

UNCLE SAM (*Knocking on* MISS LIBERTY's *door*): Miss Liberty, we need your help here. Could you come out? (LIBERTY *enters, closing the door behind her.*)

LIBERTY: I heard some commotion, Uncle.

UNCLE SAM: Yes, yes. I was just settling down to rest a bit. (*Grumpily*) And now look. These five people are accused of a crime against the country, but they're still free citizens of the United States. I want you to help them.

LIBERTY: I'll be glad to, Uncle. (*She goes downstage left and stands near the five.*)

THE FIVE (*They cluster around* MISS LIBERTY): We haven't done anything. We're innocent.

LIBERTY: If you haven't, there's nothing to worry about so just sit quietly, please. (*They sit down again.*)

THE TEN: They're guilty. They ought to be punished. They've committed a crime against the country.

UNCLE SAM (*Walking over right*) : Now—Now, just a minute. Tell me, who are you?

1ST CITIZEN (*Rising*) : We are all citizens of this country who voted in the last election.

UNCLE SAM (*Smiling at them*) : Well, well, glad to meet you. It's a pleasure.

1ST CITIZEN (*Pointing to five at left*) : But those people didn't vote.

UNCLE SAM (*Shocked*) : Didn't vote?

1ST CITIZEN : No. They neglected this most vital duty to their country. (*He sits down again.*)

UNCLE SAM : But I can't believe it.

2ND CITIZEN : It's true. (*Pointing across stage*) There's Mr. Too Lazy To Vote.

3RD CITIZEN (*Pointing*) : There's Mrs. Too Busy To Vote.

4TH CITIZEN (*Pointing*) : There's Mr. Too Dumb To Vote.

5TH CITIZEN (*Pointing*) : And there's Mr. No Use To Vote.

6TH CITIZEN (*Disgustedly, pointing*) : And there's Mr. Shilly Shally. He couldn't make up his mind *which* way to vote.

UNCLE SAM : My, my, this is a terrible charge. I still can't believe it. What shall we do, Miss Justice?

JUSTICE : We'll have to try them, Uncle Sam. Until we've proved that they're guilty of this charge, we can't do anything.

LIBERTY : Remember, whatever they've done or haven't done, they're still free citizens of the United States.

JUSTICE : You're quite right, Miss Liberty. Have your first client rise, please. (MISS LIBERTY *motions to* MR. TOO LAZY *who rises slowly, steps forward and faces a little upstage, yawning.*)

LIBERTY : Mr. Too Lazy To Vote, your honor.

JUSTICE : Mr. Too Lazy, you have heard the charge. Where were you on the first Tuesday after the first Monday in November?

MR. TOO LAZY (*Drawling*) : Why, I guess I don't remember.

2ND CITIZEN (*Rising*): I know. He was home in bed. Sleeping.

JUSTICE: You are a witness against Mr. Too Lazy?

2ND CITIZEN: Yes, your honor.

JUSTICE: Mr. Too Lazy, is it true that you were home in bed on the first Tuesday after the first Monday in November?

MR. TOO LAZY: I—I guess I was.

JUSTICE: All day?

2ND CITIZEN: Yes, your honor. We went to get him to vote, and we heard him snoring. (*He sits down again.*)

MR. TOO LAZY: I guess I can sleep if I want to.

JUSTICE: Then you admit the charge? Don't you realize that men have fought and died that you might have this privilege of voting? Don't you realize that you have neglected a solemn duty? Don't you think you should be punished?

LIBERTY: I object, your honor. There is no law that says a man cannot sleep on Election Day.

JUSTICE (*Frowning. She shrugs*): Very well, Miss Liberty. (*To* MR. TOO LAZY.) That's all. (MR. TOO LAZY *goes slowly back to chair.*) Let's hear from one of the others. (MISS LIBERTY *motions to* MRS. TOO BUSY *who rises and walks near the desk. She keeps on knitting.*)

LIBERTY: Mrs. Too Busy To Vote, your honor. (*A little sternly*) Mrs. Too Busy, stop your knitting, please, and pay attention to Miss Justice. (MRS. TOO BUSY *stops her knitting for a moment and then starts again.*)

JUSTICE: Mrs. Too Busy, you are over twenty-one years of age and a citizen of the United States of America?

MRS. TOO BUSY: Yes, Ma'am.

JUSTICE: And yet you didn't vote on Election Day?

MRS. TOO BUSY: Didn't have time.

JUSTICE: Indeed? What did you have to do that was so important?

MRS. TOO BUSY (*Rattling it off*): Cleaned the house, washed the dishes, made the beds, scrubbed the floor, dusted the furniture, cooked three meals, did a big wash, ironed a shirt—I tell you, Miss Justice, you don't know—

JUSTICE: Just a moment. All of those things were more important than voting?

3RD CITIZEN (*Rising*): Your honor, I'm a housewife too, and I found time to vote. Women fought for years to pass the nineteenth amendment to the constitution. Now we're *all* entitled to vote and still some of us don't take advantage of our rights. It's a crime, that's what it is. A crime. (*She sits down.*)

LIBERTY: I object.

JUSTICE: Yes, Miss Liberty. I know what you're going to say. It's not a crime. It's not in the books. But the lady is right. It's certainly a sad state of affairs when washing dishes is more important than voting. Next, please. (MRS. TOO BUSY *goes quickly back to her chair and* LIBERTY *nods to* MR. TOO DUMB *to rise.*)

LIBERTY: Mr. Too Dumb To Vote, your honor. (*He rises and comes forward.*)

JUSTICE: Well, Mr. Too Dumb, what have you to say for yourself? Do you admit to the charge?

MR. TOO DUMB: I didn't vote, if that's what you mean.

JUSTICE: Why not?

MR. TOO DUMB: I didn't know anything about those guys they were electing.

JUSTICE: Can you read and write?

MR. TOO DUMB: Of course I can.

4TH CITIZEN (*Rising*): Your honor, he's had a good education in our public schools. He's got a good job too, but he never takes the trouble to learn what's going on in the community, or in his country. He just thinks about himself and nobody else. (*He sits down.*)

JUSTICE: Is that true?

MR. TOO DUMB: It's not my business to worry about other people.

JUSTICE: In this world we have to think of the good of all—if not for a better reason, then for our own selfish motives. Even you ought to be able to understand that. If you don't think of other people, you, yourself, will lose out in the long run.

MR. TOO DUMB: I'll take a chance.

JUSTICE: Oh, well, if that's your attitude, you'll pardon my saying so, but yes, it *is* rather dumb. A bright lot of clients you have, Miss Liberty.

LIBERTY (*Bristling a little*): They're still free citizens. You haven't got a thing against them so far that will stand up in court, your honor.

JUSTICE: Very well. Next.

LIBERTY: Mr. No Use To Vote, your honor. (MR. NO USE *steps forward, shrugging his shoulders.*)

JUSTICE: Mr. No Use To Vote, on the first Tuesday after the first Monday in November, did you go to the polls?

MR. NO USE (*Throwing out his hands*): What was the use?

JUSTICE: Then you didn't vote.

MR. NO USE: What difference would my one vote make?

JUSTICE: I see. Suppose every citizen in the United States felt the way you do? What would happen to our country?

5TH CITIZEN (*Rising*): Your honor, I know what would happen. It happened in our town. This man is always grumbling, saying for one thing, that we need new pavements.

MR. NO USE (*Laughing*): We'll never get 'em, your honor.

5TH CITIZEN: No, we never *will* get them, not with men like you in the community. Your honor, besides voting for officials this time, we had a measure up for approval by the voters that would give us the finest pavements money can buy—and it lost—it lost by one vote. (*He sits down.*)

JUSTICE (*To* MR. NO USE): Well, do you still say it's no use to vote? (MR. No USE *shrugs and spreads out his hands again.*)

TEN CITIZENS (*Rising*): He ought to be punished—he ought to be punished!

LIBERTY: I object.

JUSTICE: Objection sustained. (*She pounds her gavel.*) Order, please. (UNCLE SAM *motions for* CITIZENS *to sit and they sit down again.* MISS LIBERTY *motions to* MR. SHILLY SHALLY *who rises.*)

LIBERTY: The last one, your honor. Mr. Shilly Shally. (MR. SHILLY SHALLY *shuffles forward. He swings from side to side as he walks or stands.*)

JUSTICE: Mr. Shilly Shally, I presume that you, too, admit to the charge of not voting?

MR. SHILLY SHALLY: Yes, your honor. I couldn't make up my mind.

JUSTICE: But that's no excuse. You have to make up your mind about *some* things every day.

MR. SHILLY SHALLY: But not about voting. It's hard to tell the difference between candidates. The butcher tells me one thing, the baker another—and then I meet another fellow and he says—

6TH CITIZEN (*Rising*): Your honor, he has a mind of his own like everybody else. I say it's his duty to decide the best way he knows how and then go to the polls and express his opinion. (*He sits down.*)

JUSTICE: I agree. Mr. Shilly Shally, the only thing that makes human beings different from dumb animals is that we have rational minds. We can judge between good and evil. Between good candidates and not-so-good candidates. And it seems to me you have failed miserably in your duty to your country. Be seated, please. (MR. SHILLY SHALLY *goes back and sits down.*)

TEN CITIZENS: He didn't vote—he didn't vote. It's not right. It's not right.

JUSTICE (*Pounding gavel*): Order, please. We'll have order. Miss Liberty, have you anything further to say on behalf of your clients?

LIBERTY: Yes, your honor. In the first place, I agree with you that the situation is deplorable. That these people did not take advantage of their great privilege in going to the polls and voting is a reflection upon them and a very dangerous state of affairs for our country. But the fact still remains that this is a *free* country and we cannot compel them to vote. They cannot be punished for neglecting their duty. Your honor, the defense rests.

TEN CITIZENS (*Babble of voices*): No—no—we don't agree. They ought to be punished. Put 'em in jail!

JUSTICE (*Pounding gavel*): Order! Order! Remember it is Miss Liberty to whom you are speaking.

7TH CITIZEN (*Rising*): Your honor, we're all for Miss Liberty —we want to keep our country free, but we can't do that, unless all the people take on their responsibilities—unless they vote.

8TH CITIZEN (*Rising*): There ought to be a law.

9TH CITIZEN (*Rising*): Make them vote!

10TH CITIZEN (*Rising*): Make them vote or they lose their citizenship.

TEN CITIZENS (*On their feet*): Make them vote. Make them vote. Make them vote!

JUSTICE (*Rapping for order*): I sympathize with your feelings. It does seem that people ought to take on their responsibilities as citizens. Perhaps there should be a law—

TEN CITIZENS: Yes. Yes. We say so and the majority rules. The majority rules. (JUSTICE *pounds the gavel and the* CITIZENS *sit down.*)

LIBERTY: Your honor, may I say another word? Of course, the majority rules but the minority has rights.

JUSTICE: Yes—yes. Miss Liberty is quite correct. But—this is very difficult. The weight of evidence seems to be all on the side of the people who have voted. But still I can't condemn these people who haven't voted to any punishment. They have broken no law. I—I don't quite know what to do.

UNCLE SAM (*Stepping forward*): Miss Justice, might I say a word?

JUSTICE: Why, Uncle Sam, of course. Whatever wrong has been done is against you. We'll certainly be glad to hear from you.

UNCLE SAM: I have been listening to all this with great interest and I might say, it's been an eye-opener. I never would have thought that there were citizens in this country of ours who didn't appreciate the privilege of voting. It just goes to show you can't take things for granted. I'm shocked—and alarmed too. But I don't think we should pass any law.

TEN CITIZENS: Not pass a law?

UNCLE SAM: No. We can't *make* people vote. We can't condemn them for the good things they don't do. That would be using force. Our country is founded on freedom—and that means the freedom of the individual. But—and this is important—if the individual doesn't make good use of that freedom, we won't have a free country any more. They say Uncle Sam is strong—well, I won't be strong for long if the people fall down on their job. For it's the people that rule this country. Don't ever forget that. Every single one of you has a job to do. If you don't do it—well, I'll probably be bitten by some "ism" or other. I may even grow sick and die—

TEN CITIZENS: No—no, that can't happen here. It mustn't happen.

OTHER FIVE: We don't want that to happen either, Uncle Sam. We just didn't realize—

UNCLE SAM: If you don't want it to happen, then do this. Keep track of what's going on in your own community, take an interest in your state government, in your national government. Watch Congress, watch your President—see if they're doing what you want them to do. If not, don't forget, the next time you go to the polls, you're the boss. Vote 'em in or vote 'em out.

TEN CITIZENS: Yes. Yes. That's right.

UNCLE SAM: But whichever side you're on, it's your duty to get out there and vote.

TEN CITIZENS: Yes. Yes. That's what we say. Vote! Vote!

OTHER FIVE: Why—why—yes. We'll do better next time. We will!

UNCLE SAM: Good! Fine! If everyone gets out and votes, we've got nothing to worry about. We can't go wrong. Because, don't forget, whichever way you vote, it's a vote for Uncle Sam.

ALL (*Cheering, raising arms*): Hooray! Hooray for Uncle Sam! (*Quick curtain.*)

THE END

Our Famous Ancestors

Characters

GEORGE PEABODY
AMY PEABODY
GREAT-AUNT HATTIE PEABODY
DICK JONES, *Amy's brother*
JANE JONES, *Amy's sister*

TIME: *The present. Thanksgiving Day.*

SETTING: *The combination living and dining room of* GEORGE *and* AMY PEABODY.

AT RISE: GEORGE PEABODY, *a nice-looking young man, is sprawled in the easy-chair, his hands behind his head and his legs stretched out in front of him, a picture of lazy contentment. He is watching his wife,* AMY, *who is putting the finishing touches on the Thanksgiving table. Under her apron she is dressed in her nicest gown for Thanksgiving. She has a dish towel in hand and is polishing a glass from the table.*

AMY: Oh, George, aren't these glasses pretty? Who gave them to us, do you remember?

GEORGE: No, I don't, Amy—we got so many wedding presents —but they're very fine milk glass.

AMY: Milk glass. Well, I hope it's all right if I use them for water. (*She sets the glass down and steps back and surveys the table.*) Oh, isn't the table beautiful?

GEORGE (*With a sigh of satisfaction*): Everything is beautiful. (*He sniffs toward the kitchen.*) The smell of that turkey and

124

mince pie is beautiful— (*He rises.*) The table is beautiful—
(*Going to* AMY) And you're beautiful. (*He kisses her.*)

AMY: Oh, George, just think. Our first Thanksgiving dinner in
our own home!

GEORGE: You're not disappointed that we aren't going over to
your folks for dinner?

AMY: Oh, no, George, and I know Mama and Papa understand.
Of course it would have been nice to have them all over here
but there are so many of them . . . Still, Thanksgiving day,
I suppose we should have had *some* company.

GEORGE: Not on your life, Amy. Two's company. (*There is a
bark from a dog offstage.*) And then there's Mutt— (*He
nods toward window laughing a little.*) He makes a crowd.
He can sit under the table and eat scraps.

AMY (*Giggling*): Maybe I should have made a place card for
Mutt too. Did you see the place car !s? (*She picks up a paper
pilgrim from near one of the pla: s*) See—George Peabody
sits here— (*Picking up another*) Amy Peabody sits here.

GEORGE: No chance of our getting lost . . . They're very nice,
Amy.

AMY: Aren't they? I copied them from an old history book.
First I thought of making turkeys but then I decided Pilgrim
fathers were more appropriate.

GEORGE: Pilgrim fathers—of course. The first Americans.

AMY: Yes, and just think, George—why, we might not be here
if they hadn't come over with Columbus.

GEORGE: Not Columbus, Amy—that was much earlier. The
Pilgrims came on the *Mayflower*.

AMY: Oh yes, and then they settled on Plymouth Rock and they
named some chickens after them.

GEORGE: Amy, my dear, you're mixed up again——

AMY: Well, I guess I don't know as much about it as you do,
George. After all, your ancestors were on that boat.

GEORGE: Now, now, Amy, don't hold that against me. You know I don't put much stock in ancestors. The important thing in America is what happens now—to us and to everyone like us.

AMY (*Blissfully*): Us.

GEORGE: Yes, Amy—and that's why I feel, at least on our first Thanksgiving Day, that we don't need any company—just us. (*He is about to take her in his arms when the phone rings.*) Now, who can that be?

AMY: Maybe it's Mama wanting to know how we're getting along.

GEORGE: Well, I'll get it. (*He goes to phone.*) Hello? Yes, yes, this is George . . . What's that? Who? . . . Good gracious —Aunt Hattie!

AMY: Oh, George. Your Aunt Hattie?

GEORGE (*To* AMY): Sh-h . . . (*Into phone again*) Yes, Aunt Hattie, I certainly didn't expect you to—I mean, it's certainly nice of you to call. How are things in Boston? . . . You don't know?—You're on your way there and you stopped off? What's that? Where? You're at the station? Oh, my! Yes, Aunt Hattie . . . Yes, Aunt Hattie . . . *Yes, Aunt Hattie* . . . (*Longer pause. Then, as though worn out*) Yes, Aunt Hattie. (*He hangs up, mops his brow with his handkerchief.*) Amy, it's my great-aunt Hattie Peabody. She's getting a taxi —she's coming right over.

AMY: For dinner?

GEORGE: Of course, for dinner. She never minds inconveniencing other people. She talks as though she's doing us a favor.

AMY: But George, a great-aunt, I think it's wonderful. We're having company after all. I'd better set another place— (*She starts left.*)

GEORGE: But Amy, wait, you don't understand—

AMY: Now, darling, don't get upset. I know it's our first

Thanksgiving but we mustn't be selfish. Why, it'll be nice meeting one of your aunts—

GEORGE: But not Aunt Hattie. There's no one like her, Amy. She'll spoil our whole Thanksgiving.

AMY: Don't be silly, George. How could she do that? Now, I'll just get another plate and things and don't you worry, we'll show Aunt Hattie a good time. (*She exits left.*)

GEORGE (*Calling after her*): But you don't understand—you can't show Aunt Hattie anything—oh, me. (*He tears his hair and looks around the room wildly, sees the glass candlesticks on the table, picks one up and looks at it, then puts it back.*) Oh, dear. (*He rushes to chest left, opens bottom drawer and takes out a pair of large, ornate candlesticks. He scowls at them, puts them on the table, taking candles from glass ones and inserting them into ornate ones. The ornate candlesticks are much too big for the table.* GEORGE *puts the glass ones on the chest, one at each end.*)

AMY (*Reëntering with plate, silver and glass*): George, what have you done to the table? Oh . . . I liked the glass candlesticks.

GEORGE: So did I, Amy, but Aunt Hattie gave us these for a wedding present.

AMY: Of course she did. Well, then, we'll have to use them. We want to please her. (*She puts dishes on table, making another place.*)

GEORGE: Amy, you cannot please Aunt Hattie—but thank goodness, she won't be here long. She's catching a plane for Boston. There's a family reunion there tonight.

AMY: Well, see, George?—a family reunion—and she thought to stop off and see us first. It's very nice of her.

GEORGE: It's not nice at all. She's been visiting Uncle Hector in Chicago and is on her way back. She never approved of Uncle

Hector's going that far west but she goes to visit him anyway just to make him uncomfortable. And now I know what's in her mind. She's coming here to look you over.

AMY: Well, I'll make a good impression. (*Giggling a little*) I make a good impression on you, don't I, George?

GEORGE: Of course, Amy, you're wonderful but—

AMY: Oh, George—kiss me.

GEORGE: Not now, Amy, there isn't time—I've got to explain. Aunt Hattie's crazy about family trees.

AMY: Trees, George? Well, we've got trees—that lovely poplar—

GEORGE: No, Amy, not that kind—*family* trees—ancestors.

AMY: Ancestors?

GEORGE: Yes, and *their* ancestors. The original hundred-percent Americans, to hear her tell it. She'll go on and on about her great-great-great-grandfather who was a drummer-boy in the Revolutionary War, and his great-great-great-uncle who came over on the *Mayflower,* and you won't be able to make head nor tail of it—I never could. But you have to listen and look interested. And mind you, if you can't scrape up a drummer-boy in your family somewhere—well, you just don't rate.

AMY: Drummer-boy—humph. Well, my uncle Jim always plays the bass drum and the cymbals in the Legion parade, and blows a cornet, too. He's a one-man band.

GEORGE: Yes, I know, Amy, he's a three-ring circus. I've seen him—but that won't do. It's got to be old—way back—ancestors—blue blood—

AMY: Blue blood? That sounds anemic, George. *Red*-blooded Americans is the way I've always heard it.

GEORGE: Amy, please—I just don't want Aunt Hattie to hurt your feelings. I remember my mother telling about when she got married. Aunt Hattie called on her and laid down the law.

She's got the whole family buffaloed. Everyone's afraid of her—

AMY: But that's silly—an old lady like that. You're not afraid of her, are you, George?

GEORGE: Who? Me? Er—why—no, of course not . . . (*He stops.*) Amy, did I hear a taxi? (*The dog starts barking off-stage and* GEORGE *goes to the window and looks out.*) Oh, my! Here she comes now. (GEORGE *now runs to the door and* AMY *runs to the window and throws it open.*)

AMY (*Calling*): Down, Mutt, down . . . He won't hurt you, Aunt Hattie—his bite's worse than his bark. He won't hurt you! (GEORGE *has gone off.*)

GEORGE (*Off*): Well, Aunt Hattie—well! Quiet, Mutt, quiet! (*The dog stops barking.*) Welcome, Aunt Hattie, welcome to our little home— (AUNT HATTIE *enters followed by* GEORGE. *She is a formidable-looking old lady.*)

AUNT HATTIE (*As she enters*): Welcome indeed—a fine welcome—that vicious dog yapping at me. (*She stamps directly across stage, taking off her cape as she goes and depositing it on back of chair. She sets small bag and umbrella near chair. Then, holding up her glasses and peering through them she turns and surveys the room.*) So this is where you live.

GEORGE: Yes, Aunt Hattie, and this is Amy . . . Amy, Aunt Hattie.

AMY (*Smiling*): Hello, Aunt Hattie. Geo—George has told me a lot about you.

AUNT HATTIE: Humph, suppose he has—well, don't believe a word of it. Come here, Amy, and let me look at you. (AMY *comes closer.*) Hmm—you're pretty enough, but that doesn't mean much. The Peabodys were never much on looks but they didn't have to be. Of course, there was great-great-great Aunt Mehitabel. She was a young girl at the time of the Revolutionary War and—

GEORGE (*He's heard it before*) : Yes, Aunt Hattie. Won't you sit down, Aunt Hattie? You must be tired, Aunt Hattie—

AUNT HATTIE: Stop fussing, George. Yes, I will sit down. (*She sits in chair.*) I've got a crick in my back from brandishing my umbrella at that vicious dog.

AMY: Oh, but he really isn't vicious, Aunt Hattie. Mutt's just playful.

AUNT HATTIE: That's what they always say. *What* do you call him?

AMY: Just—Mutt.

AUNT HATTIE: But a mutt's a dog without a pedigree.

AMY: I guess that's Mutt all right.

AUNT HATTIE: George, is that really true? You have no idea of that dog's forbears?

GEORGE: Why, no, Aunt Hattie—we—

AUNT HATTIE: Tsk—tsk. Now, you take my little dog, Lucius —I know all about him. He's from Henry the eighth, out of Guinevere—out of—

AMY: Well, we were just out of a dog and got Mutt.

GEORGE (*Clearing his throat quickly*): Amy—er—I wondered about our dinner. Hadn't you better—

AMY: Oh dear, yes. Aunt Hattie, here I am forgetting all about the dinner, and I ought to baste the turkey. (*She starts left*) If you'll excuse me for a minute—

AUNT HATTIE: Yes—yes, go on, but don't be too long. I do want to have time to talk to you while I'm here. (AMY *smiles at her and goes out.* GEORGE *walks about uncomfortably.*) Well, George, stop fidgeting about—sit down a minute so I can look at you. (GEORGE *sits on edge of chair upstage right.*) Now, then—the family will want to know all about you tonight. How you're getting along and your little wife—

GEORGE: Oh, I'm getting along fine, Aunt Hattie—fine. I like my job, and it has a great future. And as for Amy—well, you can see how wonderful she is—

AUNT HATTIE: See, nothing. You can't tell a thing by appearances, George. You have to talk to a person—know their background—their family—

GEORGE: Oh—well, Amy has lots of family, Aunt Hattie—lots of family—er—wouldn't you like to listen to the radio? (*He goes toward it.*) I was thinking—

AUNT HATTIE: Radio? Is the Boston Symphony on?

GEORGE: Why—no, I don't think so.

AUNT HATTIE: Then if you don't mind we'll not listen to the radio. (AMY *reënters, smiling.*)

AMY: Well, the turkey's just beautiful. Mr. Blutz told me he was going to be a wonderful bird.

AUNT HATTIE: Mr. Blutz?

AMY: The butcher, Aunt Hattie. He's the nicest man! He advises me on everything and he always gives me the biggest hot dogs.

AUNT HATTIE: Hot dogs?

GEORGE: Amy—

AMY: Anyhow, Aunt Hattie—now we can talk. (*She sits on straight chair near table. Brightly*) George tells me you like family trees.

GEORGE: Ohh— (*He begins walking about.*)

AUNT HATTIE: My dear, they're very important. I don't know if George has told you about the Peabodys—

GEORGE (*With a sigh*): Yes, I've told her, Aunt Hattie.

AUNT HATTIE: The Peabodys, you know, Amy, have grown with America. One might almost say America has grown with the Peabodys. The sturdy growth of the Peabody family tree is like a calendar of red letter days in American history. Wherever you find an important event there you'll find a

Peabody—the Revolutionary War—the Constitutional Convention—we go back, back, back—to Guy Ronald Boswell Peabody as he stepped off the Mayflower onto Plymouth Rock. Who in America can go back further than that?

AMY: Why, nobody, I guess, Aunt Hattie. One step further back and you'd have been an Indian.

AUNT HATTIE (*Jumping*): Humph—that doesn't necessarily follow.

GEORGE (*Nervously wiping his brow and rushing to chest*): Aunt Hattie, I—I don't believe you've seen our wedding picture. (*He takes it from the chest; shoves it at her.*)

AUNT HATTIE (*She adjusts her glasses on her nose and looks over them at the picture*): Yes—yes—very nice. People always look silly in wedding pictures. (*She hands it back to GEORGE and he puts it back on chest. Then she turns to AMY again.*) Let's see, my dear—George wrote me you were a Smith before you were married.

AMY: Oh, no, Aunt Hattie—it was Jones.

AUNT HATTIE: Jones—oh, yes—well, tell me about them. At the family reunion they'll want to know—

AMY: Oh, my, there's so much to tell. I don't know where to start. There's Dick, my brother—he was in the air corps. Then there's Jane—she's still in high school and she's got a red-headed boy friend—they're so cute together!

GEORGE: Amy, Aunt Hattie doesn't—

AMY: And then there's my older sister, she's got a baby—his name is Simon, and you know, Aunt Hattie, he makes such funny faces they call him Simple Simon.

AUNT HATTIE (*Looking aghast*): Oh, dear! Uh, Jones—I've been thinking—of course, it is a well-known name—quite illustrious in some of its branches. Now, there was John Paul Jones of naval fame—

AMY: Well, Papa wouldn't be related to that one. Papa was in the infantry during the first World War, and his name's William—all his friends call him Bill.

AUNT HATTIE: William? Is that a family name?

AMY: Oh, yes, lots of families use it.

GEORGE: Er—a—Amy, how about the dinner—the turkey?

AMY: It's all right, George, I just fixed it—remember? Oh, Aunt Hattie, I hardly know where to begin to tell you all about the Joneses—there're so many of 'em.

AUNT HATTIE: Yes, my dear, I've seen the telephone directory. But what I mean is, can't we find some one member of the family who has been prominent in the history of our country? Can't we go back—

AMY (*For the first time showing a little irritation*): Aunt Hattie, our family doesn't go back. It goes forward—we're looking forward to the future of America—

AUNT HATTIE: What's that? Now, my dear, you don't know—

GEORGE (*Desperately*): Aunt Hattie—uh—hadn't we better— well— (*The dog starts barking again. Brightly, glad of any interruption*) Oh—listen to Mutt. That was Mutt, Aunt Hattie.

AUNT HATTIE (*Shaking her head*): Mutt.

GEORGE (*Relieved*): Someone must be coming. (*Going to window. Then worriedly again.*) Oh, my. It's Dick and Jane. I wonder what they want.

AMY (*Running to door, happy again*): But that's wonderful. Aunt Hattie, you'll have a chance to meet some of the Jones family. (*She opens the door.*) Hello, Sis. Hi, Dick. Come on in.

JANE (*Off*): Mom sent us over to see how you were getting along.

AMY: Haven't you eaten yet? (JANE *enters. She is sixteen years old. She carries a jar of relish in her hand.*)

JANE (*As she enters*): No, I guess Mom wanted us out of the way while she was finishing the dinner. (DICK *enters. He is in his early twenties.*)

DICK (*As he enters*): How are you, George? (*Then taking* AMY's *hand.*) Hi, Toots! (*He swings her around and whistles the G.I. whistle of appreciation.*) Boy, you're looking sharp today. (*At the whistle* AUNT HATTIE *jumps, straightens up and stares.*)

AMY (*Giggling*): Oh, Dick, don't be silly! I want you to meet someone. George's great-aunt Hattie Peabody. (*She leads* DICK *and* JANE *across stage*) Aunt Hattie, this is my sister, Jane, and my brother, Dick.

AUNT HATTIE (*Looking at them through her glasses*): How do you do.

JANE: How do you do.

DICK (*Grinning*): Hi, Auntie! (*She starts at this.* DICK *turns to* AMY *again.*) Say, what goes on? You wouldn't come over to our house for dinner because you wanted to be alone, and now here you are with company.

GEORGE: Well, you see we weren't expecting Aunt Hattie—

AMY: But it's so nice she came. We've got such a big dinner.

JANE: That reminds me—here's some more. Mom sent over some of her homemade tomato relish.

AMY: Oh, that was sweet of her. (*She sets jar on table.*)

DICK: Say, what's the matter with you, George? (*Slapping him on shoulder.*) Where's the old pep?

GEORGE: Pep? Pep? Oh, I've got lots of pep.

DICK: Well, you don't look like it. How about a little music? (*He goes to radio and switches it on.*)

GEORGE: Oh, no, Dick, I wouldn't do that.

DICK: Why not? Need a little life in the party! (*Some noisy dance music blares forth.*) There you are—with a twist of the wrist—hot jive. Science is wonderful! (*He turns and grins at* AUNT HATTIE.) You like music, don't you, Aunt Hattie?

AUNT HATTIE: Humph, is that what you call it? And you don't seem to realize, young man. Your sister married into the Peabody family—I am not *your* aunt.

DICK: Oh, think nothing of that. Any relative of George's is just like one of the family.

AUNT HATTIE: The family?

DICK: Sure—Jones, Peabody—Peabody, Jones—what's the difference? Thanksgiving Day in America—we're all one big happy family anyhow. . . . Listen to that hot horn, Sis. What do you say we cut a rug?

JANE: O.K., big boy, start cutting. (*They go into a jitterbug dance, jumping and whirling about the room.* AUNT HATTIE *looks on scandalized.*)

AUNT HATTIE: George—George—that noise—this commotion—can't you do something?

GEORGE: I'll try. Richard—Richard—Jane! (*They pay no attention.* AMY *is watching and laughing.*)

AMY: Oh, George, let them alone. They're having so much fun. (DICK *and* JANE *are doing some extra fancy steps when a bronze medal flops out of* DICK'S *jacket and clatters to the floor. They stop dancing and* DICK *looks at coat pocket.* NOTE: *He can hold the medal in his hand and drop it when ready. Then by immediately looking in his pocket the impression will be that medal fell from that pocket.*)

DICK: Oh—oh, my hardware! (JANE *stoops over and picks it up.* GEORGE *who has sidled over to the radio takes this opportunity to turn it off.*)

JANE (*As she hands it to* DICK): Oh, Dick, your D.F.C.

AUNT HATTIE: Young man, what is that?

DICK: Oh, nothing. (*He puts it in his pocket.*)

JANE: It is, too, Aunt Hattie. It's his Distinguished Flying Cross —he won it in the war. He didn't want to get it out but Mom made him because some of the relatives hadn't seen it.

AUNT HATTIE: Hmm. Young man, let me look at that.

DICK: O.K. (*He grudgingly hands it to her. His expression is serious now.* AUNT HATTIE *examines medal through her glasses, first one side, then she turns it over.*)

AUNT HATTIE (*Reading*): Hmmm—for distinguished service to his country. May 18th— (*She breaks off.*) Young man, you ought to be proud of that. (*She hands it to him.*)

DICK (*Shoving it in pocket*): Oh, it's all right—but it's ancient history now.

AUNT HATTIE: Ancient history? It's *important* history.

DICK: So what? The way I figure it's where we go from here that counts. We kids may blow off steam with jive and stuff that you don't like, but we've got a job ahead of us—a big job. I wish more people realized it. George Washington and the rest did their stuff in their time, but they can't help us now. It's our turn.

AUNT HATTIE (*Sounding belligerent*): Just what do you mean by that? I—I—

GEORGE (*Interrupting*): Well, I don't think we have much time to discuss anything now. There's dinner—and there's dinner—

AMY: Yes, dinner. I'll bet it's almost ready.

JANE: I'll bet ours is, too. Mom said it wouldn't be long. I guess we'd better go, Dick.

DICK: I s'pose. That jitterbuggin' really works up an appetite. (JANE *and* DICK *start for door.*)

JANE: Huh, any time your appetite needs a workout! Oh, by the way, Amy—Mom says you've just got to come over for supper. We're going to eat the leftovers.

DICK: Sure, and bring Aunt Hattie, too. You'd like to gnaw on a turkey bone, wouldn't you, Aunt Hattie? (AUNT HATTIE *has her glasses up and opens her mouth to speak but* GEORGE *butts in.*)

GEORGE: Oh, Aunt Hattie won't be here. She's got to leave—

AMY: Yes, she's got to be in Boston tonight.

DICK: O.K. Well, eat a bean for me, Aunt Hattie. See you next time. So long, everybody! (*He grabs* JANE's *hand and starts out door.*)

JANE (*Turning back breathlessly*): Goodbye, Aunt Hattie, nice to have met you. (*The door closes and their voices fade.* GEORGE *sits down nervously.* AMY *starts for the kitchen.*)

AUNT HATTIE (*Sinking back in her chair*): Well, I've never seen anything like that in all my life! (AMY *turns and during next few lines moves to stage center.*)

GEORGE: Now, Aunt Hattie, I'm sorry they upset you but you mustn't mind Dick and Jane. They're young—they're full of life—

AUNT HATTIE: Humph—full of life—

GEORGE: Well, they're really not so bad.

AMY: George Peabody, what do you mean by that? They're not bad at all. You needn't apologize for them.

GEORGE (*Half rising*): Amy, please—I'm sorry. Now there's no need to get so upset—(*He sits back again.*)

AMY: I don't care. Papa always says people take us the way we are or not at all. And if people don't like us—

AUNT HATTIE: Now, my dear—it's not a matter of liking or disliking. There are just certain family traditions—

AMY: Well, there's plenty of tradition about Papa in this town. As Mr. Blutz says—if Papa does a job you know it's done right.

GEORGE: Amy—

AUNT HATTIE: Oh. That's a very excellent reputation to have. What does your father do?

AMY: He's a painter.

AUNT HATTIE: A painter. Well, that's very interesting. There was a Jones—a Rupert Jones in Maine—he specialized in marines.

GEORGE: Aunt Hattie, Amy's father does not paint marines.

AUNT HATTIE: Still-lifes?

AMY: Of course, Papa really doesn't do any of the painting himself any more. He used to when we were little, but now he's got lots of men to do it. He's got two trucks and ten ladders and scaffolds and oh, any number of drop cloths—

AUNT HATTIE: George, what is she talking about?

GEORGE: Her father's business.

AMY: It's the Jones Painting and Decorating Company, Aunt Hattie.

AUNT HATTIE: Ohhh . . . Ohh . . .

AMY: What's wrong with that?

AUNT HATTIE: Wrong? Nothing wrong, I suppose. Someone has to see that houses are painted. But it's not exactly in the Peabody tradition.

AMY: No, it's not—and I'm glad it's not.

AUNT HATTIE: Young woman, I've been trying my best to search out something about your family that I can tell Aunt Maria and the others—

AMY: Well, you don't have to search any further. You can tell them plenty! Tell them Papa's busy with the Community Chest and the City Council—and Mama's busy, too. Doing all kinds of things. They haven't got time to worry about ancient history!

GEORGE (*Rising*): Amy, my dear, there's no use your—

AMY: No, don't stop me, George. I've tried to be nice but this is too much. I know you're only interested in family trees, Aunt Hattie—well, we're concerned with grass roots. We're the real Americans—we start at the bottom and work up.

AUNT HATTIE: Well! Of all—

AMY: As far as I can see all you Peabodys do is look back and back and back— (*She stops.*) I don't mean you, George.

GEORGE: That's all right, Amy. (*He grins.*) The fat's in the fire now. (*He goes to her and puts his arm around her, facing* AUNT HATTIE.)

AMY: But we haven't got time to look back. It's just as Richard said. Today's Thanksgiving Day and we're thankful for all the things the people in the past have done, but we've got to do our part if we're going to be thankful in the future.

AUNT HATTIE (*Getting up*): Young woman, do you realize you're speaking to the oldest member of the Peabody family?

AMY (*With dignity*): I'm sorry, Aunt Hattie. Perhaps I did say too much but—

GEORGE: No, you didn't, Amy. I'm glad you said what you did. I'm proud of her, Aunt Hattie, and you can tell that to the rest of the family. I suppose you're leaving now—

AMY: It's too bad, Aunt Hattie—that you won't stay for dinner. We could have had such a nice time—and we did try to please you. Why, George even got out the candlesticks that you gave us for a wedding present.

AUNT HATTIE: Humph, thought you must have dug them out in a hurry. Well, they're too big. They look terrible.

AMY: At least we agree on one thing, Aunt Hattie. (*With a set look,* AMY *removes the big candlesticks from the table and puts the little ones on again.*)

AUNT HATTIE: Where's your phone?

GEORGE: I'll call the taxi for you, Aunt Hattie. (*He starts toward phone.*)

AUNT HATTIE (*Seeing it*): Never mind, I'll take care of it. (*She sits down and picks up phone.*) Hello . . . Operator . . . Operator—

AMY: Oh, George, I feel awful. I meant what I said, but it's kind of ruined Thanksgiving.

GEORGE: Well, we mustn't let it, Amy—

AUNT HATTIE: Operator, give me long distance. (GEORGE *and* AMY *look at one another in surprise.*)

AMY: Long distance?

AUNT HATTIE (*Into phone*): Yes, I want Boston. The Peabody residence—218 Back Bay Road . . .

AMY: George, what's she calling Boston for?

GEORGE: Search me . . .

AUNT HATTIE: Hello—is that you, Maria? This is Hattie . . . No, I'm at grand-nephew George's—I've met his wife . . .

GEORGE: Oh-oh . . . (*Through following lines* GEORGE *and* AMY *react in pantomime with looks of surprise, shrugs of shoulders, etc.*)

AUNT HATTIE: Now, don't ask a lot of questions, Maria—just listen. Listen carefully. I can't get there tonight. You'll have to have it tomorrow night . . . That's ridiculous, Maria. This is America. We can have Thanksgiving tomorrow just as well as today. It's been changed before, you know. (*Little chuckle.* GEORGE *and* AMY *begin to suspect what's going on. They smile.*) Now, don't let a little *change* upset you, Maria. I'm having dinner here and I've got a supper engagement with the Joneses—to gnaw on a turkey bone . . . You heard me . . . the Joneses. Yes, she's a Jones and a woman of spirit. Reminds me of our ancestor Mehitabel. The pretty one that told off the general. Well, I'll see you later. Tell them? Can't you ever think for yourself, Maria? Tell them—tell them I'm —keeping up with the Joneses! (*She hangs up, chuckling.* AMY *and* GEORGE, *smiling, start toward her as the curtain falls.*)

THE END

Surprise Guests

Characters

Ruth Webster	Jed Willoughby
Sue Webster	Bill Foster
Bobbie Webster	Miss Emerson
Tom Webster, *Father*	Janey Thomson
Clara Webster, *Mother*	Uncle Harry

Time: *Thanksgiving Day. Before dinner.*

Setting: *The living room of the Webster family.*

At Rise: Sue, *ten years old, is sitting at small table writing on place cards. They are cardboard turkeys and some of them stand in a row in front of her.* Bobbie, *eight, is sitting stiffly in chair downstage left. He is all dressed up and looking uncomfortable.* Ruth, *between fourteen and fifteen, is sitting on the sofa reading a newspaper.*

Bobbie (*After a pause. He sighs*): Boy, am I hungry.

Ruth (*Looking up and laughing*): Bobbie, you're always hungry.

Bobbie: But it's worse on Thanksgiving Day. You smell the turkey and everything.

Sue: Well, we certainly can't eat until our guests arrive.

Bobbie: I wish they'd hurry.

Ruth: Oh, isn't it exciting—wondering who they're all going to be! (*The doorbell rings.*) My, there's someone now. I'll go to the door. (*She rushes off right.*)

BOBBIE: I'll bet it's the one I invited, Sue. Just wait until you see—

SUE: Now, Bobbie, we promised not to tell each other. (RUTH *re-enters.*)

RUTH: Oh, it was only Dad. He couldn't get the door open. (FATHER, TOM WEBSTER, *enters carrying a small table.*)

FATHER: Sorry to disappoint you, children, but your mother wanted this old table from the garage. She's going to use it as a serving table. (*He crosses and sets table down near entrance to dining room.*) Shouldn't some of you be helping her?

SUE: I'm making the place cards.

BOBBIE: She told me to just sit and not get dirty.

FATHER (*Laughing*): I see, and what about you, Ruth?

RUTH (*Sitting on sofa and picking up paper again*): I did set the table.

FATHER: Hadn't you better see if there's anything else?

RUTH: In a minute. I just want to finish this article.

FATHER (*Dryly as he crosses and sits in chair downstage right*): The society page, no doubt.

SUE: No, it's football—that's all she's interested in lately.

BOBBIE: Me, too. I'm going to be a football star when I grow up.

FATHER: Yes, son, I knew of your interest in football, but Ruth rather surprises me.

SUE (*Singsongy*): I know why—I know why—there's a certain boy in school plays football—

RUTH: Oh, you hush up.

MOTHER (*Off left, calling*): Bobbie!

BOBBIE (*Rising*): Yes, Mom. (MOTHER, CLARA WEBSTER, *enters wearing apron over her dress.*)

MOTHER: Bobbie, our first guest arrived by the back door and you'll have to get rid of him.

BOBBIE: But Mom, who—

MOTHER (*Laughing*): It's one of your kittens. He must have smelled the turkey and he keeps getting under my feet.

BOBBIE: O.K. I'll put him in the basement. (*He starts left but stops as* SUE *speaks.*)

SUE: Look at the place cards, Mom.

MOTHER (*Going right and looking at them*): Turkey gobblers. You've done them beautifully, Sue.

SUE (*Indicating place cards*): Here are the family ones. I've written our names on them.

BOBBIE (*Running to look*): Where's mine?

SUE (*Pointing to one*): Here. (*Indicating others*) And these are for the guests. As soon as I know their names I can write them in too. Of course I know whom I invited. I've written her name in—I mean—

BOBBIE: Oh, Sue gave it away. She's invited a girl. Can I tell mine?

RUTH: No, Bobbie, of course you can't. We all agreed to keep it a secret until each guest got here. It's more exciting that way.

SUE: I'll say. Oh, I think it's going to be the most wonderful Thanksgiving we've ever had.

FATHER: Well, it's certainly going to be different.

MOTHER: That's the whole idea. Instead of having the same people we've always had, each guest as they arrive will be a surprise.

BOBBIE: And it was *my* idea.

SUE: It was not.

MOTHER: Now, children, the idea just grew. Bobbie did tell me there was someone special he wanted to invite on his very own—

SUE: But we all had someone.

FATHER: Well, anyway, it's a splendid idea, and I'll bet we'll all find we've invited someone who will appreciate a real home Thanksgiving. And isn't that what Thanksgiving means? Being thankful for what you have and—well—kind of wanting to share it with the other fellow?

RUTH (*Applauding*): Dad, you ought to make speeches. (*The doorbell rings.*)

MOTHER: Oh dear, here's someone now.

BOBBIE (*Starting right*): I'll go.

RUTH: Bobbie, wait. (BOBBIE *goes off right.*)

FATHER: Let him go.

MOTHER: My, here I am with my apron on.

FATHER: And why not? You always wear your apron on Thanksgiving.

MOTHER: But it's a little different this year.

BOBBIE (*As he re-enters*): Mr. Willoughby's at the door, Mom.

FATHER: Well, why didn't you bring him in, son?

MOTHER: Oh, I'm so relieved. Someone *did* invite Mr. Willoughby. I thought of it but then there was someone else—

SUE: I didn't invite him, Mom.

RUTH: Neither did I.

BOBBIE: I didn't.

MOTHER: Well, then, you must have, Tom.

FATHER: No, I thought you would.

BOBBIE: But he didn't come to dinner, Mom. He just wants to borrow something.

MOTHER: Oh, this is terrible. His wife is away and he's all by himself and such a near neighbor—

FATHER: Well, we can't help it, Clara. (*Rising and going toward door and calling*) Come on in, Jed.

MOTHER (*Still worrying*): The table is crowded as it is.

FATHER: Shhh. (JED WILLOUGHBY *enters right. He is an elderly man, a likable old character who pretends to be crotchety.*)

JED: Mornin', folks. Didn't mean to interrupt your festivities, but I'm doin' a little repair work on the chicken coop and ran fresh out of nails.

FATHER: Working on Thanksgiving Day, Jed?

JED: Yes, sure—just like any other day to me; never went in much for fancy festivities. (*Sniffing*) My, smells like you got turkey, all right.

MOTHER: Yes—I—er—I heard Martha had to go away.

JED: Yep, sister Sofie ain't feelin' so well and Martha went down to keep her company.

MOTHER: My, that is too bad that you have to be alone.

JED: Oh, I don't pay it no mind. If Martha was here she'd just be a fussin' and a fumin' and makin' me nervous fixin' all kinds of things to eat just for the two of us. You know, I always figger there's more to Thanksgiving than what you put in your stomach. (*Sniffing again*) My, my, that wouldn't be sage dressing you've got in that bird, would it?

MOTHER: Why, yes, it is.

BOBBIE: Mr. Willoughby, you mean you're not going to have any Thanksgiving dinner at all?

MOTHER (*In undertone nervously*): Bobbie . . .

JED: Oh, I'll eat all right—a couple of fried eggs and some salt pork maybe.

BOBBIE: All by yourself?

JED: Sure, why not? Ye can concentrate on eatin' without a lot of talkin'. (*He is walking about the room as he speaks.*) If Martha was here she'd talk, talk, talk and well—(*He chuckles.*) guess I do a bit of talkin' myself sometimes. (*Looking off into dining room*) Hmm, see you're set for a crowd of folks—guess there'll be plenty of talkin' here all right.

FATHER: Yes, I guess there will. (*He is embarrassed.*) Say— er—about those nails, Jed, what size do you need?

JED: Oh, don't matter much—say four penny maybe, but don't trouble about 'em now if you're busy. (*He starts for door right.*)

FATHER: Oh, it's no trouble, Jed. You know where they are on my bench in the garage. Why don't you just help yourself?

JED: Well, that's right nice of you and I'll be gettin' along. Good-bye, folks, and have a good time. (*He exits right.*)

FATHER (*Looking off right*): Good-bye, Jed.

SUE: Think of Mr. Willoughby preferring fried eggs to turkey.

MOTHER: Nonsense, he was only talking, and in spite of all he said he's just dying for us to invite him for Thanksgiving dinner. Oh, Tom, do you think we could somehow?

FATHER: But you said the table was crowded as it is.

MOTHER: But I could cry, thinking of Mr. Willoughby all by himself. I don't see how I can enjoy Thanksgiving. I'm going to look at the table again.

RUTH: Mother, there's no use. I could hardly fit everything on as it was—(*The doorbell rings.*)

SUE: Now, this must be somebody's guest, maybe mine. I'll go. (*She rises and runs off right.*)

MOTHER: Oh dear. Tom, you'd better get this table into the dining room.

FATHER: All right, Clara, where do you want it? (*He picks up table and starts off left.*)

MOTHER: Oh, near my end somewhere. (FATHER *exits with table.*)

SUE (*Off*): Just hang your coat on the hook here and come on in.

BILL (*Off*): Thanks, Sue. (SUE *enters followed by* BILL FOSTER, *a nice-looking boy about sixteen.*)

SUE: Look who's here. This must be your guest, Ruth. (BOBBIE *runs to* BILL.)

RUTH: My guest? Bill Foster, what are you doing here?

BILL: Bobbie invited me.

BOBBIE: Sure, he's my guest. (*Putting out his hand*) Hi, Bill!

BILL (*Shaking hands*): Hi ya, halfback. (BOBBIE *beams.*) Hello, Mrs. Webster.

MOTHER: Hello, Bill. I'm so glad to see you.

BILL: It was certainly nice of you to let Bobbie invite me. He was watching football practice the other day and I happened to mention my folks had to be away for Thanksgiving and he said, well, come to our house. (RUTH *stands back looking upset.* SUE *sits down again at table.* FATHER *enters left and sees* BILL.)

FATHER: Well—well—hello.

BILL: Hello, Mr. Webster.

BOBBIE: Well, Pop, what do you think of my guest? Say, Bill, do you want to see my kittens? Mom says one just got loose in the kitchen. (*He takes hold of* BILL'S *arm and starts pulling him left.*)

BILL (*Smiling*): Sure—sure, I'd like to. If you'll all excuse me—

BOBBIE: Come on. Besides, I've got a new football I want to show you. (BOBBIE *drags* BILL *off left.*)

RUTH: How dare Bobbie invite Bill Foster to this house!

FATHER: But why on earth not?

RUTH: Because Bill will think I put Bobbie up to it, that's why. That's what he's thinking right this minute.

MOTHER: Now, Ruth, you're making a big fuss over nothing.

RUTH: Mother, you know I asked Bill Foster to go to our club party with me and he refused.

MOTHER: But dear, maybe he had a good reason—

RUTH: He did not. He just didn't want to go with me—and now he'll think I'm trying to—I'm trying to—

SUE: Sure, Ruth, I know what you mean. All the kids at school have been teasing Ruth about Bill, Mom. They know she likes him.

RUTH: I do not like him. I never want to see him again. In fact, I—I'm going to my room and I'm not even coming down to dinner.

FATHER (*Trying to make a joke*): Well, then we'll have room for Jed Willoughby.

MOTHER: Don't be ridiculous, Tom. Ruth will eat with the rest of us. (*The doorbell rings.*) There—this may be your guest now. Go to the door, Ruth.

RUTH (*Almost crying*): All—all right, Mom, but everything's spoiled now—everything! (*She goes off right.*)

FATHER: Well, Clara, our plan doesn't seem to be working out too well.

SUE (*At table writing*): I'm writing Bill's name on his place card, Mom. Now when we see who this guest is, I can fix that.

FATHER: I hope whoever it is, he or she makes a happier impression than the last one. (RUTH *re-enters with* MISS EMERSON *who wears hat and coat.* RUTH *has recovered her poise and smiles.*)

RUTH: It *was* my guest, Mom. Here's Miss Emerson.

MOTHER: Why, how do you do?

RUTH: And there's a little girl coming up the walk—I don't know whom she belongs to.

SUE: Oh, she's mine. (*She rises and runs off right.*)

RUTH: I don't think you've met my father, Miss Emerson.

FATHER: How do you do?

MOTHER: You're Bobbie's teacher, aren't you, Miss Emerson?

MISS EMERSON: Yes, that's right, but I'm also interested in the older girls.

RUTH: She's been helping us with our dramatics club, Mom. She's wonderful.

MOTHER: Well, I'm so glad you could be with us today.

MISS EMERSON: Yes, you don't know what it means to me. I'm the only teacher who couldn't go home for Thanksgiving. I live too far away. (SUE *enters leading* JANEY THOMSON *by the hand.* JANEY *is the same age as* SUE *and wears hat and coat.*)

SUE: Mother, here's Janey Thomson.

MOTHER: Hello, Janey.

SUE (*All in a rush, indicating*): She's my mother, and here's my father and this is my sister, Ruth, and Bobbie isn't here right now—and I guess you know Miss Emerson from school.

MISS EMERSON: Of course she does.

JANEY (*Shyly*): Hello, Miss Emerson.

MOTHER: Where do you live, Janey?

JANEY: I live at the home.

MOTHER (*Puzzled*): The home?

MISS EMERSON: She's one of the little girls from the Children's Home, Mrs. Webster, and she's in Sue's class at school.

MOTHER: Of course. Janey, we're so glad you could come. Take off your hat and coat, dear. (JANEY *pulls off her hat and starts to unbutton her coat.*)

SUE: Mom, the front hall is quite full—

MOTHER: Well, you take her up to your room, Sue.

SUE: O.K. Come on, Janey. (SUE *and* JANEY *go off left.*)

RUTH (*Starting left*): And you'll want to take off your things too, Miss Emerson.

MISS EMERSON (*Starting to follow* RUTH): Yes. (*Turning*) Oh, Mrs. Webster, I'm so glad Sue invited Janey for your Thanksgiving dinner. When Ruth invited me, she told me what you were doing, and I think it's such a wonderful idea. (BOBBIE *rushes in left excitedly, almost bumping into* MISS EMERSON *but not realizing who it is.*)

BOBBIE: Mom, can I have some milk?

MISS EMERSON (*Smiling*) : Hello, Bobbie. *May* I have some milk.

BOBBIE (*Looking up*) : Hello. (*Then realizing who it is*) Oh —Miss Emerson!

MISS EMERSON : Well, don't look so surprised, Bobbie.

BOBBIE : I—I'm not but—but—gee. Did you come to dinner?

FATHER (*Crossly*) : Robert . . . Of course Miss Emerson has come to dinner. Ruth invited her. She's Ruth's guest.

RUTH (*Embarrassed*) : Yes—uh—don't you want to come upstairs, Miss Emerson? (RUTH *hurries* MISS EMERSON *off. As they go off, she says*) Aren't small boys pests, Miss Emerson?

BOBBIE : What did she mean by that?

MOTHER : After all, Bobbie, you were rather rude to your teacher.

BOBBIE : I didn't mean to be, but for gosh sakes, why did Ruth have to invite her?

FATHER (*Sitting in chair right again*) : Well, son, Ruth wasn't pleased with your choice of a guest either.

BOBBIE : Bill Foster? But he's a big football star.

MOTHER : And Miss Emerson is your teacher, Bobbie.

BOBBIE : That's just it. She'll be watching and correcting me all day. It'll spoil my whole Thanksgiving.

FATHER : Nonsense, she seems like a very nice person.

MOTHER : Bobbie, I don't like your attitude—I don't like it at all.

BOBBIE : Oh, all right, Mom. But anyhow, can I—I mean *may* I have some milk? I want to show Bill how I feed the kittens.

MOTHER : Yes, dear, you may take some milk from the refrigerator. And now mind what I told you—you're to be nice to Miss Emerson.

BOBBIE (*Running out left*) : O.K., Mom.

MOTHER (*Shaking her head*) : But he won't be. I know Bobbie.
He'll show very plainly all day that he feels uncomfortable.
Oh, everything's going wrong—everything!

FATHER: Now, Clara, maybe it isn't as bad as we think.

MOTHER: It's worse. And I feel so terrible about not being able
to invite Mr. Willoughby. At least he'd fit in better than the
guests we've got. Ruth's going to be embarrassed all day
because of Bill Foster being here and Miss Emerson will
probably feel out of place because of Bobbie—

FATHER: Well, at least that little Janey will have a good time
—that little girl from the Orphanage.

MOTHER: I don't know. If the rest of us are under a strain it
may affect her—and oh, Tom, the worst thing of all. It's my
guest.

FATHER: Your guest?

MOTHER: I'm afraid you're going to hit the ceiling when you
see whom I've invited. It's been worrying me anyway and I
know now I never should have done it.

FATHER: But Clara, who in the world— (SUE *runs in left looking distressed.*)

SUE: Mother, I don't know what to do!

MOTHER: Sue dear, what is the matter?

SUE: It's Janey. She's crying.

MOTHER: Crying? There, Tom, what did I tell you—

SUE: I don't know what could have happened. She seemed so
happy and I took her up to my room and then we came down
to the kitchen. Bobbie was there with the kitten, and all of
a sudden she burst into tears and ran upstairs again.

MOTHER: But didn't you go after her?

SUE: Yes, but she won't talk to me.

FATHER: But there must be some reason. What on earth did
you say to hurt her feelings?

SUE: Not a thing, Dad. I've thought and thought—

FATHER: Then someone else must have.

MOTHER: Nonsense, Tom. Sue, I'll go up—or no, there's something I've got to talk to your father about for a minute. You go up again and see what you can do. I'll come when I can.

SUE: All right, Mom. (*She goes out left.*)

MOTHER: Tom, I've made up my mind. I've got to tell you, so you'll be prepared. Please try to remember I thought I was doing right.

FATHER: Clara, I don't know what you're talking about.

MOTHER: The one I invited, dear—my guest. I've invited Uncle Harry.

FATHER (*Rising*): What? You've invited Uncle Harry?

MOTHER: Tom, be calm. I know you had that quarrel with him —I know you said you never wanted him in the house again— but the whole thing was so silly—just a political argument —and I thought if I got you two together— (*The doorbell rings.*) Oh, dear, I'll go. That may be Harry now.

FATHER: On the other hand it may be my guest. I'll go. (FATHER *exits.*)

MOTHER (*Calling nervously*): Oh, Tom, please try to remember that it's Thanksgiving— (RUTH *enters left.*)

RUTH: Mom, Miss Emerson wants to know if there's anything she can do to help in the kitchen. (BILL FOSTER *enters left.*)

BILL: Ruth, may I speak to you for a minute?

RUTH (*Coldly*): I thought you were Bobbie's guest. (MISS EMERSON *enters left.*)

MISS EMERSON: Now, *is* there anything I can do, Mrs. Webster?

MOTHER: Well, there's really nothing at the moment—(BOBBIE *runs in left carrying bottle of milk.*)

BOBBIE: Say, Bill, where are you? I thought you were going to help me feed the kittens.

Bill: Sure I am, Bobbie, but first— (*He turns to* Ruth.) Listen, Ruth— (Ruth *sticks up her nose and walks off left.* Bill *hesitates a minute and then follows her.*)

Miss Emerson: Why not let me help feed the kittens, Bobbie?

Bobbie: You? Oh, for gosh—I mean, all right, Miss Emerson. (Miss Emerson *smiles at him, takes his hand and they go off.*)

Father (*Off right, obviously shouting*): Harry, the trouble with your party is they're just a lot of politicians—

Harry (*Off shouting*): Don't you talk about my party!

Mother: Oh, my goodness. (Father *enters with* Uncle Harry, *who is about* Father's *age.*)

Father: Now, you listen to me, Harry—

Mother (*Going toward* Harry): Hello, Harry. I might have known what was taking you two so long, but you'll have to stop arguing—

Father: Don't look so worried, Clara, this is just an act. We cooked it up out in the hall.

Harry: Sure—sure, the only party we're going to talk about today is your Thanksgiving party. We agreed on that when Tom invited me, didn't we, Tom?

Mother: When *Tom* invited you?

Harry: Oh, you called too, Clara, but Tom got his invitation in first.

Mother: But why didn't you tell me?

Harry: Why should I? I just thought you wanted me so much that you both called.

Mother: Can you imagine that? Why, Tom, if we've both invited Harry, this makes us one guest short.

Father: Sure it does, and we can ask Jed Willoughby after all. Send one of the children over. (Sue *and* Janey *run on left both laughing.*)

Sue: Mother, Janey wasn't crying at all. She was laughing.

JANEY: I wasn't laughing. I was crying.

MOTHER: Well, there seems to be a difference of opinion. Which was it, dear?

JANEY: I—I don't quite know, Mrs. Webster. I felt so happy at being here that I started crying, and then I knew I was crying because I was happy, so I started laughing—

MOTHER: My goodness. Well, I'm glad the crying part's over. This is Sue's Uncle Harry.

HARRY: Hello, there.

SUE *and* JANEY: Hello.

FATHER: And if you little girls don't mind we've got an errand for you.

MOTHER: Yes, Sue. You and Janey get your hats and coats and run next door and invite Mr. Willoughby to dinner.

SUE: Oh, good, Mom. He won't have to eat alone after all. Come on, Janey. (*Taking her hand*) We'll go out the back door. It's quicker. (*They run off left laughing.*)

MOTHER: Well, those little girls are certainly in high spirits— I'm so relieved. And I'm so glad you two are friends again.

FATHER: We never should have been anything else. Sit down, Harry. (HARRY and FATHER *sit on sofa.*) If we ever fight over politics again, Harry, we ought to have our heads examined.

HARRY: You're right, Tom. This is a free country and we're certainly entitled to our own opinions. Have a cigar. (*He takes cigar from pocket.*)

FATHER: Yeah, thanks. (*He stops and looks at cigar.*) What? One of those El Rope-o's? Wouldn't smoke 'em on a bet. Here, have a good cigar. (*He fishes one out.*)

HARRY: You still smoking those things? Why, I wouldn't— hey, here we go again. (*They both laugh.*)

MOTHER: Oh, you two. If you want my free opinion, I wouldn't light either of those smelly cigars until after dinner.

FATHER: O.K. (*He and* HARRY *settle back comfortably on sofa.*)

MOTHER: And I suppose I ought to see about getting dinner on the table. (*She starts left and then stops as* RUTH *enters followed by* BILL.)

BILL: Listen, Ruth—

RUTH: Will you please stop following me?

BILL (*Turning to* MOTHER): Mrs. Webster, what would you do if you'd been trying to ask a girl to the Junior Prom and she wouldn't even listen?

MOTHER: Why, I don't know, Bill.

RUTH: The—the Junior Prom?

BILL: Sure, I've been trying to ask you for weeks, but you always give me the cold shoulder. That's one reason I was so glad Bobbie asked me here today. I thought it would give me a chance to talk to you.

RUTH: But I didn't know you were interested in talking to me. After all you refused my invitation—

BILL: I couldn't help it. With football practice and a test I had coming up, I couldn't go anywhere that weekend.

RUTH: And you mean you really want me to go to the Prom?

BILL: What do you think?

RUTH (*All smiles*): Oh, Bill.

HARRY (*Kidding*): If you can spare a minute you might say hello to me, Ruth.

RUTH: Why, Uncle Harry—hello! (*Leading* BILL *toward him*) Do you know Bill Foster?

HARRY (*Starting to rise*): Sure.

BILL: Don't get up, sir. (*He shakes hands with* HARRY. BOBBIE *runs in left looking happy.*)

BOBBIE: Mom—mom, what do you think?

MOTHER: Oh dear. Now what, Bobbie?

BOBBIE: Miss Emerson and I have been feeding the kittens and you ought to see her, Mom—sitting on the floor playing with them. She doesn't look like a teacher at all.

MOTHER (*Smiling*) : Indeed.

BOBBIE: She knows all about cats. She likes them, and she's got a big cat of her own, and she says I can come over and see him sometime!

BILL (*Turning, realizing he has neglected* BOBBIE) : Say, Bobbie, I still want to see those kittens of yours—

BOBBIE (*Scornfully*) : Oh, all you're interested in is girls.

RUTH: Bobbie!

BOBBIE: Well, all right, but I guess Miss Emerson and I can take care of the cats. (MISS EMERSON *enters left.*)

MISS EMERSON: Did I hear my name?

MOTHER: Yes, you did. Bobbie's certainly happy to have found someone who likes his kittens as much as he does. (FATHER *and* HARRY *rise.*) Oh, Miss Emerson, this is my brother Harry.

MISS EMERSON: How do you do?

BOBBIE: Oh, hello, Uncle Harry. (*He runs to him.* SUE *and* JANEY *enter right wearing hats and coats, one on either side of* MR. WILLOUGHBY, *holding his hands.*)

MOTHER: Well, people, here comes our last guest.

SUE *and* JANEY: Yes. Here he is.

FATHER: Hello, Jed. Does everyone here know Jed Willoughby?

HARRY: Sure. Hello, Jed.

OTHERS: Hello, Mr. Willoughby.

JED: Looks as though I've come to Thanksgiving dinner after all.

FATHER: Sorry to take you away from mending your chicken coop, Jed.

JED: Oh, that's all right. Tomorrow's another day and anyway, I figger Thanksgiving only comes once a year.

FATHER (*Going to* MOTHER) : And I think this is going to be about the nicest Thanksgiving we've ever had. How about it, Clara?

SUE: Now I can finish the place cards. Come on, Janey. (SUE *and* JANEY *run to table.*) See, here are the family's and here's yours and then, let's see, I've made Bill's—and then there's Uncle Harry and Miss Emerson and Mr. Willoughby—all the surprise guests are here. (*She starts writing.*)

BOBBIE: And they're all nice surprises, aren't they, Mom? Even Miss Emerson.

MOTHER: Why, Bobbie.

MISS EMERSON (*Laughing, going to* BOBBIE *and squeezing his shoulder. He smiles at her.*): That's all right, Mrs. Webster. When you get a lot of different people together sometimes you wonder how they're going to get along.

FATHER: Well, we're going to get along fine. And why not? This household today is just a tiny cross section of America. And what's America but a lot of different people with different ideas trying to work together for the good of all. I guess that's what we're thankful for today.

HARRY: You can say that again, Tom.

JED: Sure thing—and it just goes to show what I said—there's more to Thanksgiving than what you put in your stomach.

MOTHER: Well, in that case, I guess nobody wants any turkey. (*Exclamations from all.*)

FATHER (*Laughing*): Now, wait a minute, Clara. My speech-making hasn't spoiled our appetites. But just the same, when we enjoy that turkey, let's remember that it represents all the countless things we've got to be thankful for.

THE END

Turkey Gobblers

Characters

FATHER, *Fred Baldwin*
MOTHER, *Margaret Baldwin*
LUCILLE BALDWIN, *in early twenties*
BOB BALDWIN, *sixteen-year-old son*
JANEY BALDWIN, *six-year-old daughter*
HERBERT DODD
GRANDMA
RADIO ANNOUNCER'S VOICE

TIME: *Thanksgiving Day.*
SETTING: *The Baldwin living room.*
AT RISE: FATHER, *Fred Baldwin, is seated right and* BOB *is sprawled on the sofa.*

FATHER: Son, this is my idea of solid comfort—sitting here with all those delicious odors wafting their way in here from the kitchen.

BOB (*Grinning*): Hey, Dad, stop! I'm so hungry now— (JANEY *runs in from left.*)

JANEY: Mom just basted the turkey again and you ought to see it.

FATHER: Does it look as good as it smells, Janey?

JANEY: Better, I guess. It's getting all brown and juicy-looking.

BOB: Hey, have a heart, Janey . . .

JANEY: And Dad, you ought to see the place cards I made at

158

school. Come and look—I just put them on the table! (FATHER *rises and* JANEY *leads him to door left.*)

FATHER (*Looking left*): Hmm-m, turkey gobblers—very appropriate. My, the table looks beautiful. That centerpiece your Mother fixed—

JANEY: That's a horn of plenty—grapes and apples and—my, I'm so excited! Why does Thanksgiving only come once a year, Dad? (FATHER *goes back to his chair and* JANEY *follows.*)

FATHER: Because our forefathers thought it would be nice if we set aside one day to be especially thankful. . . . (*He puts his arm around her.*) But that doesn't mean we can't feel thankful every day in the year.

JANEY: Gee, I do. . . .

FATHER: And today you're overflowing with it . . . Well, I'm thinking about my blessings too, and you're one of them. (*He puts his finger on her nose.* MOTHER, *Margaret Baldwin, enters left, smiling. She is wearing an apron.*)

MOTHER: Well, family . . .

FATHER: And here's another.

MOTHER: Another what, Fred?

FATHER: Another blessing, Margaret . . . You, my dear.

MOTHER (*Pleased*): Oh, Fred . . . Well, I had a minute so I thought I'd come in and see if you were all hungry. (*She smiles.*)

BOB: Hey, Mom—

MOTHER: I sent your Grandma upstairs to take a nap until dinner's ready.

FATHER: Good idea, Margaret. She looked tired out from the trip.

MOTHER: She was, but of course she hated to admit it. She wanted to help. After all these years she still can't get used to the idea that I can cook Thanksgiving dinner all by myself.

BOB: After all your experience, Mom? Say, where's that candy Dad gave you? I could use a piece.

MOTHER (*Picking up the large box of candy from end table and removing the cover*): Here, but I wish you wouldn't spoil your dinner.

BOB (*Taking a piece*): As if I would—not with my appetite . . . (JANEY *comes over too, wanting a piece.*)

MOTHER (*To* JANEY): Just one piece, dear . . . How about you, Fred?

FATHER: No, thanks.

MOTHER: Does anyone know where Lucille is?

FATHER: Why, I don't know. I thought she was helping you.

MOTHER: No—not at the minute. I'm worried about her, Fred. She's all upset because she hasn't heard a word from Herbert.

BOB: Her new boy friend? Well, what did she expect to hear?

MOTHER: Well, I suppose she thought he'd send her something for Thanksgiving—a message or some flowers.

FATHER: But that's nonsense, Margaret. She saw the man only a few times.

MOTHER: Now, Fred, she was in New York visiting her cousin for three weeks.

BOB: Sure, and she met this guy the first night at a party—so she saw him every night.

FATHER: But she can't be serious!

MOTHER: I'm afraid she is serious, Fred. I only saw you a few times and it was serious, remember?

FATHER: But that was different . . . Well, I certainly wish we could meet him.

BOB: He doesn't sound like much to me.

MOTHER: Now, Bob, you mustn't—

BOB: But, Mom, an authority on food and diet—what kind of a fellow would he be, anyhow?

FATHER: Well, I'm an authority on food myself—and your

mother's the best cook in the country! Margaret, if I have to smell that turkey much longer—

JANEY: Lucille isn't hungry—not even today, she told me.

BOB: No, I don't suppose she'll eat a thing now that she's so in love, and especially with a guy who broadcasts on diet. (LUCILLE, *an attractive girl, hurries in left.*)

LUCILLE: What time is it? We've got to turn on Herbert's program—

BOB: Aw, Sis, have a heart. Have we got to listen to a guy talk about diet—on Thanksgiving?

FATHER (*Looking at his watch*): It isn't time yet, Lucille. Doesn't he come on at half past?

LUCILLE: Yes, but I don't want to miss it.

FATHER: Plenty of time. Lucille, is this Herbert of yours really one of those cranks?

LUCILLE: Cranks?

FATHER: Well, I mean—you know the way some of those diet men are—you can't eat anything but green peppers and grapes.

LUCILLE: Herbert knows his stuff. If he says green peppers are good for you—

FATHER: But what did he eat?

LUCILLE: I don't know, Dad—we didn't eat.

FATHER: Ah, no, of course you wouldn't.

BOB: You mean he never took you out and gave you a good meal all the time you were in New York? What kind of a guy is he?

MOTHER: Now, Bob—

LUCILLE: We did have a glass of milk once, I think.

JANEY: Milk?

LUCILLE: But we couldn't be bothered with eating all the time. We had so much to talk about.

BOB: But if he's an authority on diet—didn't you ever talk about food?

MOTHER: No, dear, they talked about the moon. . . . Well, I've got to get back to my dinner. (*She goes out left.*)

FATHER: Lucille, when are we ever going to meet this Herbert?

LUCILLE (*Going to radio*): I don't know, Dad—just as soon as he can get away. He's a very busy man. You can hear his voice now, though, on the radio. He'll be giving the Thanksgiving menu . . . (*She turns the radio on and after a slight pause you hear* HERBERT'S *voice from radio. The person playing* HERBERT *should sit behind the backdrop directly in back of the radio and should speak through a small megaphone.*)

HERBERT (*From radio*): Now, I do want to advise you to serve something light—

BOB: Something light? For Thanksgiving dinner?

LUCILLE: Dad, he's already started. Your watch was slow.

HERBERT (*From radio*): Perhaps a bowl of cereal and serve it with milk—not cream—

JANEY: Cereal for Thanksgiving?

HERBERT (*From radio*): And then maybe some grapes would be nice with that—

MOTHER (*Calling from off*): Lucille—can you come here a minute?

LUCILLE: But Mother—oh dear . . . (*She runs out.*)

HERBERT (*From radio*): Then I would suggest— (BOB *quickly switches radio off.*)

BOB: If anyone thinks I'm going to listen to crazy stuff like that —imagine eating sawdust for Thanksgiving!

FATHER: Now, son, cereal is all right—

BOB: But Dad—I just thought he would be someone like that. Someone who thinks you can live on greens and carrots—

FATHER: Like a rabbit?

BOB: Sure—bunny food. (LUCILLE *rushes back in.*)

LUCILLE: Mother would have to call me! (*She stops.*) Why, you've turned it off. (*She switches radio on again.*) Didn't you want to listen to Herbert?

FATHER: Well—er—we, that is—

LUCILLE: He may be finished now and I won't hear his voice.

HERBERT (*From radio*): Now, don't forget—

LUCILLE: There he is . . .

HERBERT (*From radio*): Don't overeat, don't stuff yourselves, and don't let Mother overwork . . . And now goodbye until tomorrow.

LUCILLE (*Sighing*): Oh, isn't he cute? The way he talks?

BOB: Cute??

ANNOUNCER (*From radio*): You have been listening to Herbert Dodd, outstanding authority on food and diet— (LUCILLE *switches radio off and goes to chair left and sits.*)

BOB: Don't overeat, don't let Mother overwork! How *could* she overwork fixing a bowl of cereal?

FATHER: Well, I must admit, it does seem a little drastic to me, Lucille—that menu he gave for Thanksgiving dinner.

LUCILLE: Herbert's got a lot of new ideas, Father. Besides, it's always seemed kind of silly to me—the way people eat and eat just because it's Thanksgiving.

BOB: Hey, you always did all right until—

LUCILLE: Why, Mother and I have been slaving all day—getting this dinner.

BOB: Mother has, you mean.

FATHER: Now, Bob—

LUCILLE: I helped her all morning . . . And what happens? You cook it, it gets eaten up, there's nothing but a lot of dirty dishes to wash—and then everyone has a stomach ache.

FATHER: I never had a stomach ache in my life from eating your mother's food.

LUCILLE: Well, maybe not, but you always go to sleep right after dinner.

BOB: What's wrong with that? It shows he's relaxed. (MOTHER *enters left, smiling.*)

MOTHER: In about twenty minutes, I think we can all sit down.

BOB: Hooray!

MOTHER: I've made the hot sauce for the mince pies and the cherry pudding is steaming away.

FATHER: Yum—yum. (*The phone rings.*)

BOB: I'll get it. (*Into phone*) Hello? What's that? Oh, just a moment. It's for you, Lucille.

LUCILLE: For me? (*She runs to phone.*) Hello? . . . Oh, Herbert! I thought I wasn't going to hear. How wonderful of you to call me long distance! . . . What? You're not? You're where? . . . Here? . . . but Herbert—Herbert, you're here—how wonderful!

FATHER: How can he be here? We just listened to him on the radio.

LUCILLE (*Into phone*): I just can't believe that you're at the station . . . Well, hurry, Herbert. Take a taxi and you know the street number . . . Yes, and it's the white house next to the corner . . . Oh, Herbert, goodbye! (*She hangs up.*) Mother, he's coming! He'll be here in just a little while. Herbert's coming to spend Thanksgiving with us!

FATHER: But how can he be here? We heard him on the radio.

LUCILLE: Oh, those are recordings, Father. He makes a lot of them at one time, and then they rebroadcast them—oh, isn't it wonderful?

MOTHER: But—my goodness, Herbert coming here. How long can he stay?

LUCILLE: Just a couple of hours, Mother, between trains. He's on his way to the west coast to lecture out there—oh, I'd better powder my nose and—

MOTHER: And I'd better put on another plate . . . If he's going to have dinner with us—

LUCILLE: Mother, I just happened to think—we can't serve that great big dinner—not to Herbert.

MOTHER: What?

BOB: Now, wait a minute, Sis—

LUCILLE: All those shrimps and turkey and that rich stuffing, and all those vegetables and two kinds of potatoes, and all those pies and puddings—

JANEY: Please stop talking about food, Sis, I'm so hungry.

LUCILLE: Why, we just can't serve all that, Mother. It would be revolting to Herbert.

MOTHER: Revolting? *My* dinner?

FATHER: Now, wait a minute, Lucille—this is too much. You can't call your mother's wonderful dinner—

MOTHER: I *am* hurt, Lucille. He may be an authority on food, but I can cook with the best of 'em—

LUCILLE: But Mother, you don't understand. You didn't hear Herbert's program. Father did—

FATHER: Yes, and a sillier thing I've never listened to.

LUCILLE: Father, please! Mother, Herbert gave a Thanksgiving menu, and he said serve something light—like—well, a bowl of cereal and some grapes—

MOTHER: A bowl of cereal—for Thanksgiving dinner? Why, dear, the man must be crazy.

BOB: I'll say he is!

LUCILLE: Mother, please— If Herbert says it's right, it's right. He believes in food that's good for people, so they'll be healthy.

MOTHER: Well, we're all healthy.

LUCILLE: Mother, just this once, if you could help me— He's so wonderful and I want him to like us. Couldn't you serve something like—well, like Herbert said?

FATHER: Nothing of the sort. Why, it would be an insult to

the man—a guest in our house, and you want to give him a bowl of cereal?

LUCILLE: But don't you see, Father? It would be an insult to give Herbert anything else! (*She starts to cry.*) Mother—

MOTHER (*Patting* LUCILLE's *shoulder*): Lucille, don't cry, please. I'll help—I've got an idea. . . . Bob, you bring that small table in from your father's study—we'll set it up in here—

BOB (*Getting up*): But Mom, what for?

MOTHER: We'll leave the big table set up in the dining room just as it is. (*She is near door left.*) We'll close this door and Herbert will never know.

LUCILLE: Oh, Mother, you're wonderful!

FATHER (*He has risen and is walking about*): But Margaret, what about our dinner?

MOTHER: I'll turn everything off and we can have it later.

BOB: Turn everything off? But Mom, I'm so hungry!

JANEY: You mean we've got to wait even longer for the turkey and the pudding?

MOTHER: Now, dear, it'll taste even better if you wait. After Herbert goes you can stuff yourselves to your heart's content. In the meantime, we'll have this—er—snack, so you won't get too hungry anyway.

LUCILLE: Mother, please, don't call it a snack—we've got to make it seem like a real dinner.

MOTHER: Well, dear, after all, when you're just serving cereal and grapes—

LUCILLE: But Mother, it's what Herbert gave for a Thanksgiving menu. I mean, can't we serve it nicely and—

MOTHER: I'll do my best, dear . . . Now, come along, Bob—let's get that table in here. And Janey, you can find some plates and silver.

JANEY: All right, Mom. (BOB, *looking glum, and* MOTHER *and* JANEY *go out left.*)

LUCILLE (*Nervously*): Oh dear, I do hope everything goes right.

FATHER: Lucille, you aren't really—that is, I mean are you really serious about this Herbert?

LUCILLE: Oh, Father, of course. I'd never meet another man like Herbert.

FATHER: No—I imagine not. But to spend your life with a fellow who eats in this peculiar way—

LUCILLE: But Father, you don't care what you eat when you're with Herbert! . . . Now, I do hope the table can look pretty.

FATHER: What do you expect your mother to do? Serve the cereal on a platter? (BOB *comes in with a drop-leaf table which he places center stage, and opens the leaves.* MOTHER *enters and places a white cloth on it.* JANEY *follows with plates and silver, etc. which she starts setting around.*)

BOB (*Grumbling*): For gosh sakes, if this isn't the craziest thing—

MOTHER: I just thought—we might as well let Grandma sleep right through. She's tired anyhow and we can wake her up in time for the real dinner.

LUCILLE: Oh, that's good, Mom. I don't think we could explain things to Grandma.

FATHER: You can't explain them to me so I understand them, but I suppose it's all right. (*He sits right again.*)

JANEY: Shall I get cups, Mom?

MOTHER: No, dear, glasses, I think. Perhaps we'd better serve milk to drink instead of coffee. (JANEY *goes out.*)

LUCILLE: Father, you aren't going to make remarks when Herbert's here?

MOTHER: Yes, Fred—we must be careful.

LUCILLE: If you could just kind of pretend you all like the food—

FATHER: But that's hypocrisy—I *won't* like it.

MOTHER: I don't think it would be hypocrisy in this case, Fred. (*Busy with table*) We've got to be polite.

LUCILLE: I want Herbert to think we're careful of our diet too.

FATHER: We're *sensible*.

MOTHER: Lucille, I just had an idea. I can put the cereal in the big silver bowl—that'll look nice.

LUCILLE: You're wonderful, Mom! Cereal in a silver bowl— why, it sounds like a poem.

BOB (*Disgusted*): Cereal in a silver bowl! No matter what you do with it, it's still sawdust.

MOTHER: And then some milk in the silver pitcher—that should make the table look pretty.

FATHER: But Margaret, there won't be anything *on* the table. It'll look bare.

MOTHER: I know. I could make some cole slaw—

FATHER: Yes, grate up a cabbage or something. At least it will be one more thing to chew on. I'm so hungry . . . (JANEY *comes back with glasses.*)

MOTHER: Do you suppose Herbert would object to cole slaw, Lucille?

LUCILLE: I don't know. He didn't say cole slaw in the menu, but I'm sure he couldn't object to roughage.

BOB: Roughage?

LUCILLE: That's what they call raw foods—roughage.

BOB: Oh, for gosh sakes!

MOTHER: Dear me—I'd better get into the kitchen and get things ready.

FATHER: Well, it shouldn't take you long. Don't overwork, Margaret.

MOTHER (*Smiling as she starts left*): I won't, dear . . . Janey, you can come along with me, and Bob, you can be putting some chairs around—get some extras from the dining room.

LUCILLE (*Noticing box of candy and taking it and rushing to her* MOTHER): Here, Mom, take this candy and put it somewhere. I don't want Herbert to think we're stuffing ourselves with chocolates all the time.

MOTHER: All right, dear. My goodness! (*She takes candy and goes out followed by* JANEY.)

BOB (*Grumbling*): For gosh sakes, if this isn't the craziest thing —disrupting our whole Thanksgiving Day! (*He moves some straight chairs out from the wall and puts them around the table.*)

LUCILLE: Bob Baldwin, don't you dare say anything like that when Herbert's here!

BOB: Listen, if you expect me to put on a show for this guy—

FATHER: Now, Bob, you've got to be polite—you've got to think of your sister.

BOB: Well, she isn't thinking of us—is she? Making us starve like this. (*He goes out left almost bumping into* JANEY *who enters with a bowl of grapes which she places on the table.*)

JANEY: Mom's grating up the cabbage.

LUCILLE: Fine. You'd better tell her not to put much dressing on it, Janey.

JANEY: O.K. (*She goes out left again.*)

LUCILLE: Father, I don't know why Bob has to be so difficult. Well, I guess I'd better powder my nose. (BOB *comes back with two more straight chairs, and* LUCILLE *starts toward left. The doorbell rings off right.*) He's here—Herbert's here! Oh, my goodness, and look at me!

FATHER: You look very nice.

LUCILLE: Well, I'll have to do. Father, close that door—I'll let him in and please, everyone— (*She breaks off.*) Oh, I've never been so excited in all my life! (*She rushes out right.*

FATHER *closes door left, shakes his head and walks about a little.* BOB *looks disgusted. The door left opens again and* JANEY *enters with a silver pitcher of milk which she places on table.*)

JANEY: I heard the doorbell. Is he here? (FATHER *nods and closes the door again.* LUCILLE's *voice is heard off right.*)

LUCILLE (*Off*): Oh, Herbert! . . . Herbert, I'm so glad to see you.

HERBERT (*Off*): Lucille, my dear! It's been so long. (*There is a pause.*)

FATHER: Well—well, what are they doing?

JANEY (*Whispering*): Gee, Dad, don't you know? It's like in the movies.

FATHER: Ohhh. (LUCILLE *enters holding* HERBERT's *hand. She is all smiles and so is* HERBERT. *He is tall and handsome, and carries a box with a ribbon round it.*)

LUCILLE: Father, this is Herbert . . . Herbert Dodd.

FATHER (*Extending hand*): Well—well, I'm glad to know you, Mr. Dodd.

HERBERT: Thank you, sir and please, just call me Herbert. I want Lucille's family to be my family.

FATHER: What's that?

LUCILLE: And this is my brother, Bob.

BOB: H'llo.

LUCILLE: And my little sister, Janey.

HERBERT: Well, Janey, how are you? You're as pretty as your big sister.

JANEY: What's that box you've got?

HERBERT: Why—er—it's just a little gift for Lucille. (*He smiles at her.*)

JANEY: Is it candy?

LUCILLE: Nonsense, Janey, Herbert wouldn't bring candy.

HERBERT: It's flowers— (*Hands box to* LUCILLE.)

LUCILLE: Oh, Herbert. (*She starts opening the box.*)

FATHER: Sit down—sit down, Mr. Dodd—er—Herbert. Make yourself comfortable. (BOB *has sat down on sofa, and* FATHER *sits in easy chair right.*)

HERBERT (*Sitting left*): Thanks.

LUCILLE (*Taking flowers from box*): Oh, Herbert, these are beautiful! (*She gets vase from small table, puts flowers in it, then hands vase to* JANEY.) Janey, will you put some water in this vase? Maybe we can use the flowers on the table.

BOB: Yes, it needs something. (LUCILLE *gives him a look.* JANEY *goes out left leaving door open.*)

HERBERT: You know, Mr. Baldwin, I—I suppose it was a little bold of me to just—er—barge in on you like this—especially on Thanksgiving—

FATHER: No—no, not at all—glad to have you.

HERBERT: Well, it's wonderful to be here . . . It's wonderful to be here with Lucille's family— (*Stopping and sniffing*) Say, do I smell turkey?

LUCILLE (*Quickly*): Oh, no—no—that must be the—the cereal Mom is fixing. (*She closes door left hurriedly.*) How could it possibly smell like turkey?

FATHER: Turkey? Turkey? The smell might be blowing in from next door—great people for eating next door. (*Trying to be funny.*) Turkey gobblers, you might say.

LUCILLE (*Trying to laugh*): Yes—turkey gobblers!

BOB: Turkey gobblers—phooey!

FATHER: Robert. (JANEY *enters with vase of flowers, and* LUCILLE *puts flowers on the table.* JANEY *is followed by* MOTHER *carrying a large silver bowl with cereal and a platter of grated cabbage.*)

MOTHER: Will you close the door, Janey?

JANEY: Yes, Mom. (*She does so.*)

MOTHER: Well, family— (*Stopping and smiling*) Oh . . .

LUCILLE: Herbert is here, Mother . . . Mother, this is Herbert.

MOTHER: I'm so happy you're here, Herbert. We've heard so much about you . . .

HERBERT: Mrs. Baldwin, it's so nice of you to have me.

MOTHER: We want you to feel perfectly at home. And now—I do believe we can sit down to our little—to our dinner. Let's see—yes, everything's on—cereal, cabbage, grapes. Fred, you at the end there—Herbert here, and Lucille— (MOTHER *indicates places.* FATHER *sits at right end,* HERBERT *and* LUCILLE *on upstage side facing downstage, and* MOTHER *at left end.* JANEY *sits next to* MOTHER *at downstage side with back to audience.*)

MOTHER (*Giving* BOB *a look*): Bob, will you come?

BOB: Oh, Mom. (*But he comes and sits next to* FATHER *at downstage side with back to audience.*)

FATHER: Well—well, the festive board.

MOTHER (*Nervously*): Yes, dear—will you please start things? I think we can just pass them.

FATHER (*Forgetting himself*): Yes—I can't very well carve the cereal, can I?

MOTHER: Fred. . . . (FATHER *passes cereal to* HERBERT. LUCILLE *is taking some cole slaw on her plate.*)

FATHER: Have some cereal, Mr. Dodd—er—Herbert.

HERBERT: Uh—thank you. Shall I just put it on my plate?

LUCILLE: Oh, Herbert, do you like bowls better? Mother, maybe the milk will run all over the plate.

MOTHER: Well, I can get some bowls—

HERBERT: No, no, please, a plate's fine. (*He takes a spoonful on his plate.* LUCILLE *takes cereal and passes it to* MOTHER, *and she passes slaw to* HERBERT.)

LUCILLE: Cabbage, Herbert?

HERBERT: Cabbage? Ah, full of vitamins . . . Is that what makes your eyes sparkle so, Lucille?

LUCILLE (*Giggling*): Oh, Herbert, please . . .

JANEY: I guess you like Lucille a whole lot, don't you, Mr. Dodd?

MOTHER: Janey, what a question.

HERBERT: I don't conceal it very well, I guess. And Mr. and Mrs. Baldwin, that's why I wanted to come here. I want you to know how I feel about Lucille.

MOTHER: Well, of course, we—

HERBERT: She must have told you that I hoped—

FATHER: Well, she did, but we hoped not— (*Trying to cover up his slip*) that is, I mean— Bob, will you please take some of that cabbage and pass it on to me—I'm hungry.

BOB: You can have it all. (FATHER *takes some and begins eating.*)

MOTHER (*Nervously*): Bob, you aren't eating a thing.

BOB: You're telling me? What is there—

MOTHER (*Quickly*): Never mind, dear . . .

JANEY: Mr. Dodd, why did you fall for Lucille?

FATHER: Janey, where are you manners?

HERBERT: Oh, that's quite all right. Lucille's my favorite subject, you know.

FATHER (*Trying to make a joke*): Now, I thought food was your favorite subject, Mr. Dodd—that is, diet.

HERBERT: Oh, I am very interested in food. It may seem strange to you that I've made that my career, so to speak, but it's a great field—lots of room for improvement in the way people eat.

FATHER (*Looking at his plate*): Yes, I quite agree with you.

HERBERT: And keeping healthy. You know, I think that was the first thing I noticed about Lucille. She was so glowing— so alive—the picture of health.

LUCILLE: Oh, Herbert!

BOB: Well, she didn't get healthy eating stuff like this.

MOTHER: Bob! . . . He means—

LUCILLE: He means I was—well, I guess I was just born healthy, Herbert. (GRANDMA's *voice is heard off left.*)

GRANDMA (*Off*): Well, land sakes, where is everyone?

LUCILLE (*Petrified*): It's Grandma!

GRANDMA (*Calling, still off*): Fred—Margaret—why on earth didn't you wake me up? Isn't it time for dinner?

MOTHER (*Nervously*): Oh dear me . . . (GRANDMA *enters. She stares at them all.* FATHER, BOB *and* HERBERT *rise.*)

GRANDMA: Well, land sakes, what are you doing in here? (*She stops.*) And eating, when the table's all set up in the dining room?

LUCILLE: Grandma, please—

GRANDMA (*Peering at table*): Cereal, humph. I thought you said you'd had your breakfast when you met me at the station. (*She looks at* HERBERT.) Who's this?

LUCILLE: This is Herbert Dodd, Grandma. Herbert—Mrs. Field.

HERBERT (*Bowing*): Let me get you a chair.

GRANDMA: Now, stop bobbing about, young man. I'll get my own chair. I may be old but I'm in good health.

MOTHER (*Nervously*): Herbert is a friend of Lucille's from New York, Mother—he's here between trains.

GRANDMA: Oh, and he hadn't had his breakfast?

FATHER (*Clearing his throat and cutting her off quickly*): Mr. Dodd is an authority on diet—on food.

GRANDMA: Well, land sakes, if he's an authority on food, I thought you'd have given him something decent for breakfast —like bacon and eggs maybe. Cereal, grapes, and cabbage— of all things! Isn't that some new-fangled idea? Why, you might even have given him some fried potatoes and a slab of pork—that's what I used to have on the farm. Or he could have waited for dinner—

LUCILLE (*Loudly*): This *is* dinner, Grandma.

GRANDMA: What's that you say?

LUCILLE (*Desperately*): Mr. Dodd eats very simply. This *is* dinner.

GRANDMA: Margaret, what's the matter with her? Dinner, she says, when there's a turkey in the oven and mince pies and puddings—

LUCILLE: Grandma, please. . . . (*She starts to cry.*) Oh, I knew someone would give it away! (*She rises and starts left*) And I wanted everything to go just right. Oh, I can't bear it—I just can't bear it! (HERBERT *runs after her and puts an arm around her.*)

HERBERT: Lucille—darling, what is it? Everything's all right. At first I didn't understand, but if this is breakfast—

LUCILLE: But it isn't. It was supposed to be dinner. Oh, Herbert, I wanted everything the way you said on the radio. You gave the menu for Thanksgiving dinner—

HERBERT: I gave—

LUCILLE: Yes. You said to serve something light so we did—cereal and milk and grapes. We did add the cabbage but—

HERBERT (*Beginning to roar with laughter*): But Lucille, that was breakfast!

FATHER: Breakfast?

HERBERT: I was giving that menu for breakfast—tomorrow's breakfast.

FATHER: Why, of course—we wouldn't have known. We tuned in at the middle of the program and then we turned it off.

HERBERT: I don't blame you if you imagined— (*Breaking off*) The Thanksgiving menu was given yesterday.

LUCILLE: Oh dear, and I was out shopping. I didn't listen.

HERBERT: Lucille, you *really* didn't think I was giving that menu for dinner— Why (*He turns to the others*), you folks must have thought I was some kind of a nut.

FATHER: I don't mind telling you, young man, we did. But Lucille wanted it this way—

HERBERT: Oh, Lucille, you funny darling. . . . If I remember, on today's program, I did wish everyone a happy Thanksgiving and tell them not to overeat, but I didn't expect anyone to take me seriously. (*He kisses* LUCILLE.)

JANEY: Look, Mom, he kissed her.

GRANDMA: Well, this is all very interesting, but I don't mind telling you, young man, that *I* don't even approve of this menu for *breakfast*. It wouldn't stick to your ribs worth a cent!

HERBERT: Oh, I don't know—when you've had so much to eat the day before. As I said, I'm not a crank, but I do believe in lots of vegetables and fruits—and keeping healthy.

GRANDMA: Humph, I've eaten fried potatoes and eggs and salt pork all my life, and look at me—seventy-five and as spry as a colt.

HERBERT: Yes, but I'll bet you also ate a lot of carrots and beans right out of your own garden and fresh fruit—

GRANDMA: Well, guess I did, but just the same—

LUCILLE: Grandma, please—I wish you wouldn't argue with Herbert.

GRANDMA: Why not speak my mind? It's better than beating around the bush.

HERBERT: I agree . . . Well—well, it seems we have all misunderstood one another. (*He laughs again.*) When I sat down at this table, I didn't know what to think.

BOB: I s'pose you thought *we* were all nuts, and I don't blame you.

FATHER: Well, we're not the only ones who have misunderstood one another. The whole world seems to be doing a pretty good job of it most of the time—

GRANDMA: And it all comes from beating around the bush. If more people would be honest with each other—would speak their minds the way I do—

HERBERT: Grandma, you're wonderful—

MOTHER: Well, at least in America we *can* speak our minds— that's something to think about on Thanksgiving Day.

BOB: Yes, but does anyone care if I'm thinking about turkey and sweet potatoes and brussels sprouts and mince pie—

HERBERT: So am I. Why, that's what I had on my Thanksgiving menu—

LUCILLE: Oh, Herbert, did you?

GRANDMA: Of course he did. He's got good sense. And now I'm going to speak my mind once more. Margaret, let's get that turkey on the table and all that goes with it—let's eat! (*They all start toward door left.*)

BOB: Turkey—oh boy!

JANEY: Turkey—hooray!

HERBERT: (*Laughing*): Well, Mr. Baldwin, I see you've got some turkey gobblers here too!

FATHER: Yes, sir, a whole houseful! (*They all laugh as the curtain falls.*)

THE END

A Quiet Christmas

Characters

TOM EVANS
JANE EVANS
HETTY
JOHNNIE EVANS
BILL
PHIL EVANS
RUTH EVANS
IRENE EVANS
MARIE
ANNOUNCER FROM RADIO

TIME: *Christmas Eve, about eight P.M.*

SETTING: *The Evans' living room.*

AT RISE: TOM *and* JANE EVANS *are seated in the comfortable chairs in front of the fireplace,* TOM *at right and* JANE *at left.* TOM *is reading a newspaper and* JANE *is turning over the pages of a magazine. After a moment she puts the magazine down on her lap, and looks up and smiles.*

JANE: Tom.

TOM (*Looking up*): Yes, Jane?

JANE: We remind me of that poem—"A Visit from St. Nicholas."

TOM: We do?

JANE: Yes. " 'Twas the night before Christmas, when all through the house

178

Not a creature was stirring, not even a mouse."

Tom (*Chuckling*): Hmmm—for the first time in twenty-five years, that's true—and we're very lucky. (*Then looking at paper again*) Listen to this. "Biggest Christmas on record. Ten thousand last minute shoppers jam downtown district." And look at this picture, Jane. (*He leans forward and holds paper out toward her.*) Main street near Redfields Store this afternoon.

Jane (*She leans forward and looks*): My goodness! (*Staring at it*) Oh, my goodness! Can you imagine people being silly enough to go down in that crowd?

Tom: And the stores are open late tonight. They're probably still there—milling about.

Jane (*Dramatizing it*): Yes, Tom—being pushed and jostled and stepping on each other's tired, tired feet.

Tom (*Settling back*): And here we are—at peace. No fuss, no muss—no rush, no bustle.

Jane: A quiet Christmas. It's going to be wonderful.

Tom: Well, we certainly deserve it after all these years. The Christmas spirit is fine but too much is too much. When I think of the way we turned this place inside out year after year—

Jane: Up half the night trimming the tree—and wrapping packages—

Tom: Well, now we can relax. The children are grown up.

Jane: Yes. Of course, Johnnie really isn't.

Tom: Nonsense, he's almost twenty—in college—

Jane: Yes, but he's never been away from home for Christmas.

Tom: Well, he wanted it that way, didn't he? Didn't he write and say he was going to spend Christmas with his friends there?

Jane: Of course he did. And Irene wrote that she was too busy with her job in New York.

Tom: She would be. Hmm, imagine Irene executive secretary of the social council. That's a responsible position.

Jane: Yes, and I suppose she's trying to see that everyone in the world has a Christmas.

Tom: Well, she doesn't have to worry about us. All we want is peace and quiet.

Jane: I know, but I never thought we'd have it so soon. Why, I can hardly believe the children are grown up. Just think of Phil in a home of his own with a wife and baby—right this minute, Tom, they're getting ready for their first Christmas.

Tom: Now, wait a minute, you sound almost envious.

Jane: Oh, no, I'm not, Tom.

Tom: Well, I should hope not. Think what they've got to go through in the next twenty-five years. Next year the kid will be old enough to start breaking up his toys—but of course Phil and Ruth are young. They can take it. When you get to our age—

Jane: Please, Mr. Evans. I'm not as old as all that.

Tom: Sorry, dear, I didn't mean to make us sound antique. We've just reached the age of discretion, that's all. And we're being discreet about Christmas for the first time in our lives. Sensible, that's what. (Hetty *the maid, enters left.*)

Hetty: Excuse me, Ma'am.

Jane (*Turning*): Why, Hetty, I thought you'd gone.

Hetty: Gone?

Jane: Yes. I told you that you could go to a movie.

Hetty: A movie? On Christmas Eve? I can't feature it, Ma'am.

Tom (*Making a joke*): But it's a *double* feature, Hetty.

Hetty: Humph.

Tom: Well, then how about your friend Charlie?

Hetty: Charlie?

Tom: Yes—from Regan's Grocery Store. Why not go out with him? Seems like a nice fellow.

Hetty: Hmm, nice enough, but I don't care much for riding in a delivery truck.

Tom: Oh.

Jane: Well, you know there's nothing for you to do here, Hetty.

Hetty (*Shaking her head*): Nothing to do. How about tomorrow, Ma'am?

Tom: There won't be anything to do then either.

Jane: We're eating out.

Hetty: Eating at a restaurant on Christmas?

Jane: But I told you all that, Hetty—that we'd decided—

Tom: Besides it's not a restaurant. We're eating in the dining room of the Plaza Hotel.

Jane: And you won't have to do a thing, Hetty. No fussing with a turkey or making mince pies. You can just relax.

Hetty (*Sniffing*): Humph. What kind of a Christmas is that?

Tom: Why, it'll be a wonderful Christmas. Quiet—peaceful. It's what Jane wants.

Jane: Now, Tom, it was your idea.

Tom: Nothing of the kind.

Jane: Well, it doesn't matter. It's what we both want. And tomorrow I thought you could go to your cousin's, Hetty.

Hetty: Go out? On Christmas? But Ma'am, this is my home —for over twenty years ever since the children were little and I came to you, I've spent Christmas here. Do you mind if I just stay in my room?

Jane: Why, no—no—stay in, go out—do just as you like. That's what we're doing.

Hetty: Stay in, go out. (*She looks around disapprovingly.*) Aren't you even going to put the Christmas cards on the mantel?

JANE: No, that just makes more work. They get dusty, they have to be put away. Tom, where *are* the Christmas cards? I had them on the desk.

TOM: Ah, ha, I'll show you. (*He rises and goes to desk, and opens the file drawer.*) I've taken care of the Christmas cards. (*He flips through indexed folders.*) They're all filed away—you see? From Aunt Annabel to Cousin Zeke. (*He pulls out a Christmas card, shows it, and then drops it back.*)

HETTY (*Sadly*): Christmas cards stuck away like paid bills. Tsk, tsk.

TOM: Of course, a place for everything and everything in its place. (*He starts to close drawer and it sticks.*) Jane, why does this drawer always stick when I try to close it? (*He reaches in back and pulls out a Boy Scout axe.*) Ah, here's the trouble. What on earth is this doing in here?

JANE: Oh, my, Johnnie's Boy Scout axe. I've been meaning to take that up to the attic.

TOM: Well, we needn't do it now. (*He drops scout axe into front end of drawer and closes it.*)

HETTY: Johnnie . . . I wonder what the poor little lamb is doing.

TOM: Having a good time.

JANE: And he's not exactly little, Hetty. The children are grown up.

HETTY: Well, I guess I'm not, Ma'am. (*She starts to stamp out.*)

TOM: Oh, Hetty—wait a minute.

HETTY (*Turning*): Yes, sir.

TOM: We're not forgetting Christmas entirely, you know. (*He reaches into his pocket and hands her a check.*) Merry Christmas.

HETTY (*Looking at the check a little surprised*): It's very generous, sir. (*And then sadly*) But not very merry. (*She goes off left.* JANE *stares after her for a moment.* TOM, *in pulling out* HETTY'S *check has pulled out another one which he holds in his hand.*)

TOM: Oh, and Jane, I was almost forgetting. Here's your check too. (JANE *takes it and just looks at it.*) That's what we agreed on, isn't it? Just to give the money?

JANE: Yes, we did. (*Then with a wry smile*) But Hetty's right. It isn't very merry, is it?

TOM: Nonsense—now we're certainly not going to let Hetty put us into the doldrums. Just shows what habit will do to a person. We were having a perfectly good time.

JANE: Of course. But it does seem that—well, maybe we should at least have had a Christmas tree.

TOM: But why on earth—all that mess—needles dropping—besides, it's too late to do anything about it now.

JANE: I know. (*She sighs and leans back in chair.*) My, I feel a little tired all of a sudden.

TOM (*Going to her*): You do look pale—almost think you'd been Christmas shopping in that mob this afternoon.

JANE: Yes, that's just exactly the way I feel.

TOM: Well, we'll fix that up. We're going to have plenty of rest now. Let's turn on the radio and just relax. (*He sits down in chair, reaches over and turns on radio. It blares forth with the tune of "Jingle Bells."*)

JANE: Jingle Bells. Johnnie always used to sing that so much.

TOM (*Making a little face*): Yes, let's try something else. (*He turns the knob and an* ANNOUNCER *fades in.*)

ANNOUNCER: Tonight's the night we trim the Christmas tree. And here's a suggestion to help you with yours. For artificial snow use Fluffed Up Soap Flakes. Snowier, whiter— (TOM *switches it off and looks at* JANE.)

TOM: Well—ha-ha. (*He picks up his paper.*)

JANE (*Little laugh*): Ha-ha. (*She picks up her magazine.*

There is a long moment as they turn pages, obviously somewhat unhappy. Then in the distance you hear boys' voices singing "Jingle Bells." They come nearer. TOM lowers his paper and JANE drops her magazine. They stare at one another.)

TOM: Carolers—this early?

JANE: Why, I don't know. (*The voices come still nearer.*) One of them sounds like— (*You hear a door off and JOHNNIE's voice shouting.*)

JOHNNIE (*Off*): Hi, everybody. Merry Christmas!

JANE: It is—it *is* Johnnie! (*They rise excitedly as JOHNNIE enters right followed by BILL. The boys wear warm jackets, carry zipper bags and are loaded down with bundles of holly.*)

JOHNNIE: Surprise, surprise! Hi, Mom and Dad. (*He sweeps JANE off her feet with a big hug.*)

JANE: Johnnie, my boy!

TOM (*Happily*): Well, this certainly is a surprise.

JOHNNIE (*Shaking TOM's hand up and down*): Yeah, we made it—hitchhiked all the way. Mom and Dad, this is Bill.

BILL: How do you do? I hope it's all right my coming for Christmas like this—

TOM: Of course it's all right. (*Then remembering.*) That is—

JOHNNIE: You see, all of Bill's little brothers and sisters have the measles so we couldn't go there.

JANE: My goodness.

JOHNNIE: And I would have telegraphed but it all happened so suddenly and I couldn't get a train ticket because I'd spent all of my allowance for Christmas presents. (*He kneels down and starts opening bag and pulling out packages, some wrapped in Christmas paper and some in brown paper with postage stamps on them.*) So we just started out with our thumbs. (*Looking around*) Hey, where's the Christmas tree?

TOM: The tree? Why—uh—I haven't brought it in.

JOHNNIE (*Shaking head*) : You haven't even started yet. That's the way it is in this house, Bill. They're always late—so much to do. Well, it's a good thing one of the younger generation got home to get you started.

TOM : Yes, the others aren't coming.

JOHNNIE : I know, you wrote me. Irene's busy and Phil's gone domestic on his own hook. Well, we can get going now. Here's plenty of holly.

JANE : Yes, it's beautiful.

BILL : You see, Mrs. Evans, we rode the last ten miles on a truck full of holly and the man gave us this for helping him unload.

JOHNNIE : Sure—spread it around—put some over the picture —on the mantel— (JOHNNIE *starts putting holly around and* BILL *follows suit.*) Where's Hetty? Stuffing the turkey, I'll bet. Good old Hetty!

TOM : Hetty? Hetty? Oh dear me.

JOHNNIE : She's not sick, is she?

TOM : No—oh, no. I'll go tell her you're here. (*He exits nervously left and* JANE *looks after him.*)

JOHNNIE (*Still putting holly around*) : Boy, oh boy, Mom, it's certainly good to be home. Of course, I guess we look like a couple of hoboes and we need to wash up.

JANE : And I suppose you're both hungry. There might be something in the kitchen.

JOHNNIE : Something, that's good. You ought to see our kitchen at Christmas time, Bill—full of turkey and mince pies.

JANE : Yes, of course.

JOHNNIE : Hetty's some cook. Wait till you taste her food. Well, that takes care of the holly. Guess we better go up and wash. Come on, Bill.

BILL : O.K.

JOHNNIE (*Picking up bags and starting left*) : Where are the Christmas tree decorations, Mom? Still up in the attic?

JANE: Yes, but—

JOHNNIE: Well, we'll get 'em and tell Dad to hurry with that tree. (JOHNNIE *and* BILL *go off left.* JANE *looks around the room wildly, suddenly goes to desk drawer and pulls out some Christmas cards and starts putting them on the mantel.* JOHNNIE'S *packages are left on the floor.* TOM *re-enters left looking distracted.*)

TOM: Jane, I can't find Hetty anywhere. She's not in the kitchen.

JANE: What's that? Did you try her room?

TOM: I knocked on her door. No one answered.

JANE: Oh, my—then she's gone to the movie after all. Tom, what'll we do? The boys will be down in a minute with the decorations for the tree.

TOM: But there is no tree. Oh, dear—no Hetty—

JANE: No turkey—

TOM: No tree—no presents—

JANE (*Looking at packages on floor and trying to be hopeful*): Well, of course we did send the children packages earlier, and Johnnie's brought his back with him. There it is. He hasn't opened it.

TOM: Yes, but we won't have anything for each other or Hetty and it won't be—well, the way it should be.

JANE: No. Tom, we'll just have to tell Johnnie the truth. There's nothing else to do. We can take them out to dinner tomorrow.

TOM: But what kind of a Christmas will that be for the poor boys? They've come all this way—

JANE: Well, then, you think of something. (*They stand looking at each other a little annoyed. The doorbell rings.*)

TOM: Now, who on earth can that be?

JANE (*A little acidly*): Probably someone wanting to wish us

Merry Christmas. I'll go, Tom, and you be thinking what to say to Johnnie.

TOM: Now, wait a minute, Jane. (*But she goes off right and he stands looking bewildered. He picks up a couple of packages from the floor, and looks around, wondering where to put them. Then he finally sets them down on the floor again, in just as inappropriate a place. You hear the door open offstage and* JANE *say "My goodness!" Then there is a babble of voices saying "Merry Christmas.")*

JANE (*Excitedly. Still off. She enters during speech*): Tom—it's Phil and Ruth!

TOM (*Turning*): What's that? Phil and Ruth here?

JANE: Yes—and the baby! (PHIL, *the eldest son, and his wife,* RUTH, *an attractive girl in her early twenties, enter.* PHIL *carries a baby wrapped in blankets.* RUTH *runs to* TOM *and kisses him.*)

RUTH: Merry Christmas, Father Evans!

TOM: Why—yes, of course—Merry Christmas.

PHIL: Well, Dad, we knew you'd be surprised, but you seem almost shocked.

TOM: Yes, shocked, and delighted. We didn't expect—

RUTH: Well, we tried to call you long distance this afternoon but nobody answered.

TOM: Jane, weren't you at home?

JANE: Why—uh—

PHIL: Oh, I'll bet you were all out shopping.

JANE: No—I mean—yes. Oh, look at our grandson. (*She pulls back the blanket a little.*) He's sleeping so peacefully. Tom, how he's grown. (TOM *comes over and sticks out his finger at baby.*)

PHIL: Sure, he's grown. He's a big boy now. That's why we decided to come. Wanted Phil, Jr., to have his first Christmas right in the old Evans tradition. Nobody can do it up like you folks.

RUTH: Your Christmases are so wonderful that at the last minute we couldn't stay away. And the baby is beginning to notice everything now.

TOM: What's that? Notice? At five months?

PHIL: Oh, he's a very remarkable child. You'll see. Why, I'll bet he'll remember this Christmas all his life.

TOM: So will I.

JANE: Yes, indeed. We'll *all* remember this Christmas.

PHIL: Well, then, we'd better get started. Why, you folks are even later than usual. Where's the tree?

TOM: Why—uh—Phil, my boy—there's something I guess I ought to tell you.

JANE (*Cutting him off*): Tom. We are late, Phil, but at least we've got the holly up. Johnnie brought the holly.

PHIL: Johnnie? Is that guy here? Do I want to see him! It's been six months if it's a day.

TOM: He brought a friend from school with him.

RUTH: I suppose we ought to get the baby to bed, Phil.

PHIL: That's right, so he'll be bright and happy for his merry Christmas. (*The door opens off and you hear an excited voice.*)

IRENE (*Off, calling*): Mother, Dad! Merry Christmas! Merry Christmas!

TOM (*He jumps*): Good gracious.

JANE: It's Irene!

PHIL: Well—another bad penny. (IRENE, *the daughter of the family, enters. She is attractive, brisk and full of energy. She carries a suitcase and wears hat and coat.*)

IRENE (*Setting down suitcase*): Hi, everyone. The door wasn't locked so I came right in. (*Turning to door*) Come in, Marie —come in—don't be afraid, darling. (MARIE, *a little girl about eight years old, enters shyly. She is dark and foreign-looking, wears beret and coat and hangs onto* IRENE'S *hand as the others rush over to greet* IRENE.)

JANE (*Kissing her*): Irene, my dear!

PHIL: Rene, old girl!

TOM: Well—well—well!

IRENE: At the last minute I just couldn't stand it. I had to come home. I should have let you know but it was such a rush and I knew you'd be here, and everything would be perfect. That's why I brought Marie.

TOM: Marie?

IRENE: This is my family, Marie. (MARIE *curtseys.*)

MARIE: Comment allez-vous? I mean—'ow do you do? (JANE *and* TOM *look at one another.*)

IRENE: Marie is an orphan. She's one of the children from France.

RUTH (*Feeling sorry*): Oh.

IRENE: And she's never seen an American Christmas so I wanted her to see the best.

PHIL: The very best. This is the place.

IRENE: Oh, Phil, let's see my nephew. (*Looking at baby*) Look at the baby, Marie.

MARIE (*Smiling*): Oh, he is so—'ow you say—cute! (*Looking around*) And where is the great tree you tell me about—that she will be lit up?

IRENE: Wouldn't you know? You're later than ever, Mother. I'll bet you've been working like mad all day with presents.

MARIE: Will the tree be beeg like the ones outside?

IRENE: I showed her your evergreens, Dad. That balsam you've been nursing along all these years is really something. Oh, the yard's so beautiful. It's beginning to snow.

RUTH: A white Christmas! How wonderful.

PHIL: Well, we'd better get upstairs. You take the baby, Ruth.

(RUTH *takes the baby*.) I'll get our bags. (*He goes off right.*)

JANE (*To* RUTH): You and Phil and baby can take the guest room, Ruth.

IRENE: Marie can bunk with me in my old room.

PHIL (*Re-entering with two suitcases and a couple of big wreaths*): Here, Mom, we picked up a couple of wreaths for you. (*He puts them on a table.*) And I left some presents in the hall. Will you get 'em, Dad?

JANE (*Starting left*): I'll take you all up.

IRENE (*Picking up her suitcase and taking* MARIE'S *hand*): Nonsense. You and Dad have plenty to do. As though we didn't know our way in this house. We'll be down in a minute to pitch in. (*They all start toward left.*)

JANE: Well, if you're sure you'll find everything.

PHIL: Of course.

TOM: There *is* a great deal to do. (IRENE, MARIE, PHIL *and* RUTH *go off left.*)

JANE (*Turning on* TOM): Great deal to do. You know there's nothing to do. Nothing.

TOM: I tried to tell them. I tried to tell Phil, and you cut me off.

JANE: But I couldn't bear it. The children came home expecting Christmas as usual.

TOM: Well, it wasn't as usual. We were going to relax—relax —that's funny. Well, at least I can get those presents in from the hall. (*He goes out right and re-enters with some packages, dumping them on floor.*)

JANE: Tom, that's no help, dumping presents all over the floor— no tree to put them under. (*She starts to cry.*)

TOM: Jane, dear, please, don't cry.

JANE: But you sound as though you're almost sorry that the children came home.

Tom: Of course I'm not sorry, but I don't know what to do any more than you do.

Jane: Tom, what *are* we going to do? We've got to do something and quick.

Tom: Tell them—that's the only thing.

Jane: No. Especially not when we've waited this long. Oh, if we could only find Hetty.

Tom: How can we find her if she went to a movie?

Jane: Well, she probably went to the Tivoli near here. You could go over and look.

Tom: Jane, what do you expect me to do? Go stumbling around in a darkened theater peering into people's faces?

Jane: No, but maybe you could have her paged—ask one of the ushers.

Tom: Jane! Interrupt the whole performance? They'd think I was crazy.

Jane: Oh, I know—it's ridiculous, but I just thought—Hetty might figure some way.

Tom: There *is* no way. (Marie *appears in doorway left. She has removed her coat but still wears beret and she carries a woolen sock in one hand and a long nylon in the other*.) Oh. (*Putting on a brighter look*) Uh—hello, my dear—come in —come in.

Marie: Pardonez-moi, but Miss Irene—she say— (*Holding up the stockings*) here are the—here are les bas.

Jane: Les bas—the stockings—yes, of course.

Marie (*Smiling*): We were unpacking and she say to bring them queeck before it is too late for Mr. St. Nicholas. This is mine—and this—she is Miss Irene's.

Jane: Of course. We'll hang them right up on the mantel. (Tom *goes to desk and gets some thumb tacks.*)

Tom: Yes, yes, I've got some tacks. Now— (*Taking socks*)

here, young lady, we'll put them right up. (*He pins them on the mantel.* MARIE *watches and then leans over and looks up the chimney.*)

MARIE (*Worriedly*): It is not very beeg.

TOM: No—no, it's not, but it's big enough. Santa will get down it all right.

MARIE: He will? And he will fill les bas—he will fill the stockings way up to the top like Miss Irene say?

JANE: Fill them? Oh, of course he'll fill them, darling.

TOM: Yes—yes, of course.

MARIE: Oh, it is so exciting! (*She runs off left all smiles. There is a pause. Then* JANE *goes over to fireplace and peers up the chimney.*)

TOM: Jane—Jane, what in the world are you doing?

JANE (*Straightening up and making a little face*): I don't see Santa Claus.

TOM: Jane, how in the world can you joke at a time like this?

JANE: I know. That poor little girl.

TOM: She's expecting a real Christmas.

JANE: Tom, wait a minute. We've got some things for her. I just remembered.

TOM: What's that?

JANE: I didn't want to tell you before but I went shopping this afternoon.

TOM: You went shopping?

JANE: Yes—and that picture in the newspaper—I think I recognized myself in the crowd. I was afraid you would, too.

TOM: Jane, but why in the world— (*Breaking off*) So that's where you were when Phil tried to call.

JANE: Yes, and I suppose Hetty was out, too.

TOM: Jane, you wanted a Christmas all the time.

JANE: No, it wasn't that exactly, but at the last minute I just couldn't bear not to get *anything* so I bought some toys. I thought I could send them to the Children's Hospital later.

TOM: Well, of all things.

JANE: There's a doll and several toys the little girl will like. Oh, but that doesn't help the rest of the situation, does it? (*The doorbell rings.*)

TOM: Now, who—

JANE: I don't know.

TOM: Well, it can't be any more of the children. They're all here. I'll go see. (*He hurries off right.* JANE *looks around nervously, takes out a few more Christmas cards from the desk drawer and puts them on mantel, then backs away and looks at them sadly. She leaves desk drawer open.* TOM *re-enters bearing an armful of packages all wrapped in the same kind of Christmas paper.*) Jane, it's presents from Redfields Store.

JANE: From Redfields? But who—

TOM: All wrapped for Christmas and everything. Here's one marked with your name—and Phil and Irene and Hetty—

JANE: Tom, but how—

TOM: I—I think I know what's happened. You see, every year I've had a standing order for the personal shopper there to get my stuff.

JANE: Tom Evans!

TOM: Yes, you see? And I forgot to cancel it or anything so I guess they just went ahead as usual.

JANE: Tom Evans, after all the fuss you've made every year about how hard it was to shop and how your feet hurt and here someone else did it all for you. It was all cut and dried.

TOM: Well, you always liked the stuff. And I still had to shop. You were always sending me out on last minute errands.

JANE (*Looking at one big package with a woman's natural curiosity*): Oh, I wonder what's in mine.

TOM: I don't even know. I tell 'em to pick out something they think you'll all like. They've got your ages.

JANE: Tom Evans, you told Redfields Store how old I was?

TOM: Well—

JANE: The very idea. If this isn't—

TOM: Now, wait a minute. It's a help, isn't it? At least we've got some presents.

JANE: Yes, so we have—but, oh dear. There's still no food— no tree— (JOHNNIE *enters left carrying several cardboard cartons. He has removed his heavy jacket and wears slacks and T shirt.*)

JOHNNIE: Well, I found the decorations, and here's the stand for the tree. (*He puts metal stand down at stage center.*)

JANE: The stand—

TOM: The stand—yes, of course, the stand. Now all we need is the tree.

JOHNNIE: Yeah, where is it, in the garage? I'll go get it.

TOM: No—no, wait. I'll—I'll get it. (*But he just stands, looking bewildered.*)

JOHNNIE: O.K. (*Taking stand and turning upstage left*) Where'll we put it, Mom? Up this corner—the same old place?

JANE (*Turning*): Why, yes, Johnnie. I think that'll be very nice.

JOHNNIE: Well, we'll move this chair a little. (*He shifts chair downstage a little and motions toward lamp upstage.*) Mom, can you move that lamp? (*They are busy up in the corner. Suddenly* TOM *goes quickly to desk, and with his back to others fishes out the scout axe and tucks it under his coat. Putting one hand in his coat pocket he holds axe out of sight. He starts for door right as* JANE *turns and sees him.*)

JANE: Tom, where are you going?

TOM (*Partly turning*): Why, to get the tree of course.

JANE (*Startled*): What's that? (*Covering up*) Oh, the tree—well, it's about time. (TOM *exits right.*)

JOHNNIE (*Digging through cartons which he has piled on chairs and tables, and pulling out Christmas tree decorations*): See, Mom, here are the balls, and the tinsel. Boy, this stuff certainly brings back memories. (*Now he pulls out a small angel.*) And here's the angel for the top of the tree—how long have we had her?

JANE: Ever since you were a baby.

JOHNNIE: Boy, she wears well, doesn't she? (*He is still digging through.*)

JANE: Yes, dear, but do you need to spread everything about?

JOHNNIE: Well, I'm looking for the lights. They don't seem to be here.

JANE: That's funny.

JOHNNIE (*Digging through last box*): This is the last box. They're not in here.

JANE: Oh, I remember now. There wasn't room in the boxes. Hetty wrapped them in brown paper.

JOHNNIE: Oh, well then we'll find them. (*He starts left.*) Say, where is Hetty? She's not in the kitchen.

JANE: Oh—well—she—she must have gone out for some last minute things.

JOHNNIE: I'm certainly anxious to see that old girl. She's been part of Christmas as long as I can remember. (*He goes out left.*)

JANE: Part of Christmas—oh dear. (*She desperately goes to drawer and takes out a few more Christmas cards and stands them on the mantel and then steps back, shaking her head and surveying them. You hear TOM stamping feet off and then he enters dragging a Christmas tree after him.*) Tom—Tom—a tree!

TOM: Yes, my dear. Let it never be said that the Evanses had a Christmas without a Christmas tree.

JANE: But it—it's a miracle. Where did you get it?

TOM (*Holding up axe*): Jane, I cannot tell a lie. I did it with my little hatchet.

JANE: Tom . . . George Washington Santa Claus. (*Looking at tree*) Tom, it's your favorite balsam.

TOM: Well, my dear, balsams are the best. The needles don't drop off. (*He takes the tree over and places it in the stand.*)

JANE: Oh, Tom, it's beautiful—beautiful! (*You hear a sniff or two off left and sound of crying.*)

TOM: Jane, what's that?

JANE: Someone crying—it sounds like— (HETTY *enters left wearing coat and a scarf around her head and carrying a large, paper wrapped package. She has her face buried in a hand-kerchief and is crying loudly.* JANE *rushes to her and takes her arm.*) Hetty—Hetty—oh, I'm so glad to see you.

TOM (*Rushing to her and taking her other arm. They draw her downstage between them. They are facing the audience*): Hetty, where have you been?

JANE: What's the matter? (HETTY *sniffs.*)

TOM: Here, let me take your package.

HETTY: Thank you, sir. (TOM *takes the package and holds it in front of him with both hands, staggering a little under the weight.*)

JANE: Now, what's wrong?

HETTY: I—I went to a movie, like you said.

JANE: Oh dear, was it a sad movie?

HETTY: No, Ma'am—that is, I don't know.

TOM: But then what—

HETTY: Well, you see, I'd hardly got set down near the front where I like to sit because of my eyes, sir, when the manager came.

JANE: What?

HETTY: Yes, Ma'am. (*Still sniffing*) He said the ticket I'd bought on the way in was the winning number—and he handed me that. (*She points to package and starts crying harder.*)

JANE: Don't cry, Hetty.

HETTY: Oh, but Ma'am, I never won anything before in my life and now when I have no use for it—

TOM: Now—now, Hetty, it can't be as bad as all that. What's in the package? (*Lifting it up and down*) It weighs a ton.

HETTY: Not a ton, sir. (*Crying*) Fifty-four pounds.

TOM: Fifty-four pounds of what?

HETTY: Turkey, sir. With giblets.

JANE: Turkey? (*Joyfully*) Oh, Hetty—Hetty—

HETTY: Isn't it sad, Ma'am, when we're having a quiet Christmas?

JANE: But we're not. Look. (*She twists* HETTY *around so that she can see the disordered room and the tree.*)

HETTY: A Christmas tree.

TOM: Yes, the children are home.

HETTY: The children?

JANE: Yes—all of them. And a friend of Johnnie's, and Irene's brought a little French girl.

HETTY: Oh, Ma'am, isn't it wonderful! I'll get right at that turkey—and I'll make mince pies. I'll get everything done if I have to stay up all night.

TOM: Hooray! (*Going to* HETTY) Merry Christmas, Hetty.

JANE: But Hetty, I told you not to order—have we got anything to make pies with?

HETTY: Oh. No, Ma'am.

JANE: And what about vegetables and fruit, and candy and nuts for the stockings and oh—everything.

TOM: Probably some of the stores are still open.

JANE: Not the grocery stores, Tom.

HETTY: Mr. Regan's store will open, Ma'am.

JANE: But there was a sign on it, Hetty, that he was closed at six o'clock.

HETTY: Yes, but let me use the phone. (*She crosses right and goes to phone.*)

JANE: But Hetty, what— (HETTY *is dialing a number.*)

HETTY: Just wait and see, Ma'am. (*There is a slight pause.* HETTY *speaks sweetly into phone.*) Hello, is this Charlie? This is Hetty. . . . Isn't it a beautiful Christmas Eve with the snow and all? (JANE *and* TOM *look at one another.*) Well, I just thought I'd like to hear your voice. . . . Oh, and there was something else. I forgot one or two things for the Christmas cooking, and I thought maybe— (*Pause*) Would you, Charlie? Would you really open the store? Why, that would be just wonderful of you. I'll meet you there with my list and we can have a little ride back in the truck. All right —in about half an hour. . . . Don't thank me, Charlie—a Merry Christmas to you. (*She hangs up all smiles.* JANE *and* TOM *rush to her.*)

JANE: Hetty, Hetty—you're wonderful!

HETTY: And now give me that turkey, sir. I'll get it in the kitchen before the children find out we just came by it. (*She takes package from* TOM *and hurries off left.*)

JANE (*Elated*): Oh, Tom. (*She picks up a long paper chain and a piece of tinsel and tosses them onto the tree, letting them dangle wherever they land.*)

TOM: We're off! Who wants a quiet Christmas? (*Out of a box he picks a toy tin horn and blows a loud squawk on it. Then he goes to* JANE, *puts arms around her and dances her about in a step or two.*) Jane, let's always have a Christmas.

JANE: Of course, darling. Here, all these years we've thought we were just doing it for the children.

Tom: Well, we were. I guess we're all children when it comes to Christmas. (PHIL *enters followed by* RUTH. *He is carrying a small stepladder and is in his shirt sleeves.* RUTH *has removed coat and hat.*)

PHIL: Here we are, all ready to help. The baby's asleep, and I brought the ladder from the kitchen. Hetty said we'd be needing it.

JANE: Oh, you saw Hetty?

RUTH: Yes, we all did. Johnnie's having a reunion in the kitchen right now. Hetty's getting as bad as the rest of you. She hasn't even started on the turkey.

Tom: Oh, don't you worry about Hetty. She'll get things done.

PHIL: What a bird that is she's got out there. (*He sets ladder near tree, and gets up on it.*) Come on, Ruth, let's get going on this tree. (IRENE *enters with an armful of packages and some mistletoe, followed by* MARIE *who carries an assortment of stockings, both men's and women's.* IRENE *has removed her hat and coat and* MARIE *no longer wears her beret.*)

IRENE (*She slides her packages under tree and then holds up mistletoe*): Mom, here's some mistletoe. I had it in my bag. Shall I hang it over the door as usual?

JANE: Yes.

Tom: There are thumb tacks on the desk. (IRENE *gets tacks from desk, then pulls a chair out, places it near door right and gets up on it.*)

MARIE (*Holding up stockings*): Look, everyone upstairs—they give me their stock-ings—to hang on the mantel.

Tom: You'll need tacks too, Marie.

MARIE (*She nods*): Oui. (*She stands looking around wide-eyed. Then with arms outstretched looking at tree.*) Oh, she is here—she is here! Did St. Nicholas bring her?

JANE: Yes, dear, he did. (*She looks at* TOM *and smiles and he smiles back and pretends to pull at a long white beard.*)

MARIE: She is beautiful—just like the ones we see outside.

TOM: Yes, isn't she?

JOHNNIE (*Enters singing with* BILL *who is still offstage to tune of "Here Comes the Bride"*): Here come the lights—here come the lights—tangled up as us-u-al—here come the lights! (JOHNNIE *backs in with Christmas tree lights wound around his head and shoulders and stringing out from him through the door. As he backs on stage,* BILL *follows tangled up on the other end of the lights. They stop stage center and everyone laughs.* JOHNNIE *and* BILL *continue to untangle lights till end. Everyone is busy doing something.* JANE *gets last of cards out of drawer and is happily putting them on mantel,* TOM *is picking up presents and putting them under tree and* MARIE *has taken tacks from desk and is pinning socks on mantel.*)

PHIL: What are you two doing? Playing cowboy?

JOHNNIE: Don't be silly. You should have seen 'em when we started.

BILL: They're practically untangled now. (HETTY *enters left wearing coat and a very fancy hat with fruit and flowers on it. She has a sheet of paper at least a yard long and is checking the top of it with a pencil as she hurries directly across stage.* IRENE *steps down from chair to let her pass.*)

IRENE: Why, Hetty, where are you going?

HETTY (*Turning*): Just a few last minute things to get at Mr. Regan's store. (*She holds up the list, tosses her head, smiles and off she goes.* IRENE *gets back up on chair and they all laugh.* TOM *turns on the radio.*)

TOM: I know what we need. Some Christmas music. (*They are all busy with their various tasks. "Oh, Little Town of Bethlehem" comes from the radio. After a moment they all stop and listen. Note: The volume of the music can be controlled backstage and after they listen for a moment it can be turned low so that it will not interfere with the lines, then up and full again at end.*)

IRENE: Isn't that beautiful?

MARIE: I am so happy I will cry.

RUTH (*Catching* PHIL'S *hand*): Oh, Phil.

PHIL: Merry Christmas, Ruth.

JOHNNIE: There—there's something about Christmas that kind of gets you, isn't there?

BILL: I'll say.

JANE: It's so—so peaceful, isn't it, Tom? (*She comes nearer to him.*)

JOHNNIE: What's that, Mom? With all this commotion we're making?

JANE: Peace doesn't mean just being quiet, darling. It's the way you feel inside.

TOM: That's right, and with all of you here—

JANE: And Christmas, well, we're at peace with the world.

TOM: Yes. Merry Christmas, everyone.

ALL: Merry Christmas!

THE END

The Star in the Window

Characters

OTTO   MR. BAKER
MAMA   WOMAN
MAN   MR. JONES
MRS. FLANAGAN

TIME: *Christmas Eve.*

SETTING: *A small neighborhood shop in a large city.*

AT RISE: OTTO, *an elderly little man, is rocking comfortably in a rocking chair. He holds a book in his hands and wears heavy spectacles which he peers over and under by turns as he reads. The telephone rings.* OTTO *takes no notice until it rings a second time. Then, without getting up, he puts his book on the counter, reaches for the telephone and unhooks the receiver. (He has a light accent but it need not be distinguishable as any certain nationality.)*

OTTO (*Into telephone*): Hello. Yah, Otto's Novelty and Gift Shop. . . . Christmas stars like hangs in my window? Wait a minute. (*He puts phone down, rises and goes to table and rummages around among the Christmas tree ornaments; he picks up two or three tinsel stars, then puts them down again and returns to telephone.*) Sure, we got lots of them. Fifty cents. . . . That's all. . . . Yes, just like the one in the window. . . . Sure, I know they are beautiful for fifty cents. Yes, just like it. You come in, then. Goodbye. (*He hangs up, sits in rocking chair again and takes up his book.* MAMA, OTTO's *wife, an elderly little woman, enters left. She goes straight to the cash register, pushes one of the keys and the drawer flies open.* OTTO *looks up over his spectacles.*) Ah, ha, Mama, this time I catch you. Spending more money for Christmas.

MAMA (*She has a light accent too*) : The lucky piece for the Christmas pudding, Otto. I almost forgot. (*She takes a coin out and shuts the register drawer.*) And you should see Mr. Turkey. He is all stuffed and ready for the oven.

OTTO: Fine, Mama, fine. Tomorrow we have a big Christmas dinner. I stuff myself as usual.

MAMA: Ah, you talk a lot, Otto, but you'll give the best of it to those children who are coming.

OTTO: Did you get the presents wrapped for under the tree, Mama?

MAMA: Yes, and with their names on them. I am glad you thought of having Mrs. Spinelli and her children, Papa. It gives us a chance for a happy Christmas.

OTTO: Sure, it works both ways. Poor woman. No husband— she couldn't provide much. And we have all the fun.

MAMA: I hope we've got enough presents for them, Otto.

OTTO: So what if we haven't? After dinner if they look like they want more, bring them in the store here and say: little Mr. Spinellis, little Miss Spinellis, help yourselves.

MAMA (*Laughing*) : Ah, my Otto. Such a business man you are. Everything in the store you would give away if I did not stop you.

OTTO: Ho, a lot of stopping you do, Mama. How about the little girl who has five cents to buy a doll and you give her a quarter one?

MAMA: That was once, Papa.

OTTO: Once I *caught* you, you mean. But I guess you are right, Mama. I am not much of a business man. If I was, I'd have a great big store like Mr. Jones on the avenue.

MAMA (*Thoughtfully*): Yes, Otto, maybe you might have had a big store.

OTTO: You wish I had, Mama? You wish I'd been a—a go-getter?

MAMA: No, Otto. Mr. Jones has big business—the store of the Christmas spirit, they call it. But to me, it's the wrong kind of spirit. Sell—sell—sell. Money—money—money. So commercial it is. I like our way better.

OTTO: But Mama, sometimes I worry. I don't give you much.

MAMA (*Laughing*): How you talk, Otto. We have plenty to eat, a place to live in back of the store, and each other. What more could we want?

OTTO: Nothing, for me.

MAMA: Then don't talk foolish. Otto, it's Christmas Eve. Cannot you close up soon?

OTTO: Not yet, Mama. People in this neighborhood, they work late Christmas Eve. They might need last minute things. And a lady telephoned. She's coming for a Christmas star.

MAMA: So? Then sure you must wait. I get back to my pudding.

OTTO (*Nodding toward radio*): Why don't you take the radio back, Mama, and listen while you work?

MAMA: No, when I work, I work. Later on we listen. Besides, you like to listen to the news.

OTTO: No, not tonight, Mama. I read my book. Only pleasant things on Christmas Eve. (MAMA *goes out left.* OTTO *turns to his book again. Then the door from the street opens, the bell tinkles and a* MAN *enters.* OTTO *keeps on reading his book. The* MAN *stands for a moment as though expecting someone to wait on him and then moves a little closer to* OTTO.

He stands for another moment and then coughs. When OTTO
still takes no notice he speaks.)

MAN: Are you—are you the proprietor?

OTTO (*Looking up*): What's that? Oh, yes, I'm the proprietor.
Just make yourself at home—see what you want maybe. Then
I wrap it up for you. (*He goes back to his book.*)

MAN (*He can't help smiling*): But you see I know what I want.
A star for my Christmas tree. There was one in your window.

OTTO (*He puts down his book*): A star—of course. You will
excuse me but I get so interested in my book. Christmas
stories it is, old legends.

MAN (*Politely*): Oh, yes.

OTTO (*He starts for table upstage but stops halfway*): You
have read legends?

MAN: Well, not lately.

OTTO: Most remarkable how those tales ever began. Now you
take one, it comes from the old country—it goes way back.
The animals all kneel on Christmas Eve and say their prayers.

MAN: Yes, I believe I have heard that one but it never made
much sense to me.

OTTO: Not much sense maybe but somehow the story got
started. There's a lot we don't know, I always say.

MAN: Yes, that's very true—very true. But now about my star.

OTTO: That's right, I talk too much. (*He goes to table and
rummages about, looking for star.*) Ah, here we are. (*He
holds up a tinsel star.*) Yah, that's a nice star for fifty cents.

MAN: Yes, very nice—but that isn't the one.

OTTO: No?

MAN: No. Late last night you had it in the window.

OTTO: Sure, it's still there, just like this one.

MAN: I saw that one as I came in. But I mean the one that
was there last night. I came past late and tried your door but
you were closed.

OTTO: So? I'm sorry—but still it is the same star.

MAN: No, no. This is just an ordinary tinsel star. The one I saw must have been much more expensive. Made of crystal glass perhaps and lighted from the inside. It was beautiful. I've never seen anything like it.

OTTO (*He smiles and shakes his head*): Crystal glass. No, my friend. Not in Otto's little store. You see it somewhere else maybe.

MAN: It is possible but I was quite sure—of course I could have been mistaken.

OTTO: Yah, that's right—we all make mistakes. (*The door at right opens, the bell tinkles and* MRS. FLANAGAN *enters. She carries a shabby purse.* OTTO *looks toward her and smiles.*)

MRS. FLANAGAN: Good evening, Otto.

OTTO: Ah, Mrs. Flanagan, hello. I be with you in a minute. (*She starts looking at some of the little Christmas trees.* OTTO *turns toward* MAN *again.*) Why not you try Mr. Jones' big store on the avenue? Maybe that's where you see the star. Everything they have. If anyone's got a crystal star, you find it there.

MAN: I will try there. Thank you. (*He starts for door, then turns back and picks up a package of Christmas tree lights from the table.*) But while I'm here I might as well take a set of these Christmas tree lights.

OTTO: So? Good. I see if they work. (*He takes lights from* MAN, *goes back of counter and plugs in lights. They all light.*)

MAN (*Handing him money*): Fine. (OTTO *rings sale up on cash register and gives* MAN *some change and his package of lights.*)

OTTO: Thank you, sir. And a merry Christmas to you.

MAN: Thank you—and the same to you. (*He goes out right.*)

OTTO (*Going to* MRS FLANAGAN): So, Mrs. Flanagan, it looks like we want a Christmas tree for the little ones.

MRS. FLANAGAN (*She indicates the smaller trees*): Yes, Otto, I thought maybe one of these.

OTTO: Such a little tree for such a big family?

MRS. FLANAGAN: I know, Otto. I'd like a big one but the big ones—well, the truth is, they're so expensive.

OTTO: Expensive—that's not a nice word for Christmas. Too much we hear about the expense.

MRS. FLANAGAN (*Laughing*): Yes, Otto, but when it comes down to counting the pennies—

OTTO: Yes, of course that's right, Mrs. Flanagan, but you know it's a funny thing this year. The little trees cost more than the big ones.

MRS. FLANAGAN (*Looking at him*): What do you mean, Otto?

OTTO: Well, it's just that—I guess so many people like the little ones to put on their tables—so it's—well, what you call the law of supply and demand. Now, those little ones—two dollars—three dollars some, but you look here— (*He takes her by the arm and leads her to the door downstage right. He opens the door and points outside.*) See that big one leaning against the lamp post? Too big—that kind a drug on the market—seventy-five cents.

MRS. FLANAGAN: Why, it's a beautiful tree, Otto. You mean I can have that for seventy-five cents?

OTTO: Sure, that's the price.

MRS. FLANAGAN (*She fishes into her purse and takes out some coins which she hands to him*): The children will love it. Otto, you're a fraud.

OTTO: Now, is that nice to say? (*He goes to cash register and rings up money.*)

MRS. FLANAGAN: But God bless you, Otto, and a Merry Christmas to you. (*She starts out.*)

OTTO: Now, wait. We got string outside. I tie it up for you so it's better to carry. (*He crosses right. The phone rings.* OTTO *turns left, calling.*) Mama—Mama! (MAMA *appears in doorway left.*)

MAMA: Yes, Otto?

OTTO: The phone, Mama—I tie up Mrs. Flanagan's Christmas tree. (MRS. FLANAGAN *and* OTTO *go out right, and* MAMA *goes to phone.*)

MAMA (*Into phone*): Hello? Otto's Novelty and Gift Shop. . . . Christmas stars? Yes, we have them. Made of tinsel— fifty cents. . . . Big, bright, all lighted up? No, I'm afraid not, sir. . . . But you couldn't have seen it, because we don't have 'em. We never have 'em. . . . I'm sorry, sir. Goodbye. (*She hangs up, and is about to go out left when the door opens, the bell tinkles and* PAPA *enters with* MR. BAKER, *a tall young man.* PAPA *has hold of* MR. BAKER'S *arm, and they both are smiling.*)

OTTO (*As they enter*): That's fine—that's fine—congratulations! Mama—Mama, here's Mr. Baker—and what do you think?

MAMA: The baby has come.

MR. BAKER: That's right. I wanted to tell you and Otto.

OTTO: It's a boy, Mama.

MAMA: A boy—and how is the little lady? How is your wife?

MR. BAKER: Fine—fine and so happy.

OTTO: No wonder, a baby for Christmas.

MAMA: And we are so happy *for* you.

OTTO: Yes, yes. Look at him, Mama—the picture of a proud papa, is he not?

MR. BAKER: I suppose I am. You know, it's funny. A new baby—when it happens to someone else, it seems just a common everyday occurrence, but when it happens to you, why it's—it's like a miracle.

OTTO: Yah—yah—miracles, they are all around us, it seems to me, if we just look.

MR. BAKER: Yes, that's right. Miracles all around us. You know, Otto, that's something of the idea I'm trying to get into my book.

OTTO: Ah, the writing will go well now.

MR. BAKER: It's already going well. When I got home from the hospital, I started right in on the last chapter.

OTTO: The last chapter, that is good. See, Mama, soon it will be published.

MAMA: And a best seller, I bet.

MR. BAKER: Oh, I don't know about that. Maybe no one will even want to publish it.

OTTO: But it is good. I know. The chapters you have brought me to read—they are like a fresh clean breeze in my head.

MR. BAKER: Yes, you like it, Otto, but how many people see things the way you do?

OTTO: Oh, I think lots, if they just had the chance. Some of the modern new books—I try to read them but the authors, they dig so into the mud and mire, I say to Mama, I cannot read on. I feel I need a bath.

MAMA: Papa, how you talk.

MR. BAKER: But Otto, the critics say life is like that.

OTTO: Yah—yah, there is much evil. Life *is* like that sometimes, but it need not be always if people would look up. Life, it could be—why, it could be a miracle.

MR. BAKER: Yes, that's it exactly—and the idea is clear in my mind but it's so hard to get it in writing. I've finally decided to end my book with a Christmas scene. I thought I could bring out the idea in that way.

OTTO: Yah, yah, Christmas, the greatest miracle of all—does it not sound good, Mama?

MAMA: I should say. When it is published we put it in our

window. Then we have some new books, Papa, instead of all these second-hand ones. (*She gestures toward shelves of books.*)

MR. BAKER (*Laughing*): Hmm, the reason you have so many second-hand ones is because you've bought them from people like me.

MAMA: Oh, I did not mean, Mr. Baker—

MR. BAKER: It's all right. I've said to my wife during the last year we have *eaten* my books.

OTTO: So—I did not pay you much.

MR. BAKER: More than they were worth sometimes. And to make it worse I still use them. In fact, I want to use one right now. Didn't I sell you a book of legends, Otto?

OTTO: Sure, sure, you did. Only just now I was reading it. (*He goes to counter and picks up book.*) Here—here, you take it home again.

MR. BAKER: No—no, I can look at it now. It won't take but a minute to refresh my memory. I just thought if I could find an old Christmas legend that I could use in some way, it might help to dramatize my idea.

OTTO: Here—here, you sit down, you look. (*He motions* MR. BAKER *to rocking chair and he sits down with the book.*) There was one I was just reading—about the animals kneeling.

MR. BAKER: No, no, I don't think that would do. It seems to me there was one about a star. (*His voice trails off as he starts looking through book.*)

MAMA: Star? That reminds me, Papa. The phone call. It was a man about a star. He said he saw one in our window last night—big and bright—could he buy one like it, he said.

OTTO: That's funny, Mama. Another man asked me the same thing. I tell him it must be Mr. Jones' store. Mr. Jones, he always has something unusual in his window.

MR. BAKER (*Looking up*): Here it is—the one I wanted. The Christmas Star. (*Reading from book*) There is an old, old legend, which has been told and retold for generations about the Christmas star. The villagers say a beautiful star like the one that led the wise men on the first Christmas is sometimes seen again. This star, like the first one, is really a band of angels and often they are heard singing, so that men may not forget the miracle of Christmas.

MAMA: Yes, Mr. Baker, but unless someone remembers, the star cannot come.

MR. BAKER: That's right. That's what it says here.

OTTO (*Surprised*): You read the story, Mama?

MAMA: No, Otto, I heard it—I heard it when I was—oh, so little. (*She holds her hand out to show how little.*) Sitting on my Grandpapa's knee. And he said it was true.

MR. BAKER: You mean he saw the star?

MAMA: No, *he* didn't. But when he was a boy it happened in a village not far away. Everyone was talking about the big bright star. It came at midnight and some said they heard angels singing.

MR. BAKER: It's the same story all right. Listen. (*Reading from book again*) The angels cannot draw near to the earth and cause the star to shine unless there be someone who has the true spirit of Christmas. The star must find a place to rest. And so, the villagers say, if the time should ever come when there is not one left who remembers the true meaning of Christmas, then darkness will come upon the earth and the star cannot shine.

OTTO: Hmmm. A beautiful story—is it not?

MR. BAKER: And I think I can use it. It fits in with my idea—there's a character in my book who can tell the legend. (*The door opens, the bell tinkles and a well-dressed woman enters hurriedly. She looks about and then stands waiting.*)

OTTO (*To* MR. BAKER): Yah, yah, it will be fine. I, too, see how you can use it.

WOMAN (*Somewhat impatiently*): Could someone wait on me, please?

OTTO (*Turning to her*): Oh, I am sorry. Good evening.

WOMAN: I telephoned about the star.

OTTO: Of course, I remember.

WOMAN: I hope you have some left. I notice it isn't in the window.

OTTO: Oh, but sure—it's still there—and we got lots more. (*He goes to the table and picks up a tinsel star and holds it out to her.*)

WOMAN: No—no, that's not the one.

OTTO: But my dear lady, you said like in the window. (*He goes to the window, pulls the curtain back and points it out.*) See —the same thing.

WOMAN (*Crossly*): Now, really, I don't know what your idea is. We drove past here late last night and you had a beautiful star in the window. I phoned you just a little while ago and you assured me you had more of them. I've gone to a great deal of trouble to come down here and now you show me this tinsel thing.

OTTO: But Madam, this is all I have—it's all I've ever had.

WOMAN: A likely story. I suppose the others are all gone, but you told me you still had them. You thought if you got me in here, you could still make a sale. Well, you're mistaken— badly mistaken. (*She starts for the door.*)

OTTO: I am sorry, Madam, but it's you who are mistaken.

WOMAN: It's misrepresentation, that's what it is. You ought to be reported to the Better Business Bureau! (*She slams out.*)

OTTO (*Shrugging his shoulders but disturbed*): Well, what do you think of that?

MAMA: How can she talk like that to you, Papa? Misrepresent? You who always lean over backwards the other way.

OTTO: Now, now, Mama, I guess she really thought I'd lied to her.

MR. BAKER (*Putting book down on counter, rising and coming toward them*) : But Otto, what's this all about?

OTTO: I wish I knew. I am beginning to wonder. At first I think nothing of it but now—but now if people are going to think I'm trying to cheat them—

MR. BAKER: Oh, that's ridiculous, Otto.

MAMA: But Mr. Baker, so many people say they see a big bright star in our window last night and we never have such a thing. Papa thinks it maybe must be something in Mr. Jones' window.

OTTO: Yah, yah, I'm sure that's it—and people are just confused.

MR. BAKER: But how could they confuse your little place with the Jones store?

OTTO: I don't know—but Christmas time people rush around so —they don't know where they see things. This sounds like something Mr. Jones would have, a big bright star, expensive, made of crystal glass maybe.

MR. BAKER (*Suddenly getting an idea*) : No, Otto, no! (*There is a pause.* OTTO *and* MAMA *both look at* MR. BAKER.) Not crystal glass—not crystal glass at all!

OTTO: What do you mean?

MR. BAKER: Why, the legend we've just been reading—the Christmas star!

MAMA (*Catching* MR. BAKER'S *excitement*) : Otto, do you think it could be—is it possible? Grandpapa told me—

OTTO (*Laughing a little*) : No—no, Mama. (*Then to* MR. BAKER) Mr. Baker, you save that legend for your book. In Otto's little store we have no such miracles.

MR. BAKER: But why not? You're the good people with the true Christmas spirit. It all fits.

OTTO: Hear him talk, Mama—no wonder he's an author. Such imagination.

MAMA: Yes, Mr. Baker, I suppose Otto is right. Even if it could happen it would not happen to us.

MR. BAKER (*Laughing a little too*): Well, all right—but it was an idea.

OTTO: You save those bright ideas for your book.

MR. BAKER (*Laughing*): All right, Otto, if you say so—and I guess I'd better be getting back to it.

OTTO: You sure you don't need the book, Mr. Baker, about the legend?

MR. BAKER: No—no, I'll remember. (*Starting for the door*) And a very merry Christmas to you both.

OTTO: Merry Christmas to you.

MAMA: And you take from us a merry, merry Christmas to the little lady—and to the little boy too.

MR. BAKER: Yes, I'll certainly do that. Thank you and good-night. (*He goes out and the door closes.*)

MAMA: Ah, that Mr. Baker, he is so nice. (*She sighs.*)

OTTO: Then why do you sigh about it, Mama?

MAMA: Did I, Otto? Perhaps I did. That woman—so unpleasant—it—well, it bothers me. Unpleasant things should not happen on Christmas Eve.

OTTO: Now, Mama, you are not going to let all this foolish business upset our Christmas.

MAMA: Of course, it *is* foolish. I know that.

OTTO: It's just all a mistake, Mama. We forget about the star we don't have.

MAMA: You are right. And I've still got work to do, Papa. (*She starts left.*) Cannot you close up soon? It's almost midnight.

OTTO: So? Then maybe I can. (*The door opens, the bell tinkles and* MR. JONES, *a well-dressed middle-aged gentleman enters.* MAMA *stops, as he comes in, and stands near the counter.*)

MR. JONES: Good evening—good evening—Merry Christmas—Merry Christmas.

OTTO: Merry Christmas to you, sir.

MR. JONES: What's that? Oh, yes, yes, of course, Merry Christmas.

MAMA: Thank you very much, sir, and Merry Christmas.

MR. JONES: Yes, yes, Merry Christmas—Merry Christmas—Merry Chris—well, thank goodness, it's almost over.

OTTO: Over? What's almost over?

MR. JONES: Christmas—all this Merry Christmas stuff. I'm Jones from the store on the avenue—spirit of Christmas, all that sort of thing. Merry Christmas—Merry Christmas, we've been saying it with every sale—with every phone call—

OTTO (*Very surprised*): You're—you're Mr. Jones?

MAMA: Mr. Jones from the big store?

MR. JONES: Yes, yes, been trying to get down here all evening. But it's been so hectic. Christmas is such a battle.

OTTO: A battle, Mr. Jones?

MAMA: We don't think it's a battle.

MR. JONES: No—no, you wouldn't—little place like this. But with me it's different. Terrific overhead—have to keep pushing the clerks—telling them to sell. Got to build up good will. And that's why I'm here.

OTTO: But Mr. Jones, I don't know what—

MR. JONES: Let's get right down to business. I'm here to make you an offer.

OTTO: An offer? An offer for what? I don't understand.

MR. JONES: Oh, yes, you do. This thingumbob you've had in the window.

MAMA: Papa—you hear what he's saying?

MR. JONES: People are talking about it—never saw such a real looking star, they say—so bright and shining.

OTTO: Yes, Mr. Jones, that's what they tell me too.

MR. JONES: Well, where is it? Why haven't you got it in the window now?

OTTO: But I—I haven't changed my window. People have asked about a star. We thought all along it must be something you had.

MR. JONES: No—no, I've nothing of the sort. Why, they tell me this star of yours is brighter than any light they've ever seen.

OTTO: But Mr. Jones, I tell you—all right, I show you. (*He goes to window and pulls the curtain back.*) I have never had any other star in my window but this. See? Just a tinsel star.

MR. JONES: Yes—yes, I see. (*He pulls out a fat wallet.*) That's all that's there now. But later on you'll put that other one in. You've got some unusual lighting effect or something that I don't know about.

OTTO: No—no.

MR. JONES: Look, Otto, I don't know what your game is, but I could use this star of yours. Christmas is over for you as far as selling is concerned, but next week we have bargain sales. I need something to get the people in. Why, if I could have that star of yours in my window during the rest of the holidays, starting tonight, it would be worth— (*He pulls out some money.*) five hundred dollars. (OTTO *just stands speechless.* MR. JONES *pulls out some more money.*) Six hundred—seven hundred—

OTTO: Mr. Jones, please—I don't understand. It's like we don't speak the same language. You keep your money. I have nothing to sell for that much.

MR. JONES: You have the star.

MAMA: Mr. Jones, we have told you the truth. We have no star.

MR. JONES: A thousand dollars—how about it?

OTTO: Mr. Jones, if I wanted to sell, you could buy my whole store for that. (MR. JONES *stands looking at him for a moment.*) That is all I can say, Mr. Jones.

MR. JONES: All right, if you're going to be stubborn about it, I guess there's no use my wasting any more time here. I still can't understand you. I offer you all this money—

OTTO: But Mr. Jones, I have told you—

MR. JONES (*Giving up*): Yes—yes—well, I'll be going. (*He turns toward door.*)

OTTO: I am sorry, Mr. Jones.

MR. JONES: *You're* sorry! What about me? Wasting my time when I'm all tired out. So many headaches—working late every night—now go home and my wife will expect me to be bright and cheerful. Tomorrow too—big family dinner. Christmas—I'm glad it's almost over! (*He goes out slamming the door behind him.*)

OTTO: Imagine. Glad Christmas is almost over. Such a thing to say, Mama.

MAMA: Poor Mr. Jones. Papa, I feel so sorry for him. He has the store of the Christmas spirit, but he misses all the real Christmas.

OTTO: Yes—yes. (*Sighing*) Mama, all this business about the star—I wish I knew. I just don't know what to think.

MAMA: Now, now, my Otto, I was upset before but I made up my mind not to be. We just forget about all this, like you say.

OTTO: You are right, Mama.

MAMA: It's all just some mistake.

OTTO: But what kind of a mistake? It is all so strange—ahh, well, come, Mama. We enjoy our Christmas.

MAMA: That's right, Otto. I see if there's a little Christmas music on the radio while you close up.

OTTO: Yah, Mama, that will be nice. (MAMA *goes to radio and turns it on. In a few seconds a carol is heard softly. It is "Come All Ye Faithful" and if done from a recording, it should be timed so that the final chorus starts just as* OTTO *says: "Brighter—and brighter" near end of play.* OTTO *has taken a cloth from behind counter and covers the table at center, then goes to door and locks it.*) Now, Mama, we turn off the lights and have a Merry Christmas. (*He pushes a light switch near the front door and all on-stage lights go off. There is enough light coming from the door to the living quarters left so that outlines of things on the stage can be seen. And there is a ray of light from above the window curtains which strikes the tilted mirror on the right end of high shelves. The mirror is tilted so that the ray might conceivably be reflected back toward the window.* OTTO *notices the ray of light.*) Mama—Mama, look, the mirror. (*He points at it.*)

MAMA: What is it, Otto?

OTTO: See how the light shines in the mirror.

MAMA: So? It's from the street lamp outside.

OTTO: But don't you see, Mama—that's it maybe. I think we have solved the mystery. (*He goes to the curtains, parts them a little and looks through in between them.*) Come, Mama, look. (*She crosses over and looks too. As* OTTO *looks, he points back over his shoulder toward the mirror.*) See, the light from the mirror up there, it comes back and strikes our tinsel star. With all the other lights out, it makes it shine and sparkle.

MAMA: So it does, Papa—but not so much as people say.

OTTO (*Letting curtains fall back*): No, not so much maybe. (*They come away from window.*) But that's it, Mama—that must be it. It shines some and people imagine the rest. You see, at Christmas time, people's eyes are ready for miracles, because long ago on the first Christmas happened the greatest miracle of all.

MAMA: Yes, Papa, you are right.

OTTO: Well, Mama, so that was it all the time.

MAMA: Yes, Papa, and wait till we tell Mr. Baker with all his talk about the legend. (*She stops.*) Papa, listen, the singing —it's beautiful—almost like angel voices.

OTTO: Let's take the radio in the other room, Mama. We'll be closed tomorrow and we'll want to listen to the carols.

MAMA: Yes, Papa, I get it. (*She goes to counter and leans down.*) I disconnect it— (*She rises, holding up the end of cord from radio.*) Papa—Papa!

OTTO: What's the matter?

MAMA: The radio—it was not connected, Papa.

OTTO (*Not realizing for a moment*): No, that's right. I pulled the plug out to try some Christmas tree lights and forgot to put it back.

MAMA: But Papa, Papa—the music—we hear the music.

OTTO: So—we hear— (*Then realizing*) but how—listen, they still sing. (*The voices are louder now.* MAMA *goes to* OTTO *at stage center and speaks in an awed voice.*)

MAMA: And Otto, look—the window—the light! (*The light behind curtains is gradually getting brighter as the music swells.*)

OTTO: The light—it's a bright light, Mama. (*He puts his arm around her shoulders and they stand facing right and looking up at light above window curtains.* MAMA *is downstage from* OTTO.) And getting brighter—and brighter—and brighter. (*They stand quietly looking up as the chorus swells to the end of song and the curtain falls.*)

THE END

Christmas Shopping Early

Characters

MOTHER JUDY
FATHER RICKY
BOB THE CAROLERS
RUTH

SETTING: *The living room of the Travers home on Christmas Eve.*

AT RISE: *The family are all seated admiring the Christmas tree. BOB, about seventeen, in chair at right, FATHER and MOTHER in chairs at left; RUTH, fifteen, and JUDY, eleven, on the sofa; and RICKY, eight, sprawled on the floor. The chairs have been pulled around a little so that the effect is of a semi-circle of people admiring the tree.*

RUTH: Isn't the tree beautiful?

JUDY: It's perfect.

MOTHER: And to think it's all trimmed and it's not even seven o'clock yet. I can't believe it.

FATHER: Neither can I. Usually at this time on Christmas Eve, we haven't even started on the tree.

MOTHER: Not to mention all the other things, John. Why, I don't remember any Christmas Eve that we haven't been up until two or three o'clock in the morning.

BOB: Well, didn't I tell you Christmas could be managed efficiently, Mom? Aren't you glad I took over?

MOTHER: I certainly am, Bob.

220

FATHER: Margaret, I think we've got a smart son.

RUTH: You know, Bob, I always wondered what you took that correspondence course in efficiency for. Now, I know.

JUDY (*Pointing to bookcase*): You mean all those big books of yours really told how to make Christmas simple, Bob?

BOB: No, of course not, Judy. They never even mentioned Christmas. They just showed that you can solve any problem with efficiency. Now, I'm practically an efficiency expert. You wait until I'm through school, Dad, and go into business with you, I'll bet we can make lots of changes in your business.

FATHER: Now, just a minute, Son—

BOB: But, Dad, there's no need to run anything in an old-fashioned way—

FATHER: Now let's not get carried away. It's all right for you to make Christmas more efficient, but—

MOTHER: And he certainly has.

RUTH: Just think, my presents were all bought and wrapped weeks ago!

MOTHER: Yes, isn't it a wonderful feeling? I've always read about people who did their Christmas shopping early, but I never thought I'd be one of them.

JUDY: You did yours way last July, didn't you, Mom?

BOB: That's when I told her to.

MOTHER: And I did. My, but it was hot. I wondered then if it was worth it, but I'm surely thankful now all my presents are wrapped and put away.

FATHER: So are mine. That was certainly a good idea of yours, Bob, telling me to use a personal shopping service. Why, everything's done.

BOB: Well, didn't I tell you there needn't be an uproar every Christmas Eve? What about those charts I gave you? Did you follow them?

RUTH: Sure.

BOB (*Pulling a paper and pencil from his pocket*): How long did it take you to trim the tree?

JUDY: Oh, about four hours, I guess.

BOB (*He checks and makes notes as he speaks*): Well, I'd only estimated three. Next year I'd better put three and a half. I may not have allowed enough but you probably wasted some time.

RUTH: Well, we did get to giggling over something—

RICKY: And we kept stopping to admire as much as we had done.

BOB: That's not very efficient.

JUDY: But Bob, trimming the tree is supposed to be fun.

BOB: Well, Judy, I got here in time to put on the lights, so I know that was done in record time. (*Looking at paper again*) How about the turkey, Mom? Is it ready?

MOTHER: Yes, dear, stuffed and sewed and ready for the oven in the morning.

BOB: Fine. Was it done by four-thirty this afternoon?

MOTHER: I kept right to schedule, dear. Of course I didn't put any chestnuts in the dressing.

BOB: No chestnuts? But why not?

MOTHER: Because, dear, the grocery store wasn't as efficient as I. Maybe you'd better speak to them. They didn't deliver my groceries until almost six.

BOB: That's terrible.

MOTHER: Well, I called, but they said they were swamped with Christmas orders, and it couldn't be helped.

JUDY: But Mom, no chestnuts in the dressing!

MOTHER: Judy, I guess you have to sacrifice something to efficiency. If I'd waited for them, I couldn't have kept to Bob's schedule at all.

BOB: You're right, Mom.

FATHER: Of course, and the dressing will be good anyway.

RICKY (*Rising*): Say, Bob, what about some snow? You've planned everything else, and I want a white Christmas. (*He runs to window.*)

RUTH: Sure, Bob. If you're so efficient—

BOB: But snow isn't efficient. It just tracks in and makes a lot of extra work for Mom.

RICKY: But it's starting to snow anyhow. Look!

BOB: Huh? (*Crossing to window*) Well, I'll bet it won't keep up. The flakes aren't very large. You'll see—it'll stop. (*He looks at paper.*) Now, is everything else all set? How about clothes? Last year I remember Ricky didn't have any clean shirt for church.

MOTHER: And I had to wash one out at the last minute. Well, that won't happen this year.

RUTH: I even remembered to get my dress from the cleaners— the one I'm going to wear to the Christmas party tomorrow night.

JUDY: Which dress is it, Ruth? That smooth one you made with the gold balls?

RUTH: That's right.

MOTHER: Well, Bob, I guess just everything is taken care of— thanks to you. Dinner, presents, tree—even our clothes.

BOB (*Walking about pleased with himself*): Sure, and didn't I always say it could be done efficiently? There's no need of having Christmas paper all over the living room and everyone running in and out for last minute things, and the whole place in an uproar. (*He sits down.*) Why, just look at us—

MOTHER: I know.

FATHER: Here we sit—at peace.

RICKY (*Squirming a little*): Well, what are we going to do now?

MOTHER: Why, uh, we're just going to sit here, dear, relax—

RICKY: But it's Christmas Eve.

BOB: Certainly it's Christmas Eve and for once we can enjoy it. We can admire the tree—and we can—admire the tree and—

RICKY: I did already.

BOB: Well, pretty soon we can listen to some Christmas carols.

JUDY: Not this early. The carolers never get here until late.

BOB: They will this year. I spoke to them.

RUTH: You did?

BOB: Sure. They asked my advice. They have trouble every year because people keep inviting them in for refreshments— then they don't get to some places until late.

MOTHER: But how can they help that?

BOB: I told them just to stop five minutes at each house. That way they can keep right on schedule. They'll be here any minute now.

RICKY (*Running to window again*) : I don't see them and I don't hear them either.

BOB: You will.

RUTH: In the meantime, why don't we all get our presents out and put them under the tree?

JUDY: But we never open them until Christmas morning—

MOTHER: Yes, and usually we don't have any time to admire the pretty wrappings. That's a good idea, Ruth. (*She rises.*)

RICKY (*Starting left*) : Boy, I'll say. I'm going to get mine right away. (*He rushes out.*)

RUTH (*Starting left, too*) : So am I.

MOTHER (*Following* RUTH. *She turns back to* FATHER) : Hurry up, John. Better get yours out, too.

FATHER: Ho, I hid mine away in an easy place. I can put my finger right on them. (MOTHER *and* RUTH *go off left.*)

FATHER: How about you, Bob? Know where yours are?

BOB (*He looks very strange*) : Why—er—yes, I mean—er—

(*Rising quickly*) Dad, you'll have to excuse me. I've got to go out.

FATHER: *What's* that? Out? But—

BOB: Yes—right away. (*He starts right.*)

FATHER: But Bob, what for? We're going to get our presents. Where have you got yours? In the garage?

BOB (*As he exits with a rush*): I'll see you later. (FATHER *looks after him and shakes his head puzzled.* JUDY *is standing in the middle of the floor, looking distressed.*)

JUDY: Dad, it's terrible.

FATHER: What is? Judy, I've never seen Bob look so funny. What do you suppose is the matter with him?

JUDY: I don't know. Dad, it's terrible. I can't remember— I can't remember at all.

FATHER: Can't remember what?

JUDY: Where I put my presents.

FATHER: Oh, now, Judy.

JUDY: I can't, I tell you. I remember buying them about two months ago and wrapping them, and then—then my mind is a complete blank.

FATHER: Oh, now, if you just think a minute, I'm sure you'll remember.

JUDY: What do you think I've been doing? You know how Mother always says I'd lose my head if it weren't fastened on—

FATHER: But you couldn't lose a lot of Christmas presents. Now they'll turn up. You probably put them in your room somewhere.

JUDY: I know they're not there. I just cleaned all my drawers—

FATHER (*Starting left*): Well, I'd better get mine or your mother will beat me to it. Now, you just think for a minute. (*He goes out.*)

JUDY (*Walking right, almost crying*) : Think—think? Did I put them in the front hall? No. Oh, dear. What'll I do? (RUTH *enters left with a stack of Christmas presents in one arm and a dress over the other.*)

RUTH (*As she enters*): Mother, it's terrible—oh—Judy, the most awful thing—

JUDY (*As she turns*) : You can't find your presents?

RUTH: My presents? How silly! Of course I found them. (*She dumps them on a chair.*) It's my dress—look!

JUDY: What's the matter with it?

RUTH: Half the gold balls are missing on the belt and sleeves. The cleaner must have lost them.

JUDY: But that's nothing compared to—

RUTH: Nothing! (*Crossing to telephone*) I'll have to call them right away. They'll have to do something. (*She looks through a telephone pad.*) Where's their number?

JUDY: But you could wear something else. If you knew what had happened to me—

RUTH: I haven't anything else—not that's dressy enough. (*She dials quickly.*) Hello? Quick Service Dry Cleaner? Yes, Merry Christmas to you, too, but—this is Ruth Travers. I picked up a dress this afternoon—I don't care if you're closing or not. Several of the gold balls are missing and— But they must be there. What's that? At your main plant and they're closed for Christmas? And you're just closing, too? But listen— (*She hangs up.*) Can you imagine that? They won't do anything. They're closed for Christmas.

JUDY: But, Ruth, naturally they close for Christmas. And I don't think it's so serious. If you knew what had happened to me—

RUTH: Where's Bob? He's so efficient. Why didn't he tell me I ought to examine my dress?

JUDY: I don't know where he is, and if you'd just listen to me a minute. I can't find my Christmas presents.

RUTH: Can't find—what nonsense! They're in the house somewhere, but the gold balls for my dress are in a cleaning plant.

JUDY: You can wear the dress anyway—

RUTH: Oh, of course. It will look lovely with half the trimming
missing. (*You hear* RICKY *off crying.*)

RICKY: Mom! (*Crying*) Mom—

JUDY: What's the matter with Ricky? (RICKY *enters carrying
a pile of presents. The wrappings look bedraggled and torn.*)

RICKY (*Crying*): Mom—Mom, just look—

RUTH: Mother isn't here.

RICKY (*With a sob*): Just look at my Christmas presents!

JUDY: They look as though someone had been chewing on them.

RICKY: I—I hid them up in the attic and when I went to get
them—

RUTH: The mice! Dad's been saying he thought there were
mice up there.

RICKY: Yes, the mice have eaten off the paper and fancy trimmings, and it's all Bob's fault. He said if I did my shopping
early and wrapped my stuff, everything would be all right. I
—I went to the dime store with all my money and got things
and then I wrapped 'em up pretty—and now look!

RUTH: Ricky, you never should have put them in the attic, but
now don't cry.

MOTHER (*Off*): John—John—I need you. (*She enters.*)
Where's your father? He's got to help me—my goodness!
What's the matter with everyone?

RUTH: It's my dress, Mother.

JUDY: I can't find my presents, Mother.

RICKY (*Crying*): The mice ate up all my Christmas wrappings,
Mom! (*He shows his presents.*)

MOTHER: My goodness!

RICKY: I had them in the attic. (*He cries again.*)

MOTHER: Now, now, darling, don't cry. You can rewrap them.

RUTH: Mother, you've got to help me—

MOTHER: Just a minute, Ruth.

RICKY: But I haven't got any Christmas paper, Mom.

MOTHER: No, and of course there's not a bit in the house with Bob being so efficient and having us do everything early. (*She goes to table and takes out some coins from a drawer.*) Well, here, run down to the corner—the drugstore will have some— here's the money.

RICKY: Oh, thanks, Mom! (*Happy again*) I'll be right back. (*He dumps his packages on the floor and goes out right.*)

RUTH: Mother, the cleaner's ruined my dress—half the gold balls are missing—

JUDY: My presents are missing, Mother.

MOTHER: Nonsense, they can't be—and you made some extra balls, Ruth, don't you remember?

RUTH: Why, of course, but I don't know what I did with them. Where are they?

MOTHER: On the Christmas tree.

RUTH: On the Christmas—

MOTHER: Yes, Ricky thought they were pretty and I told him he could use them.

JUDY: Sure, I remember now, too. I hung one on myself way at the top.

RUTH: I suppose they're *all* at the top—but, oh, Mom, you're a lifesaver. I'll get the step ladder. (*She rushes off left.*)

MOTHER: Now, Judy, don't look so sad. Your presents are in the house somewhere. They must be if you put them away.

JUDY: But, Mom, I just can't think—

MOTHER: They're probably in your room.

JUDY: No, Mom—or they might be on the top shelf of the closet— (RUTH *comes back with step ladder and stands it near tree and gets up on it.*)

MOTHER: Yes, Judy, and try the guest room closet—that hasn't been cleaned out in a long while. They might be there.

RUTH: I just hope I can find the balls, Mother. There's so much stuff on this tree.

JUDY (*Crossing left*): I hope I can find my presents. I thought Bob said things were going to be easy if we did our Christmas shopping early.

MOTHER: Bob—I wonder where he's got to.

JUDY: I think he went out, Mom. (*She goes off left.*)

MOTHER: Out? But why would he do that? Oh, I wish your father would hurry—

RUTH (*At tree*): Here's one—way back on this branch here. (*She takes some tinsel off and hands it to MOTHER.*) Will you take this tinsel, Mom, so I can get at it?

MOTHER (*Taking tinsel and putting it on sofa*): But, dear, I hope you're not going to have to untrim the tree—

RUTH: I've got to find the balls, Mother. There are six missing on my dress. (RICKY *runs in right with bag of paper, cords, seals, etc.*)

RICKY (*Pulling paper out of bag*): Look, Mom, I got paper with Santa Clauses on it.

MOTHER (*Patting his head*): My, that's nice, dear. Why, you're all wet. (RICKY *sits down in middle of floor with his presents and the paper, etc., all around him.*)

RICKY: Yeah, it's snowing like anything, Mom. Really like Christmas!

RUTH (*She is reaching around tree, peering, etc.*): Hmm, in spite of what Bob said.

RICKY: I saw Bob, Mom.

MOTHER: You saw Bob? But you must be mistaken, Ricky.

RICKY: No, Mom, I saw him—riding along in a taxi cab.

MOTHER: But what would he be doing that for? Judy said he

went out, too, but I'm sure he must be somewhere in the house collecting his Christmas presents— (FATHER *enters left carrying a big cardboard box.*)

FATHER: See here, doesn't my box look interesting? (*He puts it down on a chair.*) And it was so easy—came right from the store like this several weeks ago, with all the presents wrapped and everything. That was certainly a good idea of Bob's!

RICKY (*Unrolling his new Christmas paper*): I'm glad someone thinks he has good ideas.

FATHER: What's that? (*He takes a couple of wrapped gifts from box and puts them on table, then looks around.*) Say, what's happened to this room? It's a mess. What are you taking things off the tree for, Ruth? (*He takes another package from his box.*)

MOTHER: Never mind, John. You've got to help me—my presents are down in the basement and—

FATHER: You mean you haven't brought them up yet?

MOTHER: No, I can't get at them. (*She takes him by the arm.*)

FATHER (*As they go off*): What do you mean—can't get at them? (MOTHER *and* FATHER *exit left.*)

RICKY: You know, Ruth, I think I'm just going to put the new wrappings over the old ones. It'll be quicker and besides if I unwrap everything, someone might see what I've got for them. (*He begins wrapping his presents.*)

RUTH: I won't look, Ricky. (*Climbing down from step ladder*) Can you imagine? I've only found two balls and there's at least six. I'll have to disconnect these lights, I guess. (*She crawls back of tree and the lights on tree go off. Then she gets up on ladder again and takes off a string of lights.*)

RICKY: Ruth, are you going to take all the lights off the tree?

RUTH: I've got to find the trimmings for my dress, haven't I? (*She takes off some more stuff.*)

RICKY: But we'll have to decorate the tree all over again. You keep taking things off all the time.

RUTH: There's nothing else to do. You'd better hurry and get your presents wrapped so you can help me. (*Reaching way inside tree*) Oh, here's another one—way back in the branches here!

JUDY (*Entering left*): Well, I just can't find them, that's all. I looked everywhere Mother said. I turned my room upside down—

RUTH (*Turning from tree*): Oh, poor Judy!

JUDY: This is all Bob's fault—getting us to do our shopping so early. I could wring his neck.

RICKY: Judy, some of the stores are still open—maybe Dad will give you some money and you can get some more presents.

JUDY: It wouldn't be the same. I had just what I wanted for everyone—and I picked it all out so carefully—oh, I could cry. (*She almost does.*)

RUTH: Judy, as soon as I find all my balls, I'll help you look.

JUDY: There's no use looking. (*Picking up one of packages* FATHER *has put on table.*) Whose presents are these?

RICKY: Dad's, I guess.

JUDY: But—but this one says: For Cousin Doolittle.

RUTH: What? Who's he?

JUDY (*Looking at another*): And my goodness! This tag says: Merry Christmas to Aunt Hattie!

RICKY: But there's no Aunt Hattie in our family.

JUDY (*Picking up another*): And here's one for Uncle Jasper. Who are all these people?

RICKY: Search me. I never heard of them.

RUTH: Judy, Dad had a personal shopper get his presents and they've sent all the wrong stuff!

JUDY: But I thought this box came weeks ago—

RUTH: Of course, but Dad just assumed they'd be all right, I guess, and didn't look. (*She takes some more things from the tree and pounces on a ball.*) Hooray, I've found another one!

RICKY: But the tree's a wreck! (*He is still wrapping.* MOTHER *enters left. Her face has smudges on it.*)

MOTHER (*Speaking over her shoulder*): Hurry up with my presents, John. My, I'm glad we finally got them.

JUDY: Mother, you've got dirt all over your face! (FATHER *enters carrying a dusty carton. His hair is awry and his face is dirty.*)

RUTH: Dad, what on earth have you been doing? You need a bath or something. You look so funny.

FATHER (*Setting down carton*): Well, Ruth, if you'd been moving the porch furniture and the window screens, not to mention some rakes and a lawn mower, I guess you'd look funny, too. (MOTHER *starts taking out wrapped Christmas presents from carton and putting them under tree.*)

JUDY: But what have you been doing that for, Dad?

FATHER: Just a little matter of getting at your Mother's Christmas presents. (*He tries to sink into a chair but there is too much stuff on it. He wipes his brow.*)

JUDY: But I don't understand—

MOTHER: Well, Judy, I put them down there in a carton last July, and in the meantime winter has come and we've been storing stuff away. It all got piled in front of my carton.

JUDY: My goodness!

FATHER: What's happened to this room? It looks awful—and the tree—

RUTH (*Excitedly*): I've found all but one, Mother.

MOTHER (*Looking around*): Well, things *are* in a mess. I don't see how we'll ever get through in time. We'll have to get busy—

JUDY: And I still haven't found my presents, Mother—and Dad, you'll have to do something about yours.

FATHER: Mine? Nothing wrong with my presents. (*He goes over to his box.*)

RUTH: Nothing except they're for the wrong people.

FATHER: What's that? (*Looking at a package*) Cousin Doolittle. (*Looking at another*) Aunt Hattie—why—why, they've sent somebody else's things!

MOTHER: Well, John, you should have looked—

FATHER: All right—why didn't Bob tell me to check up? I thought if you had a personal shopper do it— (*Breaking off*) This is terrible. I'll have to go out or call the store or—

MOTHER: Now, John, I wouldn't worry. There are enough packages to go around, aren't there? You can give us each one—it'll be fun seeing what they are, and you can settle with the store later.

FATHER: An efficient Christmas, that's good, that is. I'd like to tell Bob a thing or two—and where is he, I'd like to know.

JUDY: This is all Bob's fault.

RUTH: Of course it is.

MOTHER: Oh, now, children—

RICKY: Sure—Bob and his goofy ideas. (BOB *enters right with an armful of packages, and looking sheepish.*)

BOB: Uh—hello, everyone. It certainly is snowing hard. In spite of what I said, I guess we're going to have a white Christmas.

FATHER (*Sternly*): Where have you been?

BOB: Why—uh—we all said we were going to—well—get our Christmas presents—

RICKY: Where'd you have yours, Bob, in a snowbank?

BOB: Well—I—guess I had mine in storage, sort of.

RUTH: Bob Travers, you didn't have them at all. Ricky saw you in a taxi. You've been out shopping.

Bob: Well, I—I guess I may as well admit it. I did forget to get mine. I was so busy planning everything else, helping all of you plan an efficient Christmas—

Father: Efficient? Young man, I'd like to tell you a thing or two. If you ever dare to mention again anything about an efficient Christmas—or doing shopping early or—

Bob: But—but what's happened? The room—the tree—what's gone wrong?

Ruth: Everything's gone wrong—everything—and it's all your fault!

Ricky: The mice ate up my paper.

Ruth: And I've had to take everything off the tree to find my dress trimmings, and Mother and Dad had to move everything in the basement, and Dad's got the wrong presents—

Judy: And I haven't got any presents at all.

Mother: Yes, dear, I don't know when we've had a more hectic Christmas Eve.

Bob: Yeah, I can see—it certainly looks as though you'd been in an uproar—

Ruth: That's putting it mildly.

Bob: And you mean nothing has worked out the way I thought it would?

Judy: Nothing! You've just ruined everything, Bob Travers.

Bob: Then I guess there's no such thing as an efficient Christmas.

Ruth: There certainly isn't—not if you have anything to do with it.

Mother: Now, children, don't be too hard—

Bob: Never mind, Mom. I guess they're right. (*Sadly he puts his packages down on the sofa, then straightens up.*) And I believed all that stuff I read in my books about efficiency. Mom, you know what I'm going to do? I'm going to throw all those books away! (*He rushes to bookcase and starts taking books out of second shelf.*)

MOTHER: Bob, there's no use your being so upset. (*He takes more books out, piling them on floor, then stops as he sees something in back of books.*)

BOB: What's all this? There's something behind the books—packages— (*He pulls out a flat package.*)

JUDY (*Rushing over*): Bob, it's my Christmas presents! Oh! Bob! (*She begins taking more flat packages off shelf.*)

BOB: Your Christmas presents?

JUDY: I remember now—I thought you knew everything in those books by heart, so you wouldn't be looking at them any more, so I decided to put my presents behind them. They were all flat packages this year.

RUTH: Judy, I'm so glad you've found them.

JUDY: Oh, Bob, thank you—thank you for showing me where they were.

FATHER: Son, your books on efficiency helped, after all.

BOB: But I was wrong, .Dad. I guess efficiency is the bunk. It won't really solve anything.

MOTHER: Now, Bob, there's nothing wrong with efficiency. It's just that—well, Christmas is a time that can't be cut and dried.

FATHER: And this Christmas certainly isn't going to be. (*He has taken a pen out and is writing on his packages.*) Margaret, look what I'm doing. I'm writing new names underneath the others on my presents. I think I'll give you the one labeled Aunt Hattie, and Bob, you can have Cousin Doolittle's—

JUDY: That'll be exciting, Dad, seeing what they turn out to be.

RICKY: I've finished wrapping my presents, Mom.

RUTH: Then you can help me retrim the Christmas tree, Ricky.

JUDY: Oh, this is fun. (*She is putting presents underneath the tree.* BOB *is watching them all.* MOTHER *smiles.*)

MOTHER: There, you see, Bob. You didn't spoil our Christmas at all. This is the way we want it to be. Doing things for one another at the last minute—laughing together— (*The* CAR-

OLERS *are heard off singing a familiar carol. The voices grad-ually get louder as though coming closer.*)

FATHER: The carolers!

RUTH: And they're as late as ever.

BOB: They didn't keep to schedule either.

MOTHER: Isn't that beautiful? Let's all sit down and listen un-til they get here. Then we'll invite them in for hot chocolate. (*They all sit down on arms of chairs, sofa or wherever they can push things aside and find room.*)

JUDY: Isn't Christmas wonderful?

RICKY: Boy, I'll say!

MOTHER: It *is* a beautiful time. Do you see now, Bob, why it can't be too cut and dried?

BOB: I think I do, Mom.

MOTHER: Christmas is affection and love and being happy to-gether. It has to come from the heart. (*The* CAROLERS *are right outside now. You hear them stamping snow off their feet, still singing.*)

MOTHER: Oh, here they are. Bob, open the door. (BOB *goes off right and comes back immediately followed by the* CAROL-ERS. *They are still singing the last verse of a carol and the family joins in to end. Then amidst shouts of "Merry Christ-mas," the curtain falls.*)

THE END

Living Up to Lincoln

Characters

FATHER
MOTHER
BOBBIE CARTER ⎤
LUCILLE CARTER ⎬ *their children*
JACK CARTER ⎦
YOUNG MAN
WIFE

TIME: *The present. The morning of Lincoln's Birthday.*
SETTING: *The Carter dining room.*
AT RISE: *The* CARTERS *are finishing their breakfast. At the right end of the table sits* FATHER, HENRY CARTER, *reading his newspaper and now and then sipping his coffee. At the left end of the table sits* MOTHER, EDITH CARTER. *At the upstage side of the table are* BOBBIE, *about nine years old, and* LUCILLE, *about twelve. At the downstage side of the table with his back to the audience is* JACK, *thirteen or fourteen.* BOBBIE *is just finishing a piece of toast.*

MOTHER: Did you eat your egg, Bobbie?
BOBBIE: Yes, Mother.
LUCILLE: So you'll grow to be a fine strong man?
MOTHER: What's that?
LUCILLE: Well, that's what you always say, Mother.
MOTHER: Of course, and Bobbie wants to grow to be a fine strong man, don't you, dear?

BOBBIE: Indubitably, Mother.

JACK: Where does Bobbie get those big words? For a kid his age—

MOTHER: He's studious, Jack.

FATHER (*Looking over his newspaper and then putting it down*) : I wonder if it pays to be studious. The more I study my newspaper the more upset I get.

MOTHER: Henry, not on top of your egg!

FATHER: I shouldn't read my newspaper on top of my egg?

MOTHER: No, you shouldn't get upset. It's bad for your digestion.

FATHER: How can I help it? All the problems in the world, and it seems I don't do much but read about them in the paper.

MOTHER: Nonsense, you do a lot.

FATHER: It seems we should all do more. If we could only see how—I tell you, Edith, all these problems of peace and housing and inflation—

MOTHER: Inflation. Now, Henry, just because you work in a bank, you mustn't always be worrying about money . . . Besides you haven't time to worry now. It's almost eight-thirty. You'd better be getting started or you'll be late.

FATHER: But I'm not going anywhere, Edith.

MOTHER: What's that? Are you sick? Then we'll call a doctor —children, you'd better go on to school—

JACK: But we're not going to school, Mother.

FATHER: And I'm not sick, Edith.

MOTHER: But then what's the matter with all of you? Not going to the bank—not going to school—

BOBBIE: It's Lincoln's Birthday, Mother.

ALL (*Laughing*) : Yes, it's Lincoln's Birthday!

MOTHER: Lincoln's Birthday—my goodness, can you imagine my forgetting all about it? Why, of course it's Lincoln's Birthday and the bank is closed and there's no school—and here I

was just thinking how lucky all of you were because you'd be
out of the way today.

BOBBIE: But why, Mother? I think we're lucky to have a holiday.

MOTHER: But that's just it, Bobbie. I'm afraid it won't be a
holiday. You see, I've planned to clean house.

LUCILLE: Clean house? In the middle of February?

MOTHER: Yes, Lucille, toward the end of winter like this the
house seems to look so down at the heels that I suddenly decided to turn everything inside out—wash the curtains and—
well, everything.

JACK: Why Mom!

MOTHER: In fact, I started last night after you were all asleep.
I guess none of you has looked in the living room—

JACK (*Rising and crossing right he peers off*): Boy, it's really
a shambles, Mom—all the furniture in the middle of the floor
and the rug rolled up. (*He comes back and sits down again.*)

MOTHER: Dear me, it *is* too bad. If I'd remembered that all of
you were going to be at home—

FATHER: But it's all right—I think it's fine, Edith. We'll all
help you.

LUCILLE: Of course we will, Mom. You know what we can do,
Jack? Fix up our recreation room in the basement.

JACK: Sure. We've been wanting to get that done for months.

FATHER: And I'll wash windows for you, Edith, and do all the
heavy work. Why, say, I'll enjoy using my muscles for a
change after sitting in that bank all day the way I do.

BOBBIE: But Mother—Father—

FATHER: Yes, Bobbie?

MOTHER: What is it, dear?

BOBBIE: It isn't that I object to doing work, Mother. I could
help too. But isn't today a holiday?

MOTHER: Well, it's Lincoln's Birthday but—

BOBBIE: Then wouldn't it be better if we all celebrated his birthday?

FATHER: We do celebrate in a way, son. There's no school. The banks are closed—

BOBBIE: But I mean why don't we celebrate the way we do for Thanksgiving and Fourth of July and—why, we always have a picnic on Fourth of July and a great big dinner on Thanksgiving and Grandma and Grandpa come.

MOTHER (*Rising and stacking breakfast dishes*): Well, we may have to have a picnic today—that is a picnic of sorts in the kitchen. We certainly can't have a great big dinner with the mess we'll be in.

BOBBIE: But a picnic in the kitchen, Mother. That's not like really celebrating.

FATHER: Bobbie, the best way we can celebrate the birthday of a great man like Lincoln is by trying to live up to him.

BOBBIE: Live up to him?

LUCILLE (*Smiling*): Sure, Bobbie, by growing up to be a fine strong man the way Mother says.

BOBBIE: Yes, Lucille, but that takes time. I'm talking about today.

FATHER (*Rising*): Well, today I'm going to wash windows. Lincoln did homely tasks like that.

BOBBIE: Lincoln chopped wood.

FATHER: Yes, son, to be exact, he split rails.

LUCILLE: Well, anyhow, Lincoln was always working and I guess there's no better way to celebrate his birthday. (*She rises and starts left*) I'm going to get started in the basement.

JACK (*Rising too*): O.K., Lucille, I'll help you. Is there anything you want me to do first, Mom?

MOTHER: Well, you might take the curtains down in the living room—they're hard for me to reach.

JACK: Sure, Mom. (*He goes off right and* LUCILLE *off left.*)

FATHER: And I'd better get at the windows, Edith. (*He goes off left.*)

BOBBIE: I still don't see what I can do, Mother.

MOTHER (*Handing him stack of dishes*): You might take these dishes out into the kitchen for me.

BOBBIE: But I didn't mean that. I mean about Lincoln. (*He takes the dishes and goes solemnly off left.* MOTHER *looks after him and then shakes her head and starts to stack the rest of the dishes.* FATHER *comes back carrying a pail of water and a squeegee.*)

MOTHER: Henry, can't you explain more to Bobbie?

FATHER: Explain? What about? (*He sets down his pail.*)

MOTHER: Lincoln's Birthday—what it means. You know, Henry, Bobbie takes everything so seriously. I think he's worried because we're all just—well, working.

FATHER: Yes, I suppose it doesn't seem much of a celebration for his hero.

MOTHER: That's it. Ever since you started him on that collection of Lincoln pennies, he's talked so much about Lincoln and now along comes his birthday and we— (BOBBIE *re-enters left.*)

BOBBIE: Mother, do you want me to take out some more dishes?

MOTHER: Not if there's something else you'd rather do, Bobbie. After all, this *is* a holiday.

BOBBIE: But everybody's working. (MOTHER *looks at* FATHER.)

FATHER: Bobbie, my boy, maybe I can explain a little more. When we think of Lincoln we think of our country, don't we?

BOBBIE: Yes, Father, because Lincoln did so much for our country.

FATHER: Exactly, and Lincoln's Birthday makes us remember that. Each one of us makes up his mind to do his best for his country, too. To keep it strong and free, the way Lincoln wanted it to be. To help solve its problems—to help each other—

BOBBIE: Problems?

FATHER: Well, there's the peace among nations—and the housing shortage all over the world—and inflation—

BOBBIE: Inflation? Is that to do with money?

FATHER: Yes, son.

BOBBIE: Well, would it help if I spent my Lincoln pennies instead of saving them?

FATHER: No, Bobbie, that would make it worse. But if we all make up our minds to help in any way we can—

BOBBIE: And is that celebrating, Father, if you make up your mind to do that?

FATHER: It's honoring Lincoln, Bobbie, in the way he'd want to be honored.

BOBBIE: Oh . . . Well, I guess I'll get my book on Famous Americans and read some more about him. (*He goes off right.* FATHER *shakes his head.*)

MOTHER: Henry, maybe you'd better go out and buy something for him. After all, holidays mean presents to children.

FATHER: I don't think so—not to Bobbie. Anyhow, the only thing he wants is that oldest Lincoln penny, and they're very hard to find. I can't even find one at the bank. (JACK *enters right carrying some curtains over his arm.*)

JACK: Here are your curtains, Mom. What'll I do with them?

MOTHER: Oh, I'll take care of them, Jack. Just put them over a chair there. (JACK *hangs curtains over back of chair.*)

JACK: O.K. I'm going down in the basement and help Lucille. (*He goes off left.*)

FATHER (*He picks up his pail*): Well, I got this far. Where do I start?

MOTHER: In the living room, Henry. The curtains are out of the way in there.

FATHER: Fine. (*Singing gaily as he exits to tune from "Pinafore"—"When I was a Lad"*) He polished up the windows so carefully—tra—la—le— (*He goes off right.* MOTHER *smiles, picks up rest of dishes in one hand and gathers the curtains over her other arm.* BOBBIE *enters slowly right, reading a large book.*)

BOBBIE: Mom, did you know that Lincoln was almost six feet four inches tall?

MOTHER: Yes I did, dear, and he probably ate his eggs every morning.

BOBBIE: I suppose . . . (*He sits down at the table facing audience and* MOTHER *goes off left.*) Let's see. (*He turns some pages of book.*) Hmmm (*Reading*) "With malice toward none; with charity for all;—" (FATHER *enters right.*)

FATHER: Bobbie, where's your mother?

BOBBIE: In the kitchen, I guess. Father, what does with malice toward none mean?

FATHER: Why, it—it means no ill will toward anyone. You like everyone.

BOBBIE: That's what I thought. I've found something that Mr. Lincoln said that fits in with what you told me. See— (*He points to page in book.*)

FATHER (*Leaning over* BOBBIE'S *shoulder*): Hmm—from Lincoln's second inaugural address. (*Reading*) "With malice toward none; with charity for all! with firmness in the right, as God gives us to see the right, let us strive on to finish the work we are in; to bind up the nation's wounds; to care for him who shall have borne the battle, and for his widow, and his orphan—to do all which may achieve and cherish a just and lasting peace among ourselves, and with all nations." (*He *pauses.*) Yes, son, that is in line with what I was telling you but Mr. Lincoln says it much better than I could ever say it. That's one of the finest things that's ever been written and it's just as true today as it was when he wrote it.

BOBBIE: But I guess we don't do all those things Mr. Lincoln said.

FATHER: I—I don't know, son. Some of us try—

BOBBIE: But you said that was the way to celebrate his birthday.

FATHER (*At his wit's end*): Oh, Bobbie, I— (MOTHER *reenters with a bucket and a mop.*)

MOTHER: Henry, I thought you were washing windows.

FATHER: I was but I got sidetracked by our son and Mr. Lincoln. Besides, I need a polishing cloth.

MOTHER: Well, there are some old rags in the bottom drawer in the kitchen, Henry. (FATHER *exits left passing* LUCILLE *and* JACK *as they enter. Their hands are dirty and they have a few smudges on their faces.*)

JACK: Say, Mom, you ought to see the basement.

MOTHER: Don't tell me you've got it cleaned up already. (MOTHER *has set down bucket and leans on mop as she listens.*)

JACK: No, but Lucille had all the newspapers and magazines off the shelves and we just took them outside for the junk man —and we set the old studio couch against the long wall—

LUCILLE: And the porch furniture that was stacked up in one corner—there's room for all of that and it just needs a little cleaning up. Why, it's going to be positively spacious down there.

JACK: It'll make a super play room.

MOTHER: I've always thought it would, and while you're doing your cleaning don't forget the washroom and the shower down there. It'll save tracking dirt through the house when you children come in from ball games and swimming next summer.

LUCILLE: Why, Mom, it'll be just like a little house of our own. And I've even got an idea we can put some curtains at the windows.

MOTHER: Of course you can. I'll find some for you when you're ready—and there's an old electric grill in the attic. You can use that for popping corn and making hamburgers.

LUCILLE: Wonderful, Mom.

JACK: Oh, boy, we can have some real parties!

BOBBIE: A party? When?

LUCILLE: Oh—oh, I see what's in your mind, Bobbie. A party for Mr. Lincoln. Well, not tonight—it won't be ready. But you're going to like that room. You'll be able to keep some of your stuff down there.

MOTHER: Yes, Bobbie, your penny collection and some of your books.

JACK: Sure, there's lots of shelf space. There are two long shelves—one for Lucille and one for me—and you can have the little one all to yourself.

BOBBIE: Oh . . . Well, why should I have the little one? I've got more books than either of you.

JACK: Maybe you have but you still get the little one.

LUCILLE: You see, we're older, Bobbie.

BOBBIE: I don't see that your being older has anything to do with it. Mr. Lincoln didn't say so.

JACK: What do you mean?

BOBBIE: His Gettysburg address—I've just been reading it. "Fourscore and seven years ago our fathers brought forth upon this continent a new nation, conceived in liberty, and dedicated to the proposition that all men are created equal." Equal. See? (JACK and LUCILLE laugh.)

JACK: Yeah, well, we'll have to think about it. Maybe we can make your shelf longer. (*FATHER enters left.*)

FATHER: Edith, I can't find those rags—

MOTHER: Oh, Henry— (*The doorbell rings.*) That's probably the mailman. Will you go and see, Bobbie?

BOBBIE: All right, Mother. (*He exits right taking his book with him.*)

MOTHER (*Setting her mop against wall and starting left*): I'll get them for you, Henry. I don't know why it is you can never find— (*She exits left.*)

FATHER: Well, you two look as though you'd been working. I haven't even started yet.

LUCILLE: We've only *just* started and we'd better get busy again too. (*BOBBIE re-enters, without his book this time.*)

BOBBIE: It wasn't the mailman. It's company.

FATHER: Company?

JACK: At this time of day?

LUCILLE: Mother will certainly be pleased with the house all—

MOTHER (*Entering left*): Here you are, Henry. (*Handing him a cloth*) It was right where I told you.

FATHER (*Taking cloth*): My dear, we have company.

MOTHER: Company?? (*A YOUNG MAN enters right followed by a YOUNG WOMAN with a baby in her arms. A large baby doll may be used for baby.*)

FATHER (*Stepping forward and hesitating a little*): How do you do?

YOUNG MAN: Excuse me, sir, but your boy left the door open— so we just walked in.

FATHER: That's quite all right. You look tired. Would you care to sit down? (*He moves one of dining room chairs toward YOUNG MAN.*)

YOUNG MAN: No, sir, but maybe my wife—

WIFE (*She sits down*): Thank you.

YOUNG MAN: I'd better explain what this is all about. We noticed you were moving, you see. The curtains being down and the furniture—

MOTHER: Moving?

YOUNG MAN: Yes, and I thought if you didn't have the renting of the place perhaps you could tell us who did.

BOBBIE: But Mister, we're not moving.

YOUNG MAN: You're not? (*He looks at* FATHER *who shakes his head.*)

MOTHER: No, it—it's just that I'm cleaning house.

YOUNG MAN: Oh, I—I see.

WIFE (*Rising*): We're terribly sorry to have bothered you. We'd better go, Dick.

YOUNG MAN (*Starting right*): Yes. I—I suppose. (*He turns back.*) Say, you don't know of any place for rent, do you?

FATHER: Why, no, I—I'm afraid I don't. I wish I did. I know how hard it is these days.

YOUNG MAN: Yes, it is. We've looked everywhere.

JACK: There was an apartment on 10th Street last week.

LUCILLE: That's gone, Jack. It wasn't vacant a day.

MOTHER: Have you tried the neighborhood just north of here?

WIFE: Oh, yes, there's nothing.

FATHER: I suppose you're one of our returned veterans?

YOUNG MAN: Yes, sir. Right now I'm working days and going to school at night on the G.I. Bill of Rights.

FATHER: That's fine—but I don't know why the country can't do something about housing for you veterans.

YOUNG MAN: I—I guess it's a problem, sir. Well, thanks anyhow, for your interest. Come along, Jean, let's go.

WIFE (*Trying to smile*): Where'll we go, Dick? (*They start right.*)

FATHER: Say, wait a minute. Haven't you two *anywhere* to go?

YOUNG MAN: Well, as a matter of fact, we had a hotel room until midnight last night—

MOTHER: Midnight? You—you mean you've just been walking about—

YOUNG MAN: No, we slept in the railroad station.

LUCILLE: But the baby—

YOUNG MAN: That's it. I could take it, but my wife and the baby—

WIFE (*Smiling a little*): Now, Dick, we've been taking it too, pretty well.

YOUNG MAN: Darling, as though I meant—

MOTHER: You poor dears. Let me get you some breakfast. (*She starts left.*)

YOUNG MAN: Oh, no, thanks. We've had breakfast.

MOTHER: A cup of coffee then. It's right on the stove. All I have to do is heat it up. (*She goes off.*)

WIFE: Your wife shouldn't bother.

FATHER: Oh, you might as well have a cup of coffee. Here, sit down. (*He pulls out chairs around the table. The* YOUNG MAN *and his* WIFE *sit down, he at right end and she left of him at upstage side.* LUCILLE *sits next to her and admires the baby.* FATHER *sits at left end and* JACK *on the downstage side.* BOBBIE *stands, watching.*)

FATHER: My name's Henry Carter by the way—and Lucille, Jack and Bobbie.

YOUNG MAN: How do you do? I'm Dick Forest—and my wife and Dick, Jr.

FATHER: Well—well—Dick, Jr.—and you're still going to school.

YOUNG MAN: At nights, sir. I'm studying law. It's a long hard grind but if we can just get a place to live, I think I can make it.

WIFE: Of course you can, Dick.

BOBBIE: You study law? Are you going to be a lawyer?

YOUNG MAN: I hope so—one of these days.

BOBBIE: Do you have Blackstone's Commentaries?

YOUNG MAN: Why, yes. Right now they're checked at the station with our bags but—

BOBBIE: Do you know how Abraham Lincoln got his Blackstone's Commentaries? He bought them in a barrel with a lot of other stuff.

YOUNG MAN: So he did. Say, this is his birthday, isn't it? (MOTHER *enters with two cups of coffee and a plate of rolls. She places the coffee in front of the* YOUNG MAN *and his* WIFE *and sets the rolls near them.*)

MOTHER: Here we are. The coffee's not quite fresh but the rolls are.

WIFE: This is so nice of you.

MOTHER: Now, don't say a word. It's the least we can do. If we could just help you find a place to live.

FATHER: If we only could. But the fact is we just don't know of a thing. Not a thing.

BOBBIE: But Father, do you think they'd mind living in a basement?

FATHER: I don't know, son. Whose basement—why—why—

MOTHER: Henry, are you thinking the same thing I am?

JACK: Of course he is. Our basement!

LUCILLE: We've just been saying what a nice room it would make!

BOBBIE: And there are shelves for your Blackstone's Commentaries.

YOUNG MAN: You mean you've got a place—

FATHER: Certainly we have—right here in this house. The basement's been there all along. I don't know why we didn't think of it before.

MOTHER: Of course it isn't much and it'll need some fixing up.

WIFE: Oh, Mrs. Carter, it'll seem like heaven to us. Dick, I can't believe we've found a place!

YOUNG MAN (*Fishing some money from pants pocket—several bills and some change. Some of the change falls on the table*): Well, say, let's pay some rent right now before these good people change their minds. How much, sir?

FATHER: Oh, that room can't be worth much. Put that money away. We'll settle that when we get to it.

YOUNG MAN: Well, all right. (*He shoves bills back into his pocket, picks up change and holds up one penny which he shows to his WIFE.*) Didn't I tell you this was my lucky penny, Jean? (*He shows it to others.*) It's just a Lincoln penny but someone gave it to me and said it was sort of valuable and I carried it all through the war.

BOBBIE: A Lincoln penny. May I look at it?

JACK: He collects Lincoln pennies. (YOUNG MAN *hands penny to* BOBBIE.)

BOBBIE: Why, it's the S VDB penny!

YOUNG MAN: The S stands for San Francisco, I suppose, where it was minted but what does the VDB mean?

BOBBIE: Why, those are the initials of the designer who made it —Victor D. Brenner. (*Still looking at it*) This is a rare one all right.

YOUNG MAN: It is, huh? Have you got it in your collection?

BOBBIE: No, it's the only one I haven't got.

YOUNG MAN: Well, you've got it now.

BOBBIE: But I—I couldn't take it, sir. It's your lucky penny.

YOUNG MAN: It's brought me enough luck today—all the luck I need. Keep it. (*He looks at his* WIFE *and then back at* BOBBIE.) To please us.

WIFE: Yes.

BOBBIE (*He is speechless*): I—I—thank you. Why—thank you.

YOUNG MAN: You'd think I'd given him a million dollars.

FATHER: It does mean a lot to him . . . Well, Bobbie, you're having a big Lincoln's Birthday after all.

BOBBIE: I'll bet I never have a better one.

FATHER: And you suggested the basement.

BOBBIE: Well, Abraham Lincoln used to give up his room at the inn when someone needed it and sleep on the counter of his store. I didn't think we should mind giving up our basement.

FATHER: Mind? We're delighted. Funny thing—here I've been worrying about the housing shortage and thinking the country should do something and still all along I could have—

YOUNG MAN: Well, sir, sometimes we don't see things right in front of our noses.

BOBBIE: We really celebrated Lincoln's Birthday after all.

FATHER: Yes, son, you've got your penny.

BOBBIE: Not only that, Father. We solved a problem.

FATHER: A prob—oh, yes, the housing shortage. We didn't solve all of it, of course.

BOBBIE: No, but you said if each one of us did his part.

FATHER: That's right. If each one of us does his part, no matter how small, all the problems, no matter how big, can be solved.

THE END

The Lincoln Umbrella

JACK   GAIL
PHIL   SILAS WILKINS
ANNE   MISS MARTIN
MARGIE   JONATHAN ASHBY

SCENE 1

TIME: *A few days before Lincoln's birthday.*
SETTING: *The sidewalk in front of a public school.*
AT RISE: *Three girls and two boys come out of school building wearing coats and carrying books.*

ANNE: If only we could decide on something. What can we do?

JACK: Nothing more now, I guess. It's getting late. We'll have to have another meeting in the morning.

PHIL: But Jack, we've got only one more day. The assembly program is on Friday.

JACK: I know that as well as you do, Phil, but we want something different.

MARGIE: If only Mr. Ashby hadn't disappointed us.

GAIL: Well, I suppose we couldn't expect him to come and make a speech at a school. An important man like that.

JACK: I suppose not, and it's my fault for counting on it. But I thought a fellow from that big museum could tell us something different. They have a Lincoln room there, you know, with all kinds of mementoes and relics of Lincoln. This Jonathan Ashby could probably have given us some new dope.

ANNE: I wonder, sometimes, if there is anything new on Lincoln.

PHIL: Why, what do you mean, Anne?

ANNE: Well, it seems to me that a great man like Abraham Lincoln is so well known that everything has been said about him that can be said. For years and years people have been writing books about him and making speeches about him.

PHIL: Sure, but there must be a new angle.

JACK: That's what we're looking for. And I guess it's up to me to think of it. I'm chairman of this program committee, worse luck!

MARGIE: We've *got* to think of something—something different, something that will be interesting to all the students.

GAIL: Could we have someone recite the Gettysburg Address?

MARGIE: Oh, no, that's been done over and over.

GAIL: Just the same, it's one of the finest things ever written. Why, it's immortal.

JACK: Of course, Gail, and if we could get Mr. Lincoln himself to give the speech for us, maybe it would be worthwhile. But as it is, everyone's studied the Address in school.

MARGIE: I know it by heart. (*Declaiming*) "Fourscore and seven years ago our fathers brought forth upon this continent a new nation—"

ALL (*Joining in*): "—conceived in liberty, and dedicated to the proposition that all men are created equal."

ANNE: You see, we all know it. If we're going to have someone recite a speech, his Second Inaugural Address would be better. It's the one that goes: "With malice toward none: with charity for all—"

JACK: But we don't want anyone to recite. What we want is human interest stuff—anecdotes—and that's what this Mr. Ashby from the museum could have given us.

PHIL: There's no use talking about him if he can't come.

JACK: You're right, Phil. It's just that I'm getting desperate. On Friday morning we've got to have some kind of a program in honor of Abraham Lincoln.

GAIL: Well, couldn't we play up the angle of his honesty and his kindness? Maybe we could have someone tell some anecdotes about him—how he went through the mud to rescue the little pig and how he walked miles because he had given some woman the wrong change.

PHIL: But everyone knows those stories about Lincoln.

ANNE: Perhaps we could have a speech about the difficulties he had. How hard he had to work to educate himself. How he became a great man in spite of such poor beginnings.

JACK: That's old stuff, too. Everyone knows he was poor—that he was a man of the people.

MARGIE: What about a debate then? We could pattern it after the Lincoln-Douglas debates.

JACK: Everyone is familiar with them, too, Margie. I guess we might as well go home. If we all sleep on it tonight, maybe we'll have some fresh ideas in the morning. (*They start off.*)

GAIL (*Stopping*): Look—coming down the street. It's old Mr. Wilkins.

MARGIE: I always like to meet him. There's something about the way he says hello that always makes me feel good.

PHIL: My dad says there's never been a man in this town who's as well liked by everyone as Mr. Wilkins.

GAIL: I wonder why.

PHIL: I don't know. It's because he's the way he is, I guess. Sincere and honest and well—I don't know. My dad says that people have gone to him for advice for years and years and he always knows the right thing to do. He's helped a lot of people around here in one way or another.

ANNE (*Looking off left*): Look at him—he *is* a dear old man. I wonder why he always carries that umbrella. I don't remember ever seeing him without it. It certainly isn't raining today.

JACK: Say, wait a minute! This has given me a wonderful idea. I don't know why I didn't think of it before.

GAIL: What do you mean?

JACK: The umbrella. I'll bet Mr. Wilkins can give us a speech about Lincoln. He must know lots of unusual things about him.

GAIL: But how? He isn't that old, is he, that he knew Mr. Lincoln?

JACK: No, of course not but—

MARGIE: And what's the umbrella got to do with it?

JACK: Everything. That umbrella once belonged to Abraham Lincoln.

ANNE: It did? But I never heard—

JACK: He doesn't talk much about it usually, but I've heard the story.

PHIL: So have I, come to think of it. My dad told me. I'd forgotten all about it.

GAIL: But an umbrella that once belonged to Abraham Lincoln —why, that would be valuable. Some museum would have paid him a lot of money for it.

JACK: I guess so, but I don't think Mr. Wilkins would part with that umbrella for any amount of money. (MR. WILKINS, *an elderly man with a lovable personality, enters left carrying a large black umbrella with a carved handle. He wears coat and hat. He smiles and waves his hand as he sees the boys and girls.*)

WILKINS: Hello there.

ALL: Hello, Mr. Wilkins.

WILKINS: Well, well, isn't it time for you young folks to go home? Or do you all like school so much that you can't bear to leave?

JACK: Maybe that's it, Mr. Wilkins. Say, could we—well, that is, we'd like to talk to you for a minute.

WILKINS: Well, now, I guess that could be arranged. In fact, there's nothing I'd like better. (*He goes toward them.*) You know, when you get as old as I am, you always seem to have plenty of time.

JACK: That's good because we—listen, Mr. Wilkins, will you do us a big favor?

WILKINS: Lots of folks have done them for me, in my time, so I'll certainly try. What is it?

JACK: We want you to make a speech.

WILKINS: What's that?

JACK: It's for our Lincoln assembly at school here, the day after tomorrow.

WILKINS: But I don't think I ever made a speech in my life, not a real speech.

JACK: But you could. If you could just tell the story of your umbrella—

PHIL: Please, Mr. Wilkins.

MARGIE: The umbrella belonged to Abraham Lincoln, didn't it?

WILKINS: Yes, it did, once upon a time, but there really isn't much of a story.

GAIL: Tell us about it.

WILKINS: Well, I've had the umbrella since I was a little boy.

ANNE: My, that's a long time.

WILKINS (*Smiling*): It certainly is. But before that, so the story goes, the umbrella belonged to my great-aunt Sophie. And Mr. Lincoln gave it to her.

GAIL: He did. But why?

WILKINS: Well, you see Great-Aunt Sophie was very much in love with a certain soldier who later became my great-uncle. But at the time when Aunt Sophie met Mr. Lincoln, my great-uncle had been taken prisoner by the Confederates and Aunt

Sophie was frantic with worry. She determined to see Mr. Lincoln somehow, by hook or by crook, and get more information. I guess she tried a few times to see him at the White House but the orderlies always stopped her with the word that the President was busy. She probably could have seen him that way eventually because President Lincoln tried to give everyone a hearing, but Sophie was young and impatient and high-spirited, so she decided not to wait for an appointment but to watch for him on the street and speak to him.

ANNE: My, that took courage.

WILKINS: I guess Aunt Sophie had plenty of that. Anyhow, she had heard that the President often went out himself to get his newspapers so she was watching for him one day when it started to rain. But that didn't stop Aunt Sophie. She waited until she saw him coming along carrying a big black umbrella and she ran up to him, so the story goes, with her hair all wet and rain streaming down her face.

MARGIE: And what did he say to her?

WILKINS: He was as nice as could be to her—told her he'd do what he could to find out about her fiancé and that he'd write her a letter. And then he offered her his umbrella.

GAIL: Oh, this is a wonderful story!

WILKINS: Yes, he insisted. Aunt Sophie didn't want to take it because, as she told President Lincoln, she might never have a chance to return it. Aunt Sophie, they say in our family, was always one to speak right up, and so she told President Lincoln that she had had such a hard time seeing him in the first place that she didn't expect ever to see him again.

JACK: And what did he say to that?

WILKINS: He said—well, an umbrella isn't very important anyhow unless it's raining and I'm practically home. You just keep it. So she did.

ANNE: And did she get a letter from him?

WILKINS: Yes, and everything turned out all right and her soldier came back.

JACK: Have you got the letter, too, Mr. Wilkins?

WILKINS: No, that must have been lost years ago. You see, I heard about all this from my grandmother when I was a little boy. They thought the umbrella was lost, too, but one day Grandmother was cleaning the attic after Aunt Sophie died and she found the umbrella among Aunt Sophie's things. That's when she gave it to me.

PHIL: Just imagine. (*He leans forward and looks at umbrella.*) May I look at it?

WILKINS: Sure. (*Holds out umbrella*)

MARGIE (*Touching it*): My, it gives you kind of a funny feeling to touch something that once belonged to Abraham Lincoln.

GAIL: This umbrella must mean a great deal to you, Mr. Wilkins.

WILKINS: I guess it does. It's been kind of a, well, a mascot for me, you might say, all my life.

JACK: The whole story is just the kind of thing we've been trying to find for our program. Will you make a speech for us, Mr. Wilkins?

WILKINS: Oh, so you're back on that, are you? Well, I tell you, if you don't call it a speech, I'll do it. Let's just say I'm going to tell the story of my umbrella.

PHIL: Fine.

JACK: It's exactly what we want.

WILKINS: When is this big affair?

JACK: Friday morning. The program starts at ten so if you could be here just a few minutes before—

WILKINS: I'll be here. And now I'd better be getting along and you boys and girls better be getting home, too.

JACK: O.K. Now don't forget to bring your umbrella, Mr. Wilkins.

WILKINS: Don't you worry. This goes everywhere I go. Goodbye. I'll be seeing you Friday.

ALL: Goodbye, Mr. Wilkins. (WILKINS *goes off right.*)

JACK: Boy, am I relieved.

PHIL: So am I.

MARGIE: He'll be wonderful.

ANNE: They can't say our committee didn't think of something good.

GAIL: And so unusual.

JACK: Now I guess we had better be shoving off. We can have a short meeting in the morning to finish making arrangements. (*They start off again as* MISS MARTIN, *a teacher, comes on wearing hat and coat.*)

MISS MARTIN: Oh, I'm so glad you're all still out here. I was going to call you at home, Jack.

JACK: What's the matter, Miss Martin?

MISS MARTIN: I've wonderful news for you. The principal's office just had a long distance call from Mr. Ashby!

JACK: From Jonathan Ashby?

MISS MARTIN: Yes. He can come and talk to us after all.

PHIL: Well!

JACK: But Miss Martin—

MISS MARTIN (*Going on*): And he's going to bring some things from the museum just as we asked him to.

JACK: Well, that—that's fine, Miss Martin, but the only thing is we—we just asked someone else to give a talk.

MISS MARTIN: You did?

JACK: Yes. Mr. Wilkins.

PHIL: And I don't see how we can tell him not to now.

MARGIE: He was so nice to say he'd do it.

MISS MARTIN: Well, don't worry, boys and girls. There's no reason why you can't have both speakers.

JACK: Why, sure, we could, couldn't we?

MISS MARTIN: Of course. In fact, I think it will make the program even better. I'll help you arrange everything in the morning. And I certainly think you're going to have a fine assembly. (*She smiles at them.*)

CURTAIN

* * *

SCENE 2

TIME: *The following Friday.*

SETTING: *The stage of an assembly hall in a school. The stage faces towards the audience. At right center is a table with old papers and photographs on it.*

AT RISE: JACK *enters from left with* MR. JONATHAN ASHBY, *a pleasant, distinguished-looking man of middle age.* ANNE *and* GAIL *are arranging newspapers and photographs on the table.*

JACK: This is our stage, Mr. Ashby. (*Gesturing toward audience*) The girls and boys will be coming into the assembly hall in a few minutes now.

ASHBY (*Nodding pleasantly*): I see.

ANNE: Are these things on the table arranged all right, Mr. Ashby?

ASHBY: Fine. Just so I can reach them as I talk. Of course, I couldn't bring our most valuable relics, but I thought the students might be interested in hearing some of the old clippings about Lincoln and in seeing some of the old pictures. (PHIL *and* MARGIE *enter left.* PHIL *carries a speaker's stand.* MARGIE *goes to table and looks at papers and pictures with* ANNE *and* GAIL.)

PHIL: Here's the stand you wanted, Jack.

JACK: Thanks, Phil. I thought you might like a stand, Mr. Ashby, in case you have notes.

ASHBY: Yes, I do have a few notes. That will be fine.

PHIL: Where shall I set it?

JACK: Why, how about right here, Mr. Ashby? (*He indicates spot near table.*)

ASHBY: That should do nicely. (PHIL *places stand.*) Oh, I meant to ask you—is my talk the only thing on the program?

JACK: No, there's one other speaker. He will come first because I imagine his talk will be rather short. And then, you, Mr. Ashby, and to end the program, our school orchestra is going to play some patriotic songs.

ASHBY: Well, well, it sounds like a splendid program.

MARGIE: The orchestra says they can bring their paraphernalia on later, Jack, after the speakers are finished. They've got it all set up off stage.

JACK: Good. We'll need some chairs for the speakers though, and I'll have to sit on stage too if I'm going to introduce them.

PHIL: I'll get some chairs. (*He goes off left.*)

MARGIE: I'll help. (*She goes off left.*)

JACK (*Looking at wrist watch*): I wonder where Mr. Wilkins is. I thought he'd be right on time.

ANNE (*Looking off left*): And so he is. Here he comes now. (MR. WILKINS *enters left wearing overcoat and carrying his umbrella.* PHIL *and* MARGIE *enter carrying three chairs.*)

PHIL *and* MARGIE (*Smiling at* WILKINS *as they enter*): Hello, Mr. Wilkins.

WILKINS: Well, well, hello there.

PHIL: Where do you want the chairs, Jack?

JACK: Behind the table here, I guess. (MARGIE *and* PHIL *place the three chairs behind table.*)

WILKINS: I hope I'm not too late, Jack.

JACK: No, we've been getting set up. This is Mr. Ashby from the museum. He's going to speak for us, too. Mr. Ashby, this is Mr. Wilkins.

ASHBY (*Shaking hands with* WILKINS) : How do you do, Mr. Wilkins?

WILKINS: Well, well, certainly glad to meet you, Mr. Ashby. So you're from that big museum.

ASHBY (*Looking at umbrella*) : That's an interesting old umbrella you have there.

WILKINS: Yes, it is. It means a lot to me.

ASHBY: And no wonder. (*Examining the handle*) That beautiful carved handle—I know of the artist.

WILKINS: You do?

ASHBY: Yes, he was a fine wood carver. We have a handle similar to this in the art room at the museum. Same fellow did it—you can't mistake his work. He was active in the late 1880's and '90's.

WILKINS (*Starting*): What? But he must have been doing some carving before that.

ASHBY: No, he couldn't have been. It's true he started quite young, but he wasn't born until the early sixties—1861, I think it was.

WILKINS (*Trying to control his voice*) : Now, isn't that odd? I—I thought this umbrella was of the period—oh, around 1865.

ASHBY: No, no, much later than that. I have a book about the artist. I can send it to you if you like. You'd probably be interested. (*Examining handle again*) My, my, this is really a fine example of his work. Oh, one of the tricks he had—he usually carved his initials in the design somewhere. (*He looks closer.*) Yes, here they are. R.S. His name was Robert—

WILKINS (*Dully*) : It doesn't matter. Then this umbrella could never have belonged to Lincoln, after all.

ASHBY: Belonged to Lincoln? Why, no. No. Did you think— (*Seeing* WILKINS' *face*) Oh, I'm sorry. I didn't know. I never would have said—

JACK (*Realizing how* WILKINS *must feel, he comes forward nervously and looks at his watch*) : Excuse me, but it's time for the students to come in now. Do you want to have a chair, Mr. Ashby—and— (WILKINS *starts off left.*) Where are you going, Mr. Wilkins?

WILKINS: Just to take off my coat. (*He goes off.*)

ANNE: Oh, poor Mr. Wilkins.

ASHBY: I'm afraid I've done a terrible thing. I never would have spoken out if I'd known the situation. Believe me, I didn't do it intentionally.

JACK: Of course you didn't. We understand. Please sit down, Mr. Ashby. (ASHBY *sits down at table still looking worried.*) And the rest of you had better get off stage. (ANNE, MARGIE, GAIL *and* PHIL *go off left as* MR. WILKINS *enters. He has taken off his overcoat but still has his umbrella.* JACK *goes toward him.*) We're all sorry about this, Mr. Wilkins.

WILKINS: It's all right. Doesn't look as though I'll have much to talk about, does it?

JACK: If you'd rather not make your speech—

WILKINS (*Hesitatingly*) : Well, no—no, I'll make it. I won't go back on my word.

JACK: All right. The students are coming in now. If you'll just sit down. (WILKINS *goes to table.* MR. ASHBY *smiles at him as though to apologize, as he sits down.* JACK *sits in chair at left of table. He looks out over audience as though waiting for the students to get settled. Then after a few moments he rises and comes to center stage.*) Members of the faculty and fellow students, our assembly this morning is in honor of one of the greatest men in the history of our country, Abraham Lincoln. We sincerely hope our program will please you. Our first speaker is a man you all know—in fact, a beloved figure in our town—Mr. Silas Wilkins. (JACK *starts the applause and there is applause from the audience. Note: A few boys and girls may be placed in audience when this play is given to start applause at proper times.* MR. WILKINS *comes forward carrying his umbrella.* JACK *sits down again.*)

WILKINS (*He smiles and clears his throat*): Well, girls and boys, I've just had kind of a shock. For years and years I've thought this old umbrella of mine (*Holds it up*) once belonged to Abraham Lincoln. And now I find that it never did. That great man never touched it as I thought or had it in his possession. (*Few exclamations from audience*) I feel sure it's true that Mr. Lincoln once did a kindly act for my great-aunt—that he once loaned her an umbrella. That story has come down through our family. But evidently that original umbrella was lost and we mistakenly thought this was the one. (*He pauses.*) Well, it isn't, and at first when I discovered it I don't mind telling you I felt as though I'd lost an old and valued friend. But then I got to thinking and do you know what I decided? This umbrella is just a symbol. (*He holds it out.*) What difference does it make whether Abraham Lincoln ever touched it or not? An umbrella is only a material object, and it's the qualities of Lincoln's *spirit* that have made an impression on me. Because I thought this umbrella had belonged to him, I grew interested in studying Lincoln, the man, and I learned a great many things about him. Oh yes, where he was born and the various facts about his life, but what was more important, those qualities of his character which made him what he was. Lincoln was an honest man—we've all heard that—but being honest doesn't just mean giving the correct change. It means trying to find out what is right to do in any situation and then doing it. Lincoln did not believe one thing and then do another. He always acted according to what he thought was true and just, no matter how difficult it might be. He reasoned a problem out and then he did what his conscience told him to do. And it's those qualities in Lincoln's character that have helped me all my life. Oh, not that I've ever done very much, but we can all *try*.

If each one of us does that we have nothing to fear. And, boys and girls, from Abraham Lincoln you can learn inspiring lessons as to what true patriotism really is. (*Applause from audience.*)

As I look out at you all, I think that perhaps one of you may be president of the United States some day; perhaps not. We can't all be presidents. But in whatever place the good Lord puts us, great or small, we can do what we honestly feel is just and right. I guess that's all I have to say. That's the story of the umbrella that never belonged to Abraham Lincoln—but it's served its purpose. It has been an inspiring and useful symbol to me, and I hope it may be to you. If you would pattern your life after a great and good man, Abraham Lincoln is a worthy example. (*The audience applauds.* MR. WILKINS *goes back to his seat smiling as the curtains close.*)

THE END

Happy Hearts

Characters

HELEN STAFFORD	BOBBIE STAFFORD
DON STAFFORD	PROFESSOR EDWARD STAFFORD
LUCY STAFFORD	RUTH JAMISON

TIME: *The afternoon of Valentine's Day.*

SETTING: *The living room of Professor Stafford's home.*

AT RISE: HELEN, *about sixteen years old, is seated in chair right and* DON, *fifteen, in chair left. He is leafing through a magazine.* LUCY, *ten, and* BOBBIE, *eight, are seated at the card table making valentines.*

LUCY (*Holding up a red paper heart*): Look, Helen. Bobbie and I are making more valentines. We're even going to write verses.

BOBBIE: I've written one already. Listen to this, Helen—do you think it will be all right to give to Ruth? (*He reads.*)

> My love I send you
> By the ton,
> And hope our hearts
> Can beat as one.

DON (*Putting down his magazine*): Say, that's all right. You're quite a poet.

HELEN: Ruth will love it, Bobbie. . . . Oh dear, I just can't believe that she's going away.

DON: Neither can I. It seems as though she's always been here —kind of taking care of us.

HELEN: She has been—for ages. Why, you and I were just little kids, Don—and Bobbie was a baby.

BOBBIE: Who's a baby?

HELEN: You were, Bobbie, when Ruth came.

DON: Hadn't Ruth been helping Mother out before that?

HELEN: Yes, she worked for all the professors' wives to help earn her way through college but then when Mother died, Dad asked Ruth if she wouldn't come and take over for a while.

DON: And she's been here ever since.

LUCY: And she isn't going to leave—I know she isn't.

HELEN: I'm afraid she is. She sounded pretty definite.

LUCY: But then who'll braid my hair and tell me stories before I go to sleep?

HELEN: I will, I guess, or maybe Dad.

BOBBIE: I don't think Dad knows any stories.

DON: Bobbie, shame on you. A brilliant guy like Dad. Why, I've heard that the college students call Dad their favorite professor. He must tell them *something* interesting.

BOBBIE: I'll bet he doesn't know the story of "The Three Little Pigs."

DON: Well, anyhow, he's always giving special lectures. How would you like a lecture on the Romance of History for a bedtime story?

BOBBIE: I don't want to hear a lecture. Besides, Dad gave me a lecture just last night, because I hadn't washed my neck. He said it made more work for Ruth.

LUCY: Helen, couldn't Dad beg Ruth to stay?

HELEN: Dad doesn't know she's leaving, and she asked me not to say anything.

DON: But why not? He'll have to know.

HELEN: Sure, but not for a few days. Ruth doesn't want to worry him because he has an extra heavy schedule this week —exams for students and special lectures and he's trying to finish his book. Ruth says when she's got everything arranged she'll tell him. She has some woman lined up to take her place here.

LUCY: Some woman? What for?

HELEN: To be a housekeeper here and take care of us all.

LUCY: I won't like her. I wouldn't like anyone but Ruth. (*She starts to cry.*)

HELEN: Lucy, for goodness sakes, stop that crying. You're a big girl now. (*She rises and goes to her.*) There, there. I thought you were going to work on your valentines.

LUCY: But why does Ruth want to leave? Doesn't she—doesn't she love us any more?

HELEN: Of course she does but—

BOBBIE (*Starting to cry too*): Then why is she going?

HELEN: Now, Bobbie, don't you start too.

DON (*Rising and walking toward* LUCY *and* BOBBIE): Listen, you kids, you've got to understand. Ruth is leaving because she doesn't want to be a housekeeper all her life and I don't blame her.

BOBBIE: A housekeeper? Ruth isn't one. She's like our mother.

DON: I know. She's been swell, and I guess you are too young to see her side of it. But I'm going to tell you anyhow. What does she do? Cook and sew and wash and clean for all of us. And what does she get? A small salary—and small thanks from any of us.

LUCY: Ruth knows we all love her. I tell her most every night.

DON: Oh, sure, but what does that mean? All any of us does is make work for her. She never has a chance to go anywhere.

BOBBIE: She does too. She takes us all to the movies.

DON (*Walking about*): And isn't that exciting? Why, Ruth is

young yet, I guess. She could do lots of interesting things
—and interesting work too. She's got her degree from the
college. She doesn't have to see that you've got a clean neck,
Bobbie, and mend my socks, and make formals for you, Helen.

HELEN: No, she doesn't have to, and all you've been saying is
very interesting, Don. In fact, I agree with most of it but it
isn't the reason that Ruth is leaving.

DON: It—it isn't? O.K. What's your theory? Come on, give.

HELEN (*Dramatically*): It's something much bigger and much
more important. I've known about it for quite a while but I
haven't said anything. No one told me either. I just guessed.

DON: Oh, so you just guessed. I don't know what you're talking
about but I'll bet you guessed wrong. Girls! Why do they
always have to cook up something dramatic? Ruth's leaving
simply because of what I said.

HELEN: Oh, no, she isn't. (*Slowly and impressively*) Ruth is
leaving because she— (*There is the sound of a door off
right.*)

DON (*Sitting down again*): Shhh! Here she comes.

BOBBIE: Oh, I'd better hide the valentine I'm making. (RUTH
JAMISON, *a nice-looking young woman with a warm smile,
enters right. She wears hat and coat and her arms are full of
packages.*)

RUTH: Hello, everyone. My, I've had fun. I've been shopping.
(LUCY *and* BOBBIE *put down their scissors, paste, etc. and run
to her.*)

LUCY (*Hugging* RUTH): Ruth, you're home!

BOBBIE: What did you bring? Have you got some valentine
candy?

RUTH (*Laughing*): Ask me no secrets and I'll tell you no lies.
But I have got some— (*She stops, staring at* BOBBIE *and*
LUCY.) Why, what—what's the matter? Have you two been
crying?

LUCY: Well, not exactly—I mean, not much.

BOBBIE: I have. I cried hard. (*He starts crying again.*) I don't want you to go away.

LUCY (*Crying too*): Please don't leave us, Ruth.

RUTH (*She places her packages on chair, kneels down and puts her arms around them*): Children . . . oh dear. (*She gets handkerchief from pocket.*) Here, blow your noses. (*Turning to* HELEN *as she pats* LUCY *and* BOBBIE) Helen, I didn't think you'd tell the little ones yet.

HELEN: Oh, I'm sorry, Ruth—I never thought. You didn't say not to.

RUTH: Of course I didn't. It's my fault. (*Rising and turning to children*) Now, now, don't cry. I won't be leaving for a while anyhow.

BOBBIE: Not for a year?

RUTH: Well, not for weeks—a week or two maybe.

BOBBIE: Two weeks! But that's so soon.

RUTH: Let's not talk about it any more. We don't want to worry your father for a few days. Everything's going to be all right—you'll see. I've found the nicest lady who's going to come and take care of you—that is, if your father likes her when he interviews her.

BOBBIE: I don't want any lady—I want you.

RUTH (*Laughing*): Oh, Bobbie, you funny darling. (*She gives him a quick kiss and then takes off her coat and hat.*)

HELEN: I'll hang up your coat, Ruth.

RUTH: Thanks, Helen. (HELEN *takes coat and hat and goes out right, returning in a moment.*)

LUCY (*Still sniffling*): Ruth, I'm sorry but I can't help crying.

RUTH: Of course you can. (*Gaily*) Now, let's forget everything but what a nice time we're going to have today. Why, this is the time when—when hearts are gay—sure enough, it's Valentine's Day! There, I made a rhyme.

BOBBIE (*Smiling now*): So did I. (*He runs to card table, then stops.*) Oh, but I can't show you yet. It's a secret.

RUTH: Maybe I could let you in on a few of *my* secrets after all. (*She picks up a brown paper bag from chair.*) In this bag are some red jelly bean hearts.

LUCY: Oh, goody!

RUTH (*Holding up an odd-shaped package*): And you could never guess what's in here—it's a cake pan.

LUCY: A cake pan?

RUTH: Shaped like a heart. I thought I'd make a heart-shaped cake. It was going to be a surprise but maybe it'll be more fun if you help me. We'll make pink frosting and decorate it with red hearts.

BOBBIE: Oh, boy!

RUTH (*Holding up a long white box*): And in here—well, it's a present for your father.

DON: For Dad?

RUTH: For you children to give him, I mean.

DON: That—that's swell, Ruth, but then we ought to pay for it.

HELEN: Yes. Lucy and Bobbie made some fancy paper hearts for him but we never thought of a real present, and I—I've spent all my allowance. I had to get something.

RUTH: Oh, my goodness, it didn't cost much. Let me pay for it this time.

BOBBIE: What is it?

RUTH: It's a tie. (*She opens box.*) Look. (*Displaying dark red tie with design in white*)

LUCY: Oh—bright red for Valentine's Day!

RUTH: It's not *bright* red, Lucy.

BOBBIE: Sure it is, with little fishes all over it!

RUTH: Not fishes, Bobbie. They're little curlicues or something. (*Worriedly*) Dear me, you don't think it's too—too splashy, do you?

HELEN: Of course not. It's lovely.

DON: It's just the thing Dad needs. It's really sharp, Ruth.

HELEN: And I'm going to see that he wears it. He's so absent-minded sometimes that he grabs the first old tie that comes to hand.

RUTH (*Handing box to* HELEN): Wrap it up pretty now. (HELEN *puts box on small table.*)

LUCY: But Ruth, if you bought the tie, it ought to be from you too.

RUTH: Oh, no—just from you children. (*Picking up other packages*) And now I'd better start baking my cake.

LUCY (*Standing at card table*): And we'd better finish our valentines. We gave away all those we made for school, Ruth, but these are family—these are special.

BOBBIE: Don't show her.

LUCY: I want to paint some flowers on mine. Where are my paints, Ruth?

RUTH: I know. Come along—I'll get them.

BOBBIE: And I want my crayons. (BOBBIE *and* LUCY *go off left with* RUTH.)

HELEN (*Walking about*): I just don't know what Bobbie and Lucy are going to do without Ruth.

DON: I wonder about us too. We're older, but—

HELEN: I know. I hate to think of it. Oh, if only Dad could see!

DON: See what?

HELEN: What's right under his nose—what I started to tell you before. And this tie business certainly proves my theory.

DON: What are you talking about? What theory?

HELEN: My theory of why Ruth is leaving. I know I'm right. She's leaving because she's—she's in love with Dad.

DON (*Rising*): Huh? Why—you're crazy.

HELEN: Oh, no, I'm not. It's the most obvious thing in the world. Buying this tie for him—

Don : But Ruth's always doing things to please us and she knew we'd like it.

Helen : That's only one thing. I've noticed others—for weeks now. The way she's always worrying about him, the way she looks at him—

Don : You're imagining things. Dad never pays any attention to Ruth. I mean, he's nice to her but he's always got his nose stuck in a book.

Helen : Exactly. I didn't say Dad was in love with *her.* I only wish he were. That would make everything all right.

Don : It would?

Helen : Certainly it would. Then Dad would propose and Ruth would accept and they would get married and she'd stay.

Don : For gosh sakes!

Helen : You mean you don't like the idea?

Don : Sure, I like the idea but it's—it's all so new to me. I'd like anything that made Ruth stay but—

Helen : Well, she can't stay the way things are now. Don't you see? It was all right as long as Ruth thought of Dad as just an employer but once she realized she was in love with him, she knew she had to go. (*Dramatically*) Don't you see how a woman would suffer being around someone she loved and knowing he didn't love her in return?

Don : Listen, Helen, you've been reading too many romantic novels! You're all wrong about this. Ruth's not leaving because of Dad, and she's not in love with him.

Helen : You talk as though no one could fall in love with Dad. Well, he may be the brilliant Professor Stafford and bookish and absent-minded, but he's a very attractive man from a woman's viewpoint.

Don (*Kiddingly*) : Who says?

Helen (*Getting angry*) : Don Stafford—

DON: O.K., Miss Romantic, go on dreaming but I'm a realist and I think you're off the beam.

HELEN: Oh, you do? Well, what's so unusual about falling in love? I guess people do it every day all over the world—and why, look at today, Valentine's Day. Think of all the messages that are being sent about hearts and flowers and love. It's love that makes the world go round.

DON: Well, it's certainly made you dizzy. I know that. (LUCY *and* BOBBIE *run in left with boxes of paints and crayons.*)

LUCY: Ruth's starting the cake. It's going to be wonderful. (*Sitting down at card table*) My, I'd better finish my valentine verses.

BOBBIE (*Sitting down and picking up crayon*): Me, too. I need a word to rhyme with love.

DON (*Disgusted*): Oh-hh. (*He sits down again. A door is heard off and* PROFESSOR EDWARD STAFFORD *enters right wearing hat and coat and carrying a brief case.*)

PROFESSOR: Children, have any of you seen my notes?

DON: Hello, Dad.

LUCY *and* BOBBIE: Hi, Dad. (*They are busy with their valentines.*)

HELEN: How was the lecture?

PROFESSOR (*Taking off coat and hat and putting them on a chair*): Fine—went splendidly. An unusual subject in a way, but the students had asked for it—"Great Lovers in History and Literature."

DON: Isn't that a little out of your line, Dad?

HELEN: It's very appropriate for today.

PROFESSOR: What? Appropriate?

HELEN: Of course. It's Valentine's Day.

PROFESSOR (*Absent-mindedly, then opening brief case and digging through his cards and papers*): So it is, so it is. . . . As I was saying, have any of you seen my notes?

HELEN : What notes?

PROFESSOR : My notes on family customs in Africa. I thought I
took them with me because I planned to go over them between
lectures so I could work on that chapter of my book tonight.
And then I found I had family customs in China instead. (*He
sits down at right and goes through his brief case again, taking out some small file cards and shuffling through them.*)
Hmm-m, these aren't the ones. These are the ones I used in
my lecture on the great lovers.

HELEN : Dad, how you can ever keep what you're saying straight
the way you shuffle those cards about, I don't know.

DON : Gosh, Dad—look, you're wearing one brown sock and one
blue.

PROFESSOR (*Looking down*): Hmm, so I am—but I guess it
doesn't really matter. (*Pulling out a tooth brush from brief
case*) Now, I wonder what this tooth brush is doing in my
brief case.

DON : Probably you planned to comb your hair with it or something.

PROFESSOR : Perhaps. (*Then looking up and smiling*) Don, you
wouldn't by any chance be laughing at your father, would
you?

DON : Well—

PROFESSOR : Because if you are, I don't blame you. But now, let
me see, I have got to find those notes—maybe you've seen
them, Helen—family customs in Africa.

HELEN : Dad, listen, how would you like to observe some family
customs right here at home for a change?

PROFESSOR : What—what's that?

HELEN : You can't work on your book tonight. We're going to
celebrate and have a special evening.

DON : Sure, Dad, come on. You can be a lot of fun when you
want to be.

PROFESSOR: But I don't want to be very often—is that the general idea? (*Rising, still holding brief case and cards*) Children, I'm sorry. I have neglected you lately. But what about tonight. Is it someone's birthday?

HELEN: No, Dad, I told you. It's Valentine's Day.

PROFESSOR: Oh, yes, hearts and flowers. Very well, since it's such an important day, I will not work.

HELEN: Good—and there's something I've got to talk to you about.

DON: Helen, you're not going to—

HELEN: Never mind, Don. Could we have a little conference, Dad?

PROFESSOR: Of course. But first I must find those notes. Maybe Ruth will know—she usually does.

HELEN: Ruth's busy, Dad. She's baking a special cake.

LUCY (*Rising*): Oh, and we promised to help her, Bobbie. I almost forgot.

BOBBIE (*Jumping up*): We'd better hurry. It may be time to scrape the frosting pan.

LUCY: Is that all the help you're going to be? (LUCY *and* BOBBIE *run off left.*)

PROFESSOR (*Starting left*): I'm going to speak to Ruth. If she does know where my notes are, maybe she can do a little typing for me.

HELEN: Dad, of course she can't. How can you expect her to do a hundred things at once?

PROFESSOR: My, my, I *am* inconsiderate. I hope you'll tell me when I am just as you've done now. Ruth does so much for us all that I sometimes forget that she only has two hands and one brain. (*He goes out left.*)

HELEN (*Sitting down abruptly*): A brain. That's all Dad ever notices. Now, if he'd notice Ruth's pretty brown eyes or the way her hair curls when it rains—

DON : Say, are you on that again?

HELEN : Oh, if I only knew how I could make Dad see how wonderful Ruth is!

DON : Helen, this may be Valentine's Day but you're not Cupid.

HELEN : If only there were something I could do.

DON : What have you got up your sleeve?

HELEN : Nothing, but I wish I did have. Oh, Don, you don't know how all this has upset me. When I think how empty this house is going to be without Ruth. Dad's wonderful and I love him but Ruth is, well, like a mother—someone to tell things to. Oh, you're a boy and you can't understand.

DON : Listen, Helen, I hate to have Ruth leave as much as you do. The only thing I can't see is this crazy theory of yours. (PROFESSOR STAFFORD *enters left, still carrying his opened brief case and looking through some file cards.*)

PROFESSOR : Ruth thinks she knows where my notes might be. She's going to look.

HELEN : Dad, I told you not to bother her.

PROFESSOR : But she thinks she can put her finger right on them. Probably she can. She's a very efficient young woman.

HELEN : Efficient?

PROFESSOR : Well, isn't she? Now, what was it you wanted to talk to me about?

DON (*Half rising*) : Uh—I guess this is my cue to leave.

HELEN : No, Don, you can stay. It's nothing private. (*Rising*) Dad, had you thought anything about presents?

PROFESSOR : Presents?

HELEN : For Valentine's Day. Don and I don't care but I know Lucy and Bobbie will be disappointed if they don't get some kind of a valentine from their dad.

PROFESSOR : Dear me, of course. And I never thought—well, I can go shopping now.

HELEN (*Going to table right and opening drawer*) : Never mind,

Dad. I was sure you'd forget so I took care of it. (*She takes out two boxes of candy from drawer. One is heart-shaped, the other square. She also takes out a flat paper bag. She holds up boxes of candy.*) See—candy.

PROFESSOR: My, my—but all this must have cost money.

HELEN: It did. I used my allowance.

PROFESSOR: Well, at least you're going to be reimbursed for your trouble. (*He takes a bill from his pocket and hands it to her.*) Two boxes, eh?

HELEN: Yes. I thought the heart-shaped one could be from you to the children.

DON (*Rising and looking at candy*): That's swell, Helen.

HELEN: And this one—well, I thought we could give this to Ruth.

PROFESSOR: To Ruth?

HELEN: I'm sure she'll appreciate some little remembrance. It can be from all of us.

PROFESSOR: Why, of course, that's a splendid idea. Ruth does so much for you children. . . . Well, you take care of it, Helen.

HELEN: Just a minute, Dad. You're not going to get off that easy. (*Taking two greeting cards from paper bag*) At least you're going to write your name on the cards.

PROFESSOR: Very well, of course. . . . Now, I wonder where my pen is. I thought I had it. Well, perhaps it's in the study. I'll see. (*He goes off left.*)

DON: Some day Dad's going to lose his head, and then where'll he be?

HELEN (*Showing cards*): Look, Don.

DON: Yes, they're nice cards all right.

HELEN (*Opening cards and looking at them*): But all they say is "Happy Valentine's Day." You don't know how much I

wanted to get one with a romantic verse for Ruth's present—
and then sign Dad's name.

DON: Hey, you couldn't do anything like that.

HELEN: No, but that doesn't mean I didn't want to. (PROFES-
SOR STAFFORD *enters left.*)

PROFESSOR: Dear me, I wonder what I could have done with my
pen. (*He is looking through his brief case again.*)

HELEN: Didn't you find it, Dad? Well, maybe it's in your overcoat pocket.

PROFESSOR: I don't think I'd put it in there.

HELEN (*Going to chair, digging in pocket of overcoat and then
holding up pen*): Well, you did—here it is. Now, sign the
cards and wrap up the candy. I got some fancy paper for you.
(*She pulls out some gift wrapping paper from bag.*)

PROFESSOR: Do they have to be wrapped? Do I have to do that?

HELEN: Well, it seems to me you ought to have a hand in these
presents somewhere. After all, I did the shopping.

PROFESSOR: Of course, of course. Well, give me the candy and
the paper.

HELEN (*Handing him cards, paper and candy*): Oh dear, I forgot to get ribbon.

PROFESSOR: Well, I have some cord in my desk. I'll take the
things into my study and fix them up. (*He has his hands full
with candy, paper, greeting cards and his brief case as he
starts left.*)

HELEN: O.K. Now fix them up nice, Dad.

PROFESSOR: I'll do my best. (*He goes out left.*)

HELEN: Oh dear, if only I had written "with love" on that card
for Ruth's present. I'll bet I could have gotten away with it
too. Dad wouldn't notice.

DON: But that would be terrible. All it would do would be to
cause a lot of embarrassment for everyone. Why, Ruth would
probably leave right away instead of in a week or two.

HELEN: What does it matter *when* she leaves as long as she's going? Besides, stop raving. I didn't do it, did I? And it was my only chance. Oh, I feel so awful. She's—she's going and there's nothing we can do to stop her.

DON (*Patting her shoulder awkwardly*): Now, Ruth. . . . (LUCY *and* BOBBIE *run in left.*)

LUCY: Helen, Don, you ought to see the cake! It's going to be beautiful.

BOBBIE: It's like a great big heart—and we helped.

DON: You probably sampled the frosting.

BOBBIE: Sure, and it tastes just like candy. (*Getting a paper valentine heart from table*) Look, Helen, do you think I ought to draw more hearts on my valentine or is it all right?

HELEN: I think you have plenty. That's very nice.

BOBBIE: Some of the hearts are kind of crooked. I guess I got tired—I drew so many.

HELEN: Ruth will love it just as it is.

LUCY: I think my valentines are done too. I drew a picture of Cupid on one of mine.

DON: You'd better give that one to Helen. (HELEN *gives him a look.*)

LUCY: No, this is the one I made for Dad. (RUTH *enters left carrying some file cards and papers.*)

RUTH: Professor Stafford—(*She stops.*) Oh, your father isn't here now.

HELEN: No, he went in the study, Ruth. He'll be back in a minute.

RUTH: Well, I found those notes he wanted on family customs in Africa. He left them on the dining room table.

DON: Oh, yeah. I remember now. He was going over them at breakfast this morning.

RUTH: I'll just leave them here. (*She puts them on a small table.*)

LUCY: Ruth, do you suppose we could give our valentines now?

BOBBIE: Yes, let's. I don't think I can wait much longer.

RUTH: All right. I thought we could have them at the dinner table but if everyone wants them now—

HELEN: Let's wait for Dad. Oh, I haven't wrapped his tie up yet! (*She takes some more gift paper from bag and starts folding it around box as* PROFESSOR STAFFORD *enters left, carrying two boxes wrapped in paper and tied with cord. He is all smiles.* HELEN *stops wrapping and puts box on table.*)

BOBBIE: Say, Dad, what have you got? Presents?

LUCY: We're going to have our valentines now, Dad.

PROFESSOR: We are? Well, that's fine. I'll hand mine out. (*Handing box to* LUCY *and* BOBBIE) This is for you, children. (*He turns to* RUTH.) And this one—well, here's a little remembrance for you, Ruth.

RUTH (*Pleased*): For me? (*She sits down in chair right and starts taking off the paper.*)

LUCY: Is this for all of us?

HELEN: Yes, Lucy, but go ahead. You and Bobbie open it.

BOBBIE: Oh, boy! (LUCY *and* BOBBIE *take the paper off their heart-shaped box of candy.*)

RUTH (*Still taking paper off*): This is so nice. I didn't expect a present. (*She has paper off and picks up a small white file card from top of candy box.*) Why, here's a card. (*Reading slowly*) "I take this opportunity to tell you how much you mean to me. I can only hope that you return the deep affection I feel for you. I love you, my dear." (*She looks up, repeating*) "I love you." (*Then breathlessly*) Oh, Edward. Edward! (*She rises, dumping card, candy and paper on chair and runs to* PROFESSOR STAFFORD.) I love you too. Of course I do. But I never dreamed you felt the same way. (*She kisses him quickly, then turns and runs left. She is crying.*) Oh, I've been so miserable and now I'm so happy. (*She runs from the room.* PROFESSOR STAFFORD *stands stunned for a moment.*)

DON (*Affected too*) : Gosh!

HELEN (*Bewildered*) : Dad, what—

PROFESSOR (*Dreamily*) : Did you hear what she said? She loves me.

HELEN : Of course she does, Dad. I've known that all along but you—

PROFESSOR : And I—why, I feel the same way about her. Isn't that wonderful, children? I feel the same way and I didn't know it. I didn't know it until this very moment.

HELEN : But Dad, you must have known. You wrote on the card.

PROFESSOR : Card? I used that card you gave me.

HELEN (*Running to chair and picking up the file card*) : No, you didn't. Why, this is a file card—the kind you use for notes.

PROFESSOR (*Looking*) : So it is. Why, it's part of my notes for my lecture today on "Great Lovers in History and Literature." It's a portion of a love letter written in the nineteenth century. I read it to the students. Now how did it get in with the candy?

HELEN (*Starting to laugh*) : I've got a pretty good idea.

PROFESSOR (*Turning*) : Well, I've got to find Ruth. (*He starts left.*) Ruth, Ruth! (*He goes out left.*)

HELEN : Can you imagine that? Isn't it wonderful?

DON : Sure, but I'm still in a daze. I don't know what's happened.

HELEN : Don't you see? Dad, in his usual fashion, mixed things up. Instead of enclosing the card I gave him in the box of candy, he enclosed this file card by mistake. He had his brief case and he'd been shuffling through his notes.

DON (*Looking at card*) : His notes on "Great Lovers in History."

HELEN : Sure, and this is part of an old love letter just as he said. Oh, isn't it wonderful that Dad's so absent-minded?

DON: Yes. If he hadn't been, Ruth would never have spoken out.

HELEN: And Dad wouldn't have realized he felt the same way about her.

LUCY (*She has been listening*): Helen, I guess I don't understand everything that's happened.

HELEN: A romance has happened, Lucy, a beautiful romance right in this very house—and on Valentine's Day.

BOBBIE: And will Ruth stay with us now and never go away?

DON: Helen, I ought to apologize to you. I was certainly wrong about everything—and you were right.

HELEN: Only half right. I never dreamed that Dad— (PROFESSOR *and* RUTH *enter left, all smiles and holding hands.*)

PROFESSOR: Children, Ruth and I—well, we have something to tell you and we hope it meets with your approval. Ruth has just consented to be my wife.

BOBBIE (*Happily*): Then that means you'll be our mother, doesn't it, Ruth?

HELEN (*Going to them*): Dad, Ruth, I'm so glad.

DON (*Kissing* RUTH *and shaking hands with his father*): So am I. Why, we're going to be one great big happy family.

RUTH: Family! That reminds me, Edward. I found those notes you wanted on family customs in Africa.

PROFESSOR: Never mind, my dear. The only family I'm going to think about right now is my own. And I understand it's the custom in my family to celebrate on Valentine's Day.

RUTH (*Smiling*): And that means happy hearts for everyone!

CHILDREN: Yes, yes! (LUCY *and* BOBBIE *run to table and get valentines.* HELEN *takes some valentines from paper bag. Everyone is laughing and giving and receiving valentine hearts as the curtain falls.*)

THE END

A Change of Hearts

Characters

Mr. Bowman	Dorothy
Miss Wiggam	Helen
Johnnie	Bill
Miss Travers	Charlie
Sue	Mr. Jenkins

Scene 1

Time: *Valentine's Day. Afternoon.*

Setting: *The principal's office of Plainview High School.*

At Rise: Mr. Bowman, *the young principal of Plainview High School, is seated at his desk looking at some papers when there is a knock at the door left. He quickly shoves the paper he is working on into the desk drawer and sits up straight.*

Mr. Bowman: Come in. (Miss Wiggam, *an elderly teacher, enters left. She wears hat and coat.*)

Miss Wiggam (*Worriedly*): Oh, Mr. Bowman.

Mr. Bowman: Yes, Miss Wiggam?

Miss Wiggam: I know I shouldn't bother you with my troubles, Mr. Bowman. As principal of this high school, you must be over-burdened as it is.

Mr. Bowman (*Smiling*): Oh, I can take it, I guess. What's the matter, Miss Wiggam? Things not going so well today?

Miss Wiggam: I should say not. My Latin classes, Mr. Bowman. The boys and girls—they just didn't have their minds

284

on the work. When I asked one boy what Pompey did after
Caesar crossed the Rubicon, what do you think he said?

MR. BOWMAN : Why, he should have said : Pompey prepared for
battle.

MISS WIGGAM : Exactly, Mr. Bowman, but he didn't. He said :
He shot an arrow into the air—it fell to earth, I know not
where.

MR. BOWMAN (*Laughing*) : Well, maybe he was thinking of
Cupid. After all, it *is* Valentine's Day, Miss Wiggam.

MISS WIGGAM : Humph. As if I didn't know. Such whispering
and giggling and writing of notes—well, I'm at my wit's end,
Mr. Bowman.

MR. BOWMAN : Now, don't worry. I suppose they all have their
minds on the Valentine party tonight. Tomorrow's another
day, Miss Wiggam.

MISS WIGGAM : Well, I don't know how you can be so opti-
mistic. But you're new—this is your first year. When you've
been here as long as I have—

MR. BOWMAN : Miss Wiggam, I'm sure things aren't as bad as
they seem. Think back now. I imagine you've turned out
some very fine citizens from Plainview High.

MISS WIGGAM : Well, yes, when you put it that way, Mr. Bowman, I guess we have.

MR. BOWMAN : Of course. And now school's over for the day.
Go home—have a rest—have a little fun.

MISS WIGGAM (*Smiling now*) : Mr. Bowman, it's always such a
help to talk to you. Thank you so much.

MR. BOWMAN : Not at all.

MISS WIGGAM : You do cheer me up. I don't know why I should
have been so worried. I suppose it's natural that young folks
should have their minds on valentines. (*She starts left and
then turns with a smile.*) You're not so old yourself, Mr.
Bowman. Maybe you've got your mind on them too.

Mr. Bowman (*A little embarrassed*) : Oh, now, Miss Wiggam—

Miss Wiggam : Well—thanks again for letting me take up your time. Goodbye. (*She goes out left.*)

Mr. Bowman (*Quickly pulling paper out of desk and looking at it*) : Now, let me see— (*He picks up a pencil, taps it on desk and looks off into space.*) Pine—valentine—my queen of hearts—I shot an arrow into the air—ohh, no. That won't do. (*Suddenly he picks up the phone and calls a number*) Oakley 211, please. . . . Hello? Jenkins Sweet Shoppe? Oh, Mr. Jenkins, this is Mr. Bowman. Have you still got that big heart-shaped box of candy? Yes, the biggest—the five dollar one. . . . Good. . . . Well, no, I don't want to order it—not yet, but I just wanted to be sure you still had it. . . . What's that? I'm slow making up my mind? No, it isn't that, Mr. Jenkins, but I'm not certain the young lady would appreciate —very well, Mr. Jenkins. I may be in later. Goodbye. (*Just as he hangs up,* Miss Wiggam *enters left again.* Mr. Bowman *jumps a little.*)

Miss Wiggam : Excuse me, Mr. Bowman—I know how busy you are, but on my way out I noticed that drinking fountain in the south corridor and I've been meaning to mention it. It squirts.

Mr. Bowman : Squirts?

Miss Wiggam : Yes—and the boys—and I regret to say the girls, too, sometimes—play with it and it makes puddles.

Mr. Bowman : Dear me.

Miss Wiggam : I thought if you'd just come and look at it, Mr. Bowman. Then you could report it to the engineer.

Mr. Bowman (*Rising*) : Very well, I— (*He sighs*) All right, Miss Wiggam. (*He crosses left following* Miss Wiggam.)

Miss Wiggam : It's just a little thing, Mr. Bowman, but it's a temptation to all the students—and it does squirt so. (*They go off. There is a pause and after a moment* JOHNNIE, *a boy about sixteen, carrying two or three textbooks, enters left followed by* MISS TRAVERS, *a pretty young teacher. She carries a square white envelope.*)

MISS TRAVERS: Johnnie, I don't like making you stay after school and bringing you to the principal's office again but— (*Breaking off as she looks toward desk*) Oh, Mr. Bowman isn't here. He must have stepped out for a minute, but you'll just have to wait for him. (*Motioning*) Sit in one of those chairs.

JOHNNIE: Yes, I know. That's where I always sit . . . But Miss Travers, you don't understand. I can't stay after school today—I just can't. I've got a very important engagement. I was to meet someone at Jenkins Sweet Shoppe.

MISS TRAVERS: You'll just have to apologize to Sue.

JOHNNIE: Oh . . . How did you know?

MISS TRAVERS: I didn't know, Johnnie, but just because I'm a teacher I'm not deaf, dumb and blind. And you should have thought of your engagement before you misbehaved in history class. (*Pulling heart-shaped valentine from envelope*) This valentine had no connection with the Wars of the Roses.

JOHNNIE: I know, Miss Travers, but I was looking at it. I was trying to think what to write on it. And the Wars of the Roses kept reminding me of roses are red, violets are blue—

MISS TRAVERS: And so when I asked you what we'd been talking about, you recited that silly verse.

JOHNNIE: It *is* a silly verse—gee, I couldn't even use it on the valentine.

MISS TRAVERS (*Looking at valentine*): The valentine has a very nice printed verse already. It wasn't necessary to think of another one.

JOHNNIE: But you don't understand, Miss Travers. I wanted to write something personal on it. A girl expects—

MISS TRAVERS: Then you should have written it before my history class.

JOHNNIE: But Miss Travers, it was my last class and I was desperate. I was going to meet Sue and I hadn't given her a valentine yet—

MISS TRAVERS: Well, I'm very sorry, Johnnie, that I had to take it away from you. But now I'll have to ask you to give it to Mr. Bowman. You show it to him. He'll have to know what foolishness you were up to when you should have been concentrating on history.

JOHNNIE: But that's *ancient* history, Miss Travers. My life, that's history in the making. If I don't meet Sue—

MISS TRAVERS (*Trying not to smile*): As I said, I'm very sorry, Johnnie, but you'll just have to wait for Mr. Bowman. I must go now, but I know I can trust you.

JOHNNIE (*Sadly*): Yeah, it's too bad, but I guess you can, Miss Travers.

MISS TRAVERS (*Slipping valentine back in envelope and handing it to him*): And show him the valentine. And tell him you're to study your history—all the assignments on the Wars of the Roses.

JOHNNIE: O.K. (*He goes and sits down in one of the chairs near desk and* MISS TRAVERS *goes out left.* JOHNNIE *sighs. He pulls the valentine out of the envelope and looks at it.*) Women . . . They cause more trouble. (*He shoves it back in the envelope.* MR. BOWMAN *enters left, stops as he sees* JOHNNIE. JOHNNIE *rises*) Hello, Mr. Bowman. I'm here again.

MR. BOWMAN (*As he goes to his desk*): So I see.

JOHNNIE: Miss Travers brought me in.

MR. BOWMAN (*Smiling*): Miss Travers? Oh, Miss Travers was in. Well . . . well.

JOHNNIE: Yes, she said I'm to stay here and study my history

—oh, and she said to give you this. (*He hands envelope to* Mr. Bowman.)

Mr. Bowman: Oh? (*He takes envelope and opens it.*)

Johnnie: Yeah, Miss Travers said—

Mr. Bowman (*Looking at heart*): Why—why—this—this is a valentine!

Johnnie: Yes, Mr. Bowman. You see—

Mr. Bowman (*Reading verse*): My heart is yours, forever thine,

Won't you be my valentine?

(*Excitedly. Up in the clouds*) Why, this is wonderful! Wonderful! Isn't that a beautiful verse?

Johnnie: Yes, it is nice, isn't it? (*Noticing* Mr. Bowman *has stuffed the valentine into his pocket*) But are you going to keep the valentine?

Mr. Bowman: Why, certainly I'm going to keep it. Of course I'm going to keep it. (*Rising from desk in a daze*) And you'll have to excuse me—I've got an errand—a very important errand. I'll have to go out.

Johnnie: But Mr. Bowman, didn't you hear me say that I had to stay after school?

Mr. Bowman: What's that?

Johnnie: Yes, I told you. Miss Travers wants me to stay in here and—

Mr. Bowman: Dear me. Then I suppose I'll have to stay too.

Johnnie: Yes. You see, I wasn't concentrating on my history so she brought me in here to you—

Mr. Bowman: Then you're under my supervision, Johnnie, aren't you? Maybe you could run the errand for me.

Johnnie: Well, gee, I'd be glad to, Mr. Bowman, but I hope it doesn't take too long.

Mr. Bowman: No, this is just around the corner. Jenkins Sweet Shoppe.

JOHNNIE: Jenkins Sweet Shoppe? Gee, Mr. Bowman, that's where I'm supposed to be right now if I hadn't got into trouble.

MR. BOWMAN: Oh? Well, you run over there— (*Taking bill from his wallet*) Here, take this five dollars—

JOHNNIE: Yes, Mr. Bowman.

MR. BOWMAN: And buy the big box of candy—it's heart-shaped —the biggest one they have.

JOHNNIE: Yes, Mr. Bowman.

MR. BOWMAN: Have Mr. Jenkins wrap it up nicely and bring it back here to me.

JOHNNIE: Yes, Mr. Bowman.

CURTAIN

* * *

SCENE 2

SETTING: *Jenkins Sweet Shoppe.*

AT RISE: SUE, DOROTHY *and* HELEN, *three girls of about sixteen, are seated at one of the tables. Two of them have sundaes and one is sipping a soft drink.* MR. JENKINS *is back of the counter straightening up things.*

SUE: I just can't understand what's happened to Johnnie. He was supposed to meet me here right after school.

DOROTHY: Stop fuming, Sue. Johnnie's always late. Look at the valentine Bill gave me—isn't it gorgeous? (*She displays a fancy valentine.*)

HELEN: Did you see what Charlie sent me? (*She holds up a pretty valentine*) And that's not all. I think he's getting me a corsage for the party tonight.

DOROTHY: What did you get from Johnnie, Sue?

SUE: Nothing, yet. That's what worrying me. But I sort of had an idea he might be going to buy me something here.

DOROTHY: Oh, Sue, wouldn't it be wonderful if he got you that big heart-shaped box of candy? (*They all look toward the candy counter.*)

SUE: I've been thinking about that. Oh, I'd give anything to have it.

HELEN: Don't get your hopes up, Sue. No boy we know would have that much money.

SUE: Johnnie might have saved up—and he said so especially that he wanted to meet me here.

HELEN: But he always meets you here.

SUE: Just the same, he might get it. (*She calls to* MR. JEN-KINS) Oh, Mr. Jenkins, you haven't sold that big heart, have you?

MR. JENKINS: Well, I can't rightly say I have and I can't rightly say I haven't, Miss Sue.

SUE: My goodness. You mean you're holding it for someone?

MR. JENKINS: I couldn't say that either. Let me put it this way. I got someone interested. Yes, sir. Someone's mighty interested.

SUE: Did you hear that, girls? You—you couldn't tell us who it was, could you, Mr. Jenkins?

MR. JENKINS (*Wiping counter*): No, can't mention no names —that wouldn't be fittin', but this certain party, well, he's been inquirin' about it—

HELEN: Oh, Sue, isn't this exciting?

DOROTHY: It must be Johnnie.

SUE: Do you really think this—this certain party's going to buy it, Mr. Jenkins?

MR. JENKINS: Well, mebbe, yes, mebbe no. 'Course I realize it's an expensive item. Lots of fellows been askin' about it, but when I tell 'em the price, they just go out lookin' sad. As I say, though, this certain party—mentionin' no names of course—he's really interested.

SUE (*To girls*) : Oh my, wouldn't it be perfectly super? I'm just so excited. I can't wait for Johnnie to come. (BILL and CHARLIE, *boys about sixteen, enter right and come toward table. The girls are all smiles at the sight of them, except for* SUE.)

BILL: Hi, gals.

DOROTHY: Bill!

HELEN: Charlie!

CHARLIE: How are you doing, Helen? H'llo, Dorothy. H'llo, Sue. (*They pull chairs over and sit down at table.*)

SUE: Charlie, where's Johnnie? Didn't he come with you?

CHARLIE: Johnnie had to stay after school. (*Calling*) Say, Mr. Jenkins. How about a couple of cokes?

MR. JENKINS: Coming right up.

SUE: Johnnie had to stay after school today when he was supposed to meet me?

BILL: Sure. I guess Miss Travers took him to Mr. Bowman's office.

SUE (*Getting angry*) : Well! If he doesn't care enough about meeting me to stay out of trouble just once—

DOROTHY: I don't see how anyone could get into trouble with Miss Travers. She's one of the nicest teachers we've ever had.

HELEN: And so pretty and sweet.

BILL: Sure, but you see Johnnie was fooling around in class. He was—

SUE: I don't care what he was doing—I've a good mind to go on home.

DOROTHY: Oh, Sue. (MR. JENKINS *brings over two glasses with straws and sets them on table.*)

MR. JENKINS: Here are your cokes.

BILL: O.K., Mr. Jenkins. (BILL *and* CHARLIE *hand coins to* MR. JENKINS, *and he goes back behind the counter and rings money up on cash register.* JOHNNIE *enters right, hurriedly.*)

CHARLIE: Sue, look—here's Johnnie now.

SUE: Johnnie!

JOHNNIE (*Embarrassedly*): Hello, everybody—

SUE: Johnnie, what do you mean by being so late?

JOHNNIE: Gee, I'm sorry, Sue. I couldn't help it, but I haven't got much time now. (*He starts to cross toward counter.*)

SUE: *You* haven't got much time? Well, I like that. You keep me waiting and waiting—

JOHNNIE (*Hesitating*): I know—I said I was sorry.

SUE: And you haven't even given me a valentine.

JOHNNIE: I know. I would have had one for you but something happened—

SUE: That's just too bad. Well, if you don't care about a date with me, I don't care about a date with you. I'm not going to the party with you tonight. (*She rises.*)

JOHNNIE: Sue, listen, don't say that. You've got to go to the party—we're going to have a lot of fun—

SUE (*Preparing to leave*): You'll have it without me.

JOHNNIE: But Sue, wait—

SUE: I've waited all I'm going to wait for you.

JOHNNIE: Sue, I—I can explain everything but we'll have to talk later. I've got something very important to do right now—

SUE: Oh, you have? Well, so have I. I'm going home.

JOHNNIE: Oh, for gosh sakes. (*He walks over to counter as* SUE *starts to leave*) Mr. Jenkins, I want to buy that big box of candy— (*He goes to downstage end of counter*) This one right here. (*The boys and girls at table turn and stare.* SUE *stops.*)

HELEN: Sue, did you hear that? (SUE *starts to smile and crosses to counter.*)

MR. JENKINS: Well—well—well. Have you got the money for it, Johnnie?

JOHNNIE: Sure. (*Pulling five-dollar bill from his pocket*) Here it is, Mr. Jenkins. And will you wrap it up kind of pretty, please?

MR. JENKINS: I certainly will, my boy. This here's a fine present for someone. (*He starts wrapping candy.*)

SUE (*Touching* JOHNNIE'S *arm, all smiles*): Oh, Johnnie, to think I could have been angry with you—

JOHNNIE (*Turning, surprised*): Sue . . . you mean you aren't angry any more?

SUE: Of course I'm not.

JOHNNIE: Boy, I'm glad you changed your mind.

MR. JENKINS (*Still wrapping*): I'll have it ready in a minute, Johnnie.

SUE: Oh, Johnnie, you're wonderful, you're just wonderful!

JOHNNIE: I—I am?

MR. JENKINS (*Handing box of candy to* JOHNNIE *and then ringing money up on cash register*): Here you are.

SUE (*Taking box of candy from* JOHNNIE): Of course you're wonderful. To think all along you planned to get me this wonderful heart!

JOHNNIE (*Trying to get it back*): But Sue, wait—you don't understand—

SUE (*Hugging heart to her*): Of course I understand. You didn't want me to know—you wanted to walk over to the table and surprise me—but I guessed right away.

HELEN: Oh, Sue, it's just super!

DOROTHY: It's the most gorgeous valentine any girl ever had.

MR. JENKINS: You've got right good taste, Johnnie. Miss Sue, I wouldn't be surprised if you've got the finest box of candy to be had in this whole town. Yes, sir, a mighty fine present it is.

SUE: It's wonderful, Mr. Jenkins. Oh, Johnnie—

JOHNNIE: Sue, listen, you've got to let me explain—

SUE: Johnnie, you don't have to. It doesn't matter about your being late or anything now.

JOHNNIE: But about that heart—

SUE: I love it! I just love it! I've never had such a wonderful present in all my life. (MISS TRAVERS *enters right wearing hat and coat now. She carries a large white envelope.* JOHNNIE *and* SUE *are downstage near counter so she doesn't see them right away. The other boys and girls smile at her.*)

CHARLIE, BILL, DOROTHY *and* HELEN: Hello, Miss Travers. How are you, Miss Travers?

MISS TRAVERS (*Smiling at them*): Hello, everyone. (*She walks toward counter*) Mr. Jenkins, do you carry stamps in here? I have something that should be mailed and I didn't want to go to the post office—

MR. JENKINS: Well, guess now I could oblige you, Miss Travers.

JOHNNIE (*Turning*): Miss Travers. . . . Oh, boy!

MR. JENKINS (*Going on*): I always keep a few stamps in the cash register—

MISS TRAVERS (*Seeing* JOHNNIE): Why Johnnie—Johnnie, what are you doing here? You're supposed to be staying after school. (*She comes downstage to* JOHNNIE *and* SUE.)

JOHNNIE: Gee, Miss Travers, I know, but I had to come and buy a box of candy—

MISS TRAVERS (*Seeing* SUE *holding the box of candy*): You're in here buying valentines when I sent you to the principal's office?

SUE: Oh, Miss Travers, please—don't be angry with Johnnie. It *is* Valentine's Day and you see, he'd planned to buy me this big heart—

MISS TRAVERS: Johnnie, I'm certain that Mr. Bowman wouldn't have dismissed you as soon as this—

JOHNNIE: No, he didn't dismiss me, Miss Travers, but you see—

MISS TRAVERS: Then you skipped out.

JOHNNIE: No—no, I didn't. That is—

MISS TRAVERS: You must have, and I thought I could trust you. Johnnie, this is serious.

SUE: Oh, Miss Travers, don't be too hard on him.

MISS TRAVERS: I don't want to be hard on him at all, but I'm afraid we'll have to call Mr. Bowman and let him know—

JOHNNIE: Oh, no, please—don't do that, Miss Travers.

MISS TRAVERS: You and I will have to have a talk, Johnnie. You'll have to explain—

SUE: I—I guess I'd better be going then. But oh, Miss Travers, try to understand how it is on Valentine's Day. And Johnnie, I just love the candy. Thanks so much.

JOHNNIE: But Sue, wait, you can't go.

SUE: But Miss Travers wants to talk to you, Johnnie. And I've got to get home anyway and get my dress ready for the party tonight. Wait till you see it, Johnnie. (*She smiles at him and then stops at table where others are.*) Are you kids coming?

HELEN: Yes. I guess we'd better be going too.

BILL: I'm finished. . . . Come along, Charlie. (*They all rise and start toward door.* JOHNNIE *looks after them desperately.*)

SUE: Goodbye, Johnnie. I'll see you tonight.

JOHNNIE: But Sue— (*He gives up, his shoulders slumping.*)

CHARLIE (*As they start out door*): Boy, I hope Johnnie isn't in trouble.

DOROTHY: I do, too—oh, Sue—that wonderful heart. I just can't believe it.

SUE: I can't either. I'm so happy. (*They all exit right.*)

MISS TRAVERS (*Crossing to one of tables*): Now, Johnnie,

maybe you'll explain to me. Do you want to sit down at the table here?

JOHNNIE (*Sadly*): I don't care—all right, Miss Travers. (*He pulls out a chair for her and seats her with her back toward the door, then sits down opposite her.*)

MR. JENKINS (*Coming over, worriedly*): Miss Travers, I s'pose I shouldn't be buttin' in. I know you're a teacher and teachers have got to have rules—but I've been runnin' this place here near the school a long time and seen a lot of young folks come in and out, and by and large they ain't so bad.

MISS TRAVERS: Of course they're not, Mr. Jenkins.

MR. JENKINS (*Putting arm on* JOHNNIE'S *shoulder*): And Johnnie here—well, I've known him since he was knee high to a grasshopper—and he's a mighty fine boy even if he don't use his head much sometimes.

MISS TRAVERS: I'm sure you're right, Mr. Jenkins. Thank you you for telling me. (MR. JENKINS *goes back to counter shaking his head*) Johnnie, the thing that bothers me is this. I thought I could trust you.

JOHNNIE: But you can, Miss Travers. You don't understand what happened. Oh, gosh, what am I going to do? I'm in the worst jam—

MISS TRAVERS: Oh, now, it's not as bad as all that.

JOHNNIE: It's worse—it's much worse.

MISS TRAVERS: Then why did you skip out in the first place?

JOHNNIE: But I didn't. I'm trying to tell you. Mr. Bowman sent me over here on an errand—

MISS TRAVERS: Mr. Bowman? On an errand?

JOHNNIE: Yes. He sent me over to buy that big box of candy.

MISS TRAVERS: But why would Mr. Bowman do that?

JOHNNIE: Why does any fellow want to buy a box of candy, Miss Travers? I suppose he wanted to give it to some girl.

MISS TRAVERS (*Coolly now*): To a girl. I see. Well, I must say—

JOHNNIE: Sure, and while I was buying it Sue came over and she thought the candy was for her—and I couldn't get it away from her. What am I going to do now? The candy is gone —and the five dollars is gone and what am I going to tell Mr. Bowman? (MR. BOWMAN *enters right wearing hat and coat.*)

MR. BOWMAN: Johnnie, I was beginning to wonder what happened to you— (JOHNNIE *rises startled.* MR. BOWMAN *breaks off as he sees* MISS TRAVERS. *He takes off his hat, smiling, a little embarrassed.*) Why, Miss Travers— Mary . . .

MISS TRAVERS: Mr. Bowman.

MR. BOWMAN: Did you get the candy all right, Johnnie—or was it gone?

JOHNNIE: It's gone all right, Mr. Bowman, but—

MISS TRAVERS (*Interrupting*): Mr. Bowman, I recognize that you're the principal of Plainview High School, and I suppose I shouldn't say this, but when I send a boy into your office I don't think you should dispatch him on a foolish errand. (JOHNNIE *steps upstage a little not quite knowing what to do.* MR. BOWMAN *steps opposite* MISS TRAVERS.)

MR. BOWMAN: But Miss Travers—Mary—it wasn't a foolish errand—it was very important. You see, I wanted a particular box of candy for a particular young lady—

MISS TRAVERS: I'm not interested in whom you wanted it for, Mr. Bowman.

MR. BOWMAN: But I—I thought you would be. When you sent me that valentine—

MISS TRAVERS: I sent you a valentine? What are you talking about?

MR. BOWMAN (*Pulling valentine from pocket*): Why—why this. It says: My heart is yours, forever thine, Won't you be **my** valentine?

MISS TRAVERS: Ohhh—ohh—and you thought I sent—why, that's Johnnie's valentine. He was going to give it to Sue. Johnnie, didn't you explain to Mr. Bowman?

JOHNNIE: Gee, I tried to, but nobody ever lets me explain anything.

MISS TRAVERS: Mr. Bowman, how could you think that I'd give you a valentine with a verse like that on it? Johnnie was concentrating on this valentine instead of his history so I told him to give it to you, to show you what foolishness he'd been up to.

MR. BOWMAN: I guess Johnnie isn't the only one. You're right, Miss Travers. I did send him on a foolish errand. You see, I wanted that big heart box for you.

MISS TRAVERS: For me? You wanted it for me? Oh, Phillip. I mean Mr. Bowman—

MR. BOWMAN: Yes, but of course you aren't interested in valentines.

MISS TRAVERS: Oh, but I am. (*She rises, holding out her envelope*) Look, in spite of all I said I *was* sending you a valentine. (*She hands it to him.*)

MR. BOWMAN (*Looking at it surprised*): Why, it's—it's addressed to me. (*He opens it and looks at it. Then smiling*) From Guess Who.

MISS TRAVERS: Yes, it's not very grammatical, but I didn't want you to know it was from me.

MR. BOWMAN: Why on earth not?

MISS TRAVERS: I didn't think you'd be interested. For weeks you've been acting so standoffish—

MR. BOWMAN: *I've* been standoffish? I asked you to have dinner with me and you turned me down—then I saw you out with Professor Green—

MISS TRAVERS: But he'd asked me first and I had to be fair to him. I kept hoping you'd ask me again—

MR. BOWMAN: How I wanted to—but I was afraid— (*He breaks off*) Ah, well, Mary—everything's all right now.

MISS TRAVERS: It certainly is . . . Oh, Phillip, to think you bought me that lovely big candy heart—

JOHNNIE (*Interrupting*): But Miss Travers, have you forgotten? Sue's got it.

MISS TRAVERS (*Turning to* JOHNNIE *and laughing*): So she has.

JOHNNIE: But it isn't anything to laugh about . . . Gee, I feel terrible, Mr. Bowman. I was buying the heart and then Sue thought it was for her and now she's got it and your five dollars is gone. I—I can save up and pay you back—

MR. BOWMAN: Oh, I don't think that will be necessary. If you'll just let me keep this valentine— (*He holds up original heart intended for* SUE) buy it from you—

JOHNNIE: Well, that's all right, Mr. Bowman, but it only cost a quarter.

MR. BOWMAN: It's been worth five dollars to me. In fact, a great deal more than that.

JOHNNIE: Yes, but Miss Travers still hasn't got any heart—

MR. BOWMAN: I know she hasn't, but I think I can find one to give her in its place if she'll have it.

MISS TRAVERS: Oh, Phillip. (MR. BOWMAN *leans over as though he is going to kiss her. Then he remembers* JOHNNIE.)

MR. BOWMAN: Uh—Miss Travers, don't you suppose that Johnnie has stayed after school long enough?

MISS TRAVERS (*Smiling*): Yes, I think he has.

MR. BOWMAN: Johnnie, you may be excused.

JOHNNIE: Excused? (*Light dawning*) Oh, you mean excused. (*Grinning as he goes out right*) Well, *excuse* me.

MR. BOWMAN (*Putting hand on* MISS TRAVERS' *shoulder*): Now, Mary—to return to this business of the hearts—yours and mine— (*A little embarrassed,* Miss Travers *looks toward* Mr. Jenkins.)

Mr. Jenkins (*Smiling*) : Don't mind me, you two. You're not the first couple I've caught kissing in here and don't worry— I never report them to the principal.

THE END

A Date with Washington

Characters

LEWIS HENDERSON, *father* JUNIOR HENDERSON
CORA HENDERSON, *mother* BRUCE CAMERON
MARY HENDERSON

TIME: *Washington's Birthday. Late afternoon.*
SETTING: *The Henderson living room.*
AT RISE: MOTHER *is seated on sofa sewing on a party dress.*
FATHER *enters left smiling and holding out a newspaper.*

FATHER: Well—well, our daughter's picture in the newspaper!
What do you think of that? Quite a splurge.

MOTHER (*Smiling too*): Yes, isn't it?

FATHER: Oh, you've seen the paper?

MOTHER: Yes, I got one this afternoon. It's on the table there.
(*She indicates paper on table at left.*) It *is* exciting. (*She
puts dress down on sofa and crosses to* FATHER.)

FATHER (*Still holding out paper*): Look at that. Mary Henderson, winner of George Washington Essay Contest. Girl of fifteen writes brilliant theme on the Father of our Country.

MOTHER (*Looking too*): And isn't it a nice picture?

FATHER: Certainly is. Fine picture—fine-looking girl. Smart
as they come. I tell you—

MOTHER: Now, Lewis, it's all right to be proud—

FATHER: Why, of course I'm proud. I tell you George Washington has nothing on me. He was the Father of our Coun-

302

try but I'm the father of Mary Henderson. (MOTHER *laughs.* MARY, *a pretty girl of fifteen, enters.*)

MOTHER: Mary dear, we were just talking about you.

FATHER: I should say we were. Admiring your publicity.

MOTHER: Admiring is hardly the word. Your father's been boasting his head off.

FATHER: Why not? (*Pinching* MARY'S *cheek*) And how do you feel about it?

MARY (*Not too enthusiastically*): It's fine. Wonderful. But Mom, have there been any phone calls for me?

MOTHER: No, dear, not yet— (*She goes to sofa and holds up party dress.*) But look at your dress. I'm just putting the finishing touches on it.

MARY: It's lovely—but what good will a pretty dress do me?

MOTHER: Now, don't you worry, Mary. You'll be the guest of honor and you'll have a good time.

MARY: How can I? (*She almost starts to cry*) Oh, Mom. (*She runs off right.*)

FATHER (*Staring after her*): What on earth is the matter with her?

MOTHER: Shh-h—

FATHER: But has she been working too hard—is she overtired? Has all this been too much for her?

MOTHER: No, dear. It's nothing like that.

FATHER: But she ought to be the happiest girl in town. An honor like this.

MOTHER: I know, Lewis, but she has to attend the Washington's Birthday party tonight because she's the guest of honor—and she hasn't an escort.

FATHER: She hasn't? Why not?

MOTHER: Well—because none of the boys has asked her.

FATHER: Not asked her? A pretty girl like Mary. (*He points to paper*) Why, look at that picture.

MOTHER: Yes, I know, but Mary is so brilliant in her studies—

FATHER: What's that got to do with it? All the more reason—

MOTHER: Lewis, you know boys. Men too for that matter. They shy away from women who know as much as they do.

FATHER: Nonsense. I never heard of—

MOTHER: Oh, yes, you have. Remember the first time you asked me for a date? Then you found out I had all A's on my report and you tried to get out of it.

FATHER: Cora, I did not. I don't remember anything about it—

MOTHER: No? Well, perhaps not, but I do, and boys are just the same today. And besides that, Mary is shy—she hasn't learned how to manage boys yet.

FATHER: Manage, humph.

MOTHER: Well, they do have to be managed, dear. (*She smiles at him*) Men, too. (JUNIOR, *a boy about sixteen, enters left wearing jacket, carrying hockey stick, and with a pair of skates slung over his shoulder. As he enters he leans the hockey stick against the wall near the door.*)

JUNIOR: Hi, Mom—hi, Dad.

FATHER: Hello, son. Enjoying the holiday?

JUNIOR: Yeah. I'm all in favor of George Washington. We ought to celebrate his birthday every day. Boy, did we have a game of hockey!

FATHER: Junior, is the living room the best place for a hockey stick?

JUNIOR: Why, I don't know, Dad—when it's a good hockey stick—

FATHER: And I take it, that is a good one?

JUNIOR: You ought to know—you gave it to me—and just this afternoon down at the pond a new fellow—he's only been in school a few days—offered to swap me his stick and three dollars to boot.

FATHER: Hmm, very interesting.

JUNIOR: It was a good offer all right, but I said no. (*He starts to put his skates on chair left.*)

MOTHER: Now, don't put your skates on the chair, Junior.

JUNIOR: O.K., Mom. (*He drops them to floor and then takes off his jacket and throws it over back of chair left. As he does so he notices paper on the table*) I see you got the paper. Mary got quite a write-up, didn't she?

MOTHER: Yes. This ought to be a happy time for her and I'm afraid it's all going to be spoiled because of that party.

JUNIOR: Nobody's asked her yet, huh?

MOTHER: No.

FATHER: Too bad. Too bad. What's your explanation of it, son?

JUNIOR: Well, I tell you, Dad. Sis is all right but she's too darned smart.

FATHER: Of course she is. Takes after her father.

JUNIOR: Gee, I always heard Mom was the one who got the good grades.

FATHER: Well—

MOTHER: Now, Junior, grades or no grades, everyone always speaks of your father as a very brilliant man.

JUNIOR (*Grinning*): Yeah? I always thought I was like Dad and Mary took after you, Mom. Anyhow, Mary just scares the fellows off. She's too standoffish. If she'd go up to a fellow sometimes and say, "Hi ya, Toots"—

MOTHER: My goodness, is that what you have to do?

JUNIOR: Sure—unbend a little. And if *one* of the boys started to notice her, they all would. She's not bad-looking—

FATHER: Bad-looking? She's beautiful.

JUNIOR: Sure. She could be a regular glamour-puss if she put her mind to it.

FATHER: Humph, glamour-puss. Well, can't you do something, son? You know all the boys.

JUNIOR: Gee, Dad, I've tried—even about the party tonight. I've hinted around, but it's just no soap.

MOTHER (*With a sigh*): Well, then, Junior, there's only one thing to do. *You'll* have to take Mary to the party.

JUNIOR: But Mom, I'm taking Betty Gibson.

MOTHER: I know, but you'll have to take Mary too.

JUNIOR: Oh, for gosh sakes. What would Betty think? I can't do it, Mom—I just can't.

MOTHER: But the party's in honor of Mary—that is, in honor of Mary and George Washington.

JUNIOR: Sure, and wouldn't we be a cosy little foursome? Betty and me and Mary and George Washington.

FATHER: Son, this is no time for funny remarks.

JUNIOR: There's nothing funny about it. It's serious. I can't take my kid sister—

MOTHER: Either that, Junior, or you'll have to think of something else. I'm not going to have Mary attend that party alone.

JUNIOR: Oh, for gosh sakes. (*He slumps into chair right, frowning.*)

FATHER: Well, now that's settled, perhaps I can look at the rest of the paper. (*He opens paper to middle sheet and sits down on left end of sofa, pushing dress a little as he does so.*)

MOTHER: Be careful of that dress, Lewis—and I'd better finish it. (*She sits down on right end of sofa and starts sewing. There is a pause.*)

JUNIOR (*Sitting up straight. An idea has dawned*): Listen, I've got an idea—it's wonderful. I don't know why I didn't think of it before. (MOTHER *stops sewing and* FATHER *looks up from over his paper.*)

MOTHER: What is it, son?

JUNIOR: Well, look—this new fellow—the one I met at the pond this afternoon—Bruce Cameron his name is—

FATHER: You mean he might take Mary to the party? But do they know each other?

JUNIOR: No—no, of course they don't. He doesn't really know any of the kids yet. But if I can get him over here—and Mary plays her cards right—I'll coach her—

MOTHER: Now, wait a minute, Junior.

JUNIOR: But Mom, you said I had to do something.

MOTHER: I know, Junior, but there hardly seems time for such intrigue.

JUNIOR: Yeah, there isn't much time—but he only lives up the street and if I could just get him over here— (*Another idea dawning*) I know! Gee, I hate to do it but when a fellow's desperate—I will. I'll do it. (*He rises and starts right.*)

FATHER: Where are you going?

JUNIOR: I'm going to call Bruce Cameron up. I'll tell him if he comes over right away, I'll go through with his deal on the hockey stick.

MOTHER: But Junior—

JUNIOR: And listen, if you could get Mary in here—I want to talk to her before he gets here. (*He goes off right.*)

MOTHER: Lewis, I'm not sure I like this. After all, you gave him the hockey stick—

FATHER: Well, Cora, you gave him the ultimatum. (*Laughing a little*) If you women will push men into corners, they're apt to do desperate things.

MOTHER: Well, I don't like being an accomplice, but I guess I'd better get Mary in here. Besides her dress is finished. (*She rises carrying dress and goes toward right, calling*) Mary . . . Come look at your dress. (*Calling again*) Mary! (MARY *enters right still looking unhappy.*)

MARY: Yes, Mom?

MOTHER: Here's your dress, dear—all done. (*She holds it up to* MARY.)

MARY: It's beautiful. Thanks so much . . . (*She touches dress and then gives it back to* MOTHER) Oh, Mom, what will I do?

MOTHER: Now, Mary, don't worry. You're going to the party with Junior—or—or someone else.

MARY: Someone else?

MOTHER: Maybe. Junior has a friend coming over.

MARY: A friend? You mean he called someone up and told them I didn't have a date?

MOTHER: No, dear, of course not—

MARY: Well, then, what has he done? What's going on? I guess I've got a right to know. (JUNIOR *enters right.*)

JUNIOR: Hi, Sis.

MARY: Junior, what have you been up to?

JUNIOR: Now, take it easy. You know that new fellow in school?

MARY: Yes, I've seen him. All the girls have been talking about him. He's so good looking. (MOTHER *goes back to the sofa and sits down.*)

JUNIOR: Well, I met him this afternoon—his name's Bruce Cameron. And he'll be over here in just a few minutes now.

MARY: He'll be here? Junior, what did you tell him about me?

JUNIOR: Not a thing—I didn't even tell him I had a sister. He's coming over on private business. But I know he hasn't got a date for the party tonight.

MARY: And I suppose the minute he sees me he'll ask me.

JUNIOR: Not right away maybe but I'll introduce you and it's up to you to do the rest—

MARY: Junior, it isn't fair getting a boy over here and pushing him into—

JUNIOR: You won't be pushing him into anything. He'll like you —he'll want to take you to the party if you act right. Now, listen, just for once, be smart and act dumb.

MARY: Dumb?

JUNIOR: Sure—and whatever you do, don't let him know you're

the one who won that essay contest. His folks are new in town—they may not buy the paper yet. We hope not anyhow.

MARY: I don't go around bragging.

JUNIOR: Of course you don't, but you're apt to start talking about how Washington crossed the Delaware—

MARY: No, I wouldn't. I didn't even mention that in my essay. My main effort was to paint Washington's real character so that people of today might realize—

JUNIOR: Yes, yes, but don't talk about that either. You know how the other girls talk.

MARY: I know but—

JUNIOR: Give it the light touch—come up with a wise crack now and then. Hum a little from a hot song maybe— (*He hums a snatch of tune ending with some da de das*) and then go into a dance step.

MARY: But Junior, I'd feel silly.

JUNIOR: Why? The boys eat it up. And if things are going kind of slow and he doesn't seem to know what to say, pull something like this. (*He looks off into space for a moment for inspiration and then grabs* MARY *by the arm*) Come on, don't be a sad sack all your life. Let's cut a rug! (*He dances her around a few steps, and then stops*) You can do it.

MARY: Well, I—I could try.

JUNIOR: Sure, you can. You've got to play up to the boys. Know how to handle 'em. Why—why, look at Mom. If she can do it, you can. (FATHER *jumps and looks startled.*)

MOTHER: Junior, what on earth are you talking about? If you're insinuating that I ever carried on in any such manner—

JUNIOR: No, Mom, but you know how to keep Dad happy. Aren't you always telling him how smart he is?

FATHER (*Rising and stalking right*): Well, this is too much. I shall go elsewhere and read my paper. (*He turns and glares*) And perhaps chew up a rug. (*He exits.*)

JUNIOR: Poor Dad.

MOTHER (*Rising and shaking her head*): Well, I don't know. Mary, I've got to press this dress a little.

MARY: I could do it, Mom.

MOTHER: No—no, you stay here with Junior. (*She goes out right still shaking her head a little.*)

JUNIOR: Listen, Mary, this is the way we'll work things. I've got three brand-new records in the rumpus room. You just mention them and he'll want to hear them—

MARY: Do you think so?

JUNIOR: Sure. Then we'll take him down there. And those records are hot stuff. Right away he'll want to dance. And that may remind him of the party tonight. If it doesn't you steer the conversation around—

MARY: Junior, do you really think I can?

JUNIOR: Sure—and just think, Mary—the new boy in school. Think of the rest of the girls when you walk in there tonight with Bruce Cameron. (MARY *smiles and the doorbell rings off*) There he is. Now, don't forget, Mary. (JUNIOR *goes off left.* MARY *pats her hair and straightens her dress nervously. She picks up a heavy textbook from table right and starts reading, then quickly puts it down and picks up a picture magazine.* JUNIOR *enters with* BRUCE CAMERON, *a tall nice-looking boy of about his own age.* BRUCE *wears jacket and carries a hockey stick.*)

JUNIOR: Enter the Henderson castle, Bruce. Make yourself at home.

BRUCE: Thank you. Nice to be here. I haven't had a chance to talk to many of the fellows.

JUNIOR: Nor the girls either, I guess . . . Oh—Mary, this is Bruce Cameron . . . Bruce, this is my sister, Mary.

MARY (*Shyly. She puts her magazine down*): How do you do?

(*Then somewhat nervously trying to act her part*) I mean hi —hi ya, Bruce.

BRUCE (*Smiling at her*): Hello, Mary.

MARY (*Rather low. Trying*): Well—uh—shed your coat, won't you? We're no eskimos.

BRUCE (*Not understanding*): Pardon me?

MARY: I said—won't you take off your coat?

BRUCE: Thanks. (*He leans hockey stick against back of chair, takes off his jacket and throws it on top of* JUNIOR'S.)

MARY (*Still trying, brightly*): I—I've heard a lot about you.

BRUCE: You have?

MARY: Yes. The girls—that is, the girls at school talk a lot about you.

BRUCE: They do? But they don't know me.

MARY: No, I guess not, but—but— (*Getting more fussed*) Junior, didn't you have some business to transact?

JUNIOR (*Giving her a disgusted look*): Oh, yes, I guess we might as well take care of that. (JUNIOR *gets his hockey stick from against wall,* BRUCE *fishes out three dollars from his pocket and hands it to* JUNIOR.)

BRUCE: It's my last three bucks but it's worth it. (*He takes the stick from* JUNIOR *and examines it admiringly.*)

MARY (*Surprised*): Junior, are you selling your hockey stick?

JUNIOR: Not exactly. I'm swapping it for this one— (*He indicates stick* BRUCE *brought in*)—with three dollars to boot. (*He pockets the money.*)

MARY: But Junior—I don't understand—

JUNIOR: There's nothing to understand, Mary. It's a good deal. We're both satisfied, aren't we, Bruce?

BRUCE: I certainly am. (*Smiling, looking at his stick*) Say, I wonder if it's too late to go back to the pond again—

JUNIOR (*Quickly*): Oh, it's much too late. Besides we want you to stay here a while, don't we, Mary?

MARY: Why, yes, we'd like—I mean we'd love it.

JUNIOR: We've got a swell rumpus room downstairs—with a ping pong table and a record player— (*He looks at* MARY *meaningly.*)

MARY (*Getting into action again suddenly*): And three new hot records!

JUNIOR: Come on down and look it over, Bruce.

BRUCE: Well—fine—I'd like to. (*He places hockey stick across table near chair at left and on top of the newspaper*) Oh—is this a good newspaper? Dad wants to subscribe to one—

JUNIOR (*Nervously*): Yeah, that's a good rag all right but you don't want to look at that now. Come on.

BRUCE: O.K. (*He starts right following* MARY *and* JUNIOR. JUNIOR *nudges* MARY.)

MARY: Do you—do you dance, Bruce?

BRUCE: Oh, I try to.

JUNIOR: Try? I'll bet he's a whizz.

BRUCE (*Looking a little worried*): Well, no, I—I really am not very good. (*There is a slight pause and* JUNIOR *nudges* MARY *again.*)

MARY (*Making a big effort*): Oh, come on, big boy, don't be a sad sack all your life. Let's cut a rug! (*She grabs his arm and they exit right.* JUNIOR *smilingly follows them off. There is a pause. After a moment* FATHER *sticks his head in at right, then seeing no one, enters still carrying his newpaper. He sits down on sofa as* MOTHER *enters right.*)

MOTHER: Did the young man get here, Lewis?

FATHER: Well, I'm no detective but— (*He points to jacket on chair*) there's an extra coat— (*He points to hockey stick*) and an extra hockey stick— (*The music starts off right*) and a lot of bad music from the room downstairs—what do you think?

MOTHER: Why, yes—yes, they must be down there. Well, Mary's dress is all ready. I've laid it out on her bed. Oh dear, I hope everything works out all right. (*She sits on sofa too.*)

FATHER: Listen, Cora, any boy that doesn't appreciate Mary is crazy. I've been reading her essay in the paper here—it's wonderful. Why, the ideas that girl has—

MOTHER: I know, dear, but as Junior says, I don't think the boys would appreciate them.

FATHER: Well, anyway, I've learned more about George Washington than I ever knew before— (JUNIOR *enters.*)

JUNIOR: Shh-h—

FATHER: What's the matter, son?

JUNIOR: Don't mention George Washington. Mary's doing fine.

FATHER: Humph, as though she could hear me with that racket.

JUNIOR: But it might put a jinx on the whole set-up. She's doing everything I told her—

FATHER: You mean to say she's chewing the rug?

JUNIOR: Not chewing, Dad. Cutting. But honest, you ought to see Mary—she's snapping her fingers in time to the music and giving out with cute remarks—

MOTHER: Indeed? Is the young man enjoying it?

JUNIOR: Well, if I'm any judge. You can tell by the look on his face that he's never seen anyone like Mary before. (BRUCE *appears right. He looks wildly about and then starts directly across stage to door left.*)

BRUCE: Excuse me—I—I just remembered. I've got to go. I— I've got to get home— (*He grabs his jacket from chair.*)

JUNIOR: But you haven't even met my mother and father. Dad, Mother, this is Bruce Cameron.

MOTHER: How do you do, Bruce?

BRUCE: How do *you* do?—How are you?—Goodbye. (*He exits left putting on his coat as he goes. The music stops off.*)

MOTHER (*Staring after him*) : Well, of all things!

FATHER: What on earth was the matter with your friend, Junior?

JUNIOR: Search me. What do you suppose happened?

MOTHER: I can't imagine. Where's Mary?— (*She rises and starts for door right just as* MARY *appears crying*) Mary— Mary dear, you're crying.

MARY: Oh, Mom, it was terrible—

JUNIOR: But Sis, what's the matter?

MARY: He didn't like me—he didn't like me at all.

JUNIOR: Didn't like you? But when I left everything was going fine.

MARY: That's what you thought. Don't you ever dare to tell me how to act again! I can't do those things you said—I just can't. It isn't natural. Why, Bruce looked at me as though I were crazy—

MOTHER (*Patting* MARY'S *shoulder*) : Mary dear—

MARY: And now there's no chance that anyone will ask me to the party. Oh, I wish I were dead.

FATHER: Nonsense. (*Tapping his newspaper*) Any girl that can write a fine essay like this one—

MARY: Don't you mention that old essay to me—I wish I'd never written it—I wish I were dumb—

JUNIOR: Gee, Mary— (*The doorbell rings off left*) I'll go, Mom. (*He goes off left.*)

MOTHER: Now, Mary, stop crying. You can go to the party with Junior.

MARY: Mother, I don't want to go with Junior. (BRUCE *enters hurriedly followed by* JUNIOR.)

BRUCE: I'll get it, Junior. Er—excuse me for interrupting you again like this, but I—I forgot my hockey stick. (*He rushes in, grabs up the hockey stick and in so doing, knocks the newspaper on the floor. He is about to rush out again when* FATHER *loses his temper.*)

FATHER (*Rising*) : Now, wait a minute, young man—

BRUCE (*Stopping*) : Y-yes, sir.

FATHER : Do you realize what you just did?

BRUCE : No, sir.

FATHER : You knocked a picture of my daughter onto the floor.

BRUCE : I did?

FATHER : Yes, in that newspaper—and you'll be so kind as to pick it up.

BRUCE : Yes, sir. (*He stoops, picking up paper, then suddenly stares at it. Reading*) "Mary Henderson, winner of George Washington Essay contest"— (*Breaking off*) Why, Mary, that's you. You're not the girl who won that big contest?

MARY : Why—why, yes, I am. (FATHER *sits down again.*)

BRUCE : But—but—why, that's wonderful. I've been wanting to meet you—

MARY : You have?

BRUCE (*Looking at paper again*) : Of course. Anyone who could write a prize essay—but I—I just can't believe that you—

MARY : You mean you didn't think I had brains enough to write it? Well, I don't blame you after the way I acted.

JUNIOR : Gee, that was my fault, Bruce. I've been telling Mary she ought to act more like the other girls.

BRUCE : Oh, that was a mistake. Always let people be themselves. (*Looking at paper*) I see they've printed the whole essay— I'll want to read it. (*Scanning parts*) Say, this is fine. This bit here. (*Reading*) "Some have said that Washington will always remain a mystery as to his character, because he never wrote or talked about his own personal feelings. But perhaps this was because he was just not as interested in himself as he was in service to his country and his fellow man." (*He looks up*) That's really good.

MARY (*Smiling*): I'm glad you like it. Then I go on to tell how in spite of his high purpose he had a great faculty for enjoying life—especially his home—

BRUCE: I see you do . . . (*Scanning further*) And why—this part—I really go for this. Listen to this, will you? (*Reading*) "Some may ask, why read about Washington these days? Why study our early history? That time may seem far away and long ago, but there is much we can learn. The examples which great men like Washington set are guides for us today. In spite of all that our early heroes accomplished for our country, there is still more to be done. Our problems may be different now but we must attack them with the same courage and spirit of service—" (*He breaks off*) That's wonderful, isn't it? (*He puts paper back on table.*)

FATHER: Of course. What did I tell you, Cora? That essay is remarkable.

MOTHER: Yes, dear.

BRUCE: Mary, what you've written—it's so exactly the way I feel. Why, we've *got* to be interested in our country—especially we young people. We'll have to take over in a few years. You know, at Brown High School where I came from, I'd started some discussion groups on democracy, and a Junior Town meeting—I want to do some things like that here.

JUNIOR (*Who has been staring at* BRUCE): Gee, I—I didn't think you'd be interested in things like that.

BRUCE: Why not?

JUNIOR: Well, I don't know—you play a good game of hockey and you seem like a lot of fun—

BRUCE (*Laughing*): Well, can't you have fun and think a little too?

JUNIOR: I—I guess so—

BRUCE: Listen, fella, it's not smart to be dumb any more.

JUNIOR (*Grinning*): Maybe I've got a lot to learn. Gee, Mary, maybe I'll have to take a tip or two from you.

BRUCE: Mary, I wish I'd met you sooner.

MARY: Why?

BRUCE: Then I could take you to that party tonight. We could could talk some more right away.

MARY: Maybe we still can.

BRUCE: You mean you would go with me?

MARY: Why, yes, if you want me to.

BRUCE: Oh, boy, this is my lucky day! And now this time I— I'd really better be going. I've got to get home and get cleaned up—oh, by the way, would you like some flowers?

MARY (*Hesitating*): Why, I—

BRUCE: What kind do you like?

MARY: Well, there are some pretty little corsages at the florist's around the corner—

BRUCE: There are? Well, I wonder how much they cost. I shouldn't ask that but I've only got three— (*Remembering*) Oh, gee. I forgot . . .

MARY: Well, never mind, Bruce.

JUNIOR: Oh, it's O.K., Bruce. We can take care of that. (*He picks up* BRUCE's *old hockey stick, takes the three dollars from his pocket and offers the stick and the money to* BRUCE) Here you are, Bruce.

BRUCE: Junior, you mean you're really willing to swap again?

JUNIOR (*All smiles*): Oh, sure—anything for my little sister.

BRUCE: Well, thanks, thanks a lot . . . (*He takes stick and money from* JUNIOR *and hands* JUNIOR *the other hockey stick*) And now, I'll have to dash. (*He turns and smiles at* MOTHER *and* FATHER) It's very nice to have met you, Mr. and Mrs. Henderson. (*They nod and smile*) I'll be seeing you, Junior.

JUNIOR: O.K., Bruce.

BRUCE: And Mary, what time shall I pick you up?

MARY: Oh, I guess about quarter to eight. I'll see you to the door, Bruce. (*They cross left together, all smiles.* MOTHER, FATHER *and* JUNIOR *watch and listen.*)

BRUCE: You know, Mary, that essay is wonderful.

MARY: Thanks. I worked hard on it. I spent weeks reading and studying about George Washington.

BRUCE (*Enthusiastically*): We're going to have a lot to talk about . . . (*Then grinning*) Although I guess if you're so well acquainted with George Washington you may find me pretty tame.

MARY: Oh, no, Bruce. You know I was just thinking—it seems that you have some of Washington's qualities.

BRUCE: I—I do? (*They are off.* JUNIOR *is staring after them,* MOTHER *and* FATHER *are still smiling.*)

MARY (*Off stage*): Yes. You're inclined to be reserved the way he was—and yet you have a sense of fun. Then besides you want to serve your country— (*Her voice fades out.*)

JUNIOR: Well, what do you think of that? Little Mary is learning fast.

MOTHER: Why, what do you mean?

JUNIOR: She's being herself all right, but something new has been added. When you compare a fellow to George Washington, you're really giving him a build-up.

THE END

Thanks to George Washington

Characters

MARY ROGERS, *14*
GERALD WILLIAMS, *15*
JOHN ROGERS
ETHEL ROGERS

CHARLIE WILLIAMS
DORA WILLIAMS
DELIVERY MAN

TIME: *February 22nd, about 6:00 p.m.*

SETTING: *The living room of the Rogers home.*

AT RISE: MARY ROGERS *is standing in front of the mirror fussing with her hair. She pushes her hair on top of her head and then twists her head this way and that looking at herself. The doorbell rings and* MARY *goes right and opens the door.* GERALD WILLIAMS *enters excitedly.*

MARY: Gerald Williams, what are you doing here?

GERALD: I had to come, Mary. Something terrible has happened. (*Pushing past her and looking around the room*) Did the desk get here yet?

MARY: What desk?

GERALD: My desk.

MARY: Junior, what are you talking about?

GERALD: And don't call me Junior. It's bad enough my mother and father do but I thought you of all people—

MARY: All right, Gerald. But why should your desk be in our house?

GERALD: Because your mother bought it. I was just over at the

319

Washington's Birthday bazaar and I saw her. She bid twenty-two fifty and she got my desk.

MARY: But why did you donate your desk to the bazaar if you didn't want someone to buy it?

GERALD: I didn't donate it. My mother must have done it while I was at school. The desk was up in the attic and Mom told me I could fix a corner and study up there. Then she must have been looking for stuff to give to the bazaar and she took my desk. It was an old desk.

MARY: Then no wonder my mother bought it. If she sees something old she's always sure it's an antique. Look at those chairs— (*Pointing to one of the straight chairs upstage*) We don't dare sit on them. If your desk was anything like those chairs, you ought to be glad to get rid of it.

GERALD: Mary, you don't understand. Behind one of the drawers I discovered a secret compartment where I kept— well, confidential papers.

MARY: Confidential papers?

GERALD: Yes. There was a note I'd written to you, Mary. I always write them just before I go to bed at night and put them in there for safekeeping.

MARY (*Pleased*): Do you really, Gerald? (*An afterthought*) I wondered why the notes were kind of smudgy and dusty sometimes.

GERALD: Well, I guess I ought to dust out that desk. Anyhow, I'd written a note last night and I was going to give it to you at school today. Then I forgot it this morning and when I looked at noon the desk was gone.

MARY: Oh, Gerald, I wondered why you didn't give me any note today. I thought maybe you were mad about something. (*Light dawning*) Oh, but this is awful, isn't it? If Mother finds that note—

GERALD: Yes—exactly. I don't know why your parents can't understand that you're grown up enough to have a boy friend.

MARY: My parents? What about yours? Don't they still call you Junior as though you're about ten years old?

GERALD: Mary, we haven't got time to argue. What about the note? If they'd only deliver the desk before your folks come home so I could get the note out.

MARY: Well, maybe I could get it out—if you'll tell me how to work the secret compartment. (*A car is heard stopping off right.*)

GERALD: Mary, I hear a car. Maybe they're delivering the desk now.

MARY: Maybe. (*She runs to window.*) It's Father, Gerald!

GERALD (*Scared*): Your father? I've got to get out of here. (*He starts left.*)

MARY: Yes—the back door. But the note—can't you tell me how—

GERALD: Yes—no—there isn't time.

MARY: But what'll we do?

GERALD: I'll go back to the bazaar. Maybe the desk will still be there.

MARY: But what if it isn't?

GERALD: I don't know. I'll have to think of something. (*He rushes off left.* MARY *takes a deep breath as the door opens right and* JOHN ROGERS, *her father, enters, carrying a package and a battered metal box such as fishermen use for their tackle. He is wearing hat and coat.*)

JOHN: Hello, Mary—is your mother home? I'm hungry.

MARY: No, Dad, she's at the Washington's Birthday bazaar. I thought you were going to stop off there on your way home from work.

JOHN: I did stop, but I didn't see her. (*Holding up package*)

But I saw six of her cherry pies in the bakery booth and I know she doesn't like it if they don't all sell so I bought 'em. (*Holding up box*) And look at this.

MARY: Why, that looks like your old box of fishing tackle.

JOHN: It is. (*He deposits box on floor near easy chair right and takes off his hat and puts it on chair.*) Thank goodness I was in time to get it. This is the second year your mother has donated my fishing tackle to the bazaar and the second time I've been lucky enough to buy it back.

MARY (*Emphatically*): Well, it just seems to me that people shouldn't donate things that other people want.

JOHN: What's the matter with you? She didn't donate anything of yours, did she?

MARY: No, but—well, terrible things might happen from people donating other people's belongings to bazaars—things that would change the whole course of their lives.

JOHN: Oh, now, I hardly think it's that bad. But I am getting a little tired of these annual bazaars. Of course, I suppose raising money for a new town hall is as good a way as any to honor Washington's Birthday but—here, can't you do something with these pies? (*He holds out the package toward her. She takes the package and during next few lines JOHN removes his coat.*)

MARY: But what should I do? Six pies!

JOHN: It does seem like a lot, but there were only four of Mrs. Williams' Washington cakes left over—and we can't let her get ahead of your mother, can we?

MARY: No, I suppose not. But I'm sure I can't eat six pies. Shall I fix some for you?

JOHN: No, thank you—not pies just now. I'd like my dinner. It's funny I didn't see your mother at the bazaar.

MARY: Well, did you look where they were selling the furniture?

JOHN: Yes, knowing your mother's weakness for so-called

antiques I looked there first, but I hope she didn't buy any of that junk. People certainly must have cleaned out their attics this year.

MARY: Yes, I should say they did.

JOHN: What do you mean by that?

MARY: Uh—nothing, Dad. I'll put these pies in the kitchen.

JOHN: Well, here, be a good girl and hang up my hat and coat.

MARY: O.K. (*He puts hat and coat over her arm and she goes off left. JOHN sits down in easy chair right and starts to lean back comfortably when the doorbell rings. He rises, goes to door right and opens it. A* DELIVERY MAN *enters and stands just inside the door. He is carrying a small desk. It has spindly legs, and one or more drawers. It is old, if not antique.*)

MAN: Hello, Mr. Rogers. I have a desk for you.

JOHN: A desk? But I haven't ordered a desk.

MAN: It's from the bazaar. Mrs. Rogers bought it. It's an an-tick.

JOHN (*Resignedly*): Oh, all right—bring it in. (MAN *crosses to stage center and sets the desk down facing left.*) Hmmm, antique—do you suppose it'll hold together until my wife gets home?

MAN: Yeah, I know what you mean. It doesn't look like much to me either, but your Missis says it's a find. She told me to be extra careful with it and she even came out to the truck to see I got it loaded on right.

JOHN: She did? That's where she must have been when I was looking for her. Well, I guess it's here to stay so thanks for bringing it.

MAN: Oh, that's all right, glad to be of service. There's a dollar delivery charge.

JOHN: Oh, I see. (*He fishes into his pocket.*) These bazaars must be good for your business.

MAN: Sure thing. I picked this up at the Williams house down the street this morning and delivered it here tonight.

JOHN: Well—well—and I suppose you collect going and coming?

MAN: Yeah, but a Washington Birthday bazaar *should* be good for business, I always say. Washington, America, freedom, free enterprise—see what I mean?

JOHN: Why, yes, of course. (*Handing him the dollar*) The enterprise part doesn't seem quite free to me at the moment, but yes, I see what you mean.

MAN: Thanks, Mr. Rogers—well, so long. (*He exits right, closing the door.* JOHN *sits down at right and looks at the desk, shaking his head.* MARY *enters left, sees the desk.*)

MARY: Oh, Dad, the desk! I mean, where did that come from?

JOHN (*Little laugh*): One guess.

MARY (*Quickly examining the desk*): I wonder if the drawers work. (*She opens one a little.*)

JOHN: I wouldn't touch it if I were you, Mary. It might fall apart. I'll bet the Williamses were glad to get that out of the way.

MARY: I don't know about that. Maybe it was valuable to someone.

JOHN: Don't worry about that. Charlie and Dora Williams wouldn't give away anything that was valuable. They're nice people, of course, and good neighbors—

MARY: You don't talk as though they were.

JOHN: Well, after all, Charlie might have returned that garden hose he borrowed early last summer. He sent that kid of his over—

MARY: Kid?

JOHN: Well, you know—what's his name?

MARY: Gerald, Father, and you could hardly call him a kid. He may be elected president of his class at school.

JOHN: President or not, I wish he'd bring my hose back.

MARY: The Williamses aren't the only ones who borrow. Haven't you got their lawn mower down in the basement?

JOHN: What's that? Maybe I have, but I fixed the handle on it. Wobbled up and down. I fixed it. (*He watches* MARY *as she continues to examine the desk.*) Mary, what's this sudden interest in old furniture? I hope you're not taking after your mother in that respect.

MARY: Well, I—I was just looking at the drawers. There's something about this desk—uh, Dad, don't you want to get that fishing tackle out of the way before Mother comes?

JOHN: No, I'll just shove it back here. (*Without getting up he slides the box upstage from the chair out of sight*) Anyhow, she'll have to know I bought it sometime. (*The door opens and* ETHEL ROGERS *enters.*)

ETHEL: Well, here I am—ohh, my desk came. Isn't it a beauty, John? (*She bustles about taking off her hat and coat and putting them on arm of sofa, then goes to desk, touching and admiring it as she talks.*) Don't you think so, Mary?

MARY: I—

JOHN: I won't say a word, Ethel.

ETHEL: Now, John, just look at it. I'm sure it's a rare piece. (*She partly opens one of the drawers.*)

JOHN: It's rare all right.

MARY: I wouldn't pull at those drawers, Mother.

ETHEL (*Stepping back*): Look at those legs—the lovely curve.

JOHN: If they don't drop off.

ETHEL: I really haven't half examined it yet. Just look at the drawers—come here, John—I do want to show you.

JOHN: Now, Ethel, couldn't we wait until after dinner to examine the desk? I'm so hungry.

ETHEL: Well, all right then, but just let me get my breath. (*She sits down left.*) I've worked so hard at the bazaar.

JOHN: How did the bazaar go?

ETHEL: Fine—and do you know—every one of my cherry pies sold.

JOHN: They did? Well— And how did Dora Williams' cakes go?

ETHEL: Well, the funniest thing—four of them were left over and then I saw Charlie Williams come in and buy them himself. Can you imagine that?

JOHN: Well—uh—yes, I can imagine it but— (MARY *laughs a little and* JOHN *frowns at her.*)

ETHEL: Of course, not that Dora's cakes aren't good to eat, but why a cake for Washington's Birthday, is what I always say. Just because her cook book calls this cake Washington cake—

JOHN: What's in the cake?

ETHEL: Raspberries of all things. I think cherry pies are much more suitable.

JOHN: So do I.

ETHEL: Of course Dora says they aren't because Washington never really cut down the cherry tree. She says that's just a legend.

JOHN: Oh, well—

ETHEL: As I told her, there was never even a rumor that he cut down a raspberry bush.

MARY: Mother, I don't see why you're always criticizing the Williamses.

ETHEL: But Mary dear, I'm not criticizing them. Whatever gave you that idea?

JOHN: Ha, speaking of the Williamses, do you know where that beautiful antique came from? (*He nods toward desk.*)

ETHEL: Why—uh—from the bazaar.

JOHN: Sure, but who donated it? The Williamses—fresh out of their attic.

ETHEL: John! I—I don't believe it.

JOHN: Well, it's true. The delivery man told me.

ETHEL: I—I did wonder where it came from. But it seems impossible.

JOHN: Yes. Did you ever know Charlie or Dora to give away anything worthwhile?

ETHEL: No, but— (*Emphatically now*) this time they must have made a mistake. Yes, that's it—a mistake. Dora never did realize the value of fine things—and this is fine, John. (*Rising and going to desk and rubbing her hand over it*) Look at the patina.

MARY: The what, Mother?

ETHEL: The fine old finish, dear.

JOHN (*Rising and rubbing the desk, imitating* ETHEL'S *movement. Then, looking at his hand*): The fine old dust, dear. Don't the Williamses ever clean their house?

MARY: Well, after all, we don't clean our attic either.

ETHEL: Now, stop being silly, you two. This is a beautiful desk. I think it's the finest piece I've ever discovered.

JOHN: I hope it stands up better than that chair over there. (*Pointing upstage*) I sat on it the other day and it almost collapsed.

ETHEL: You must be more careful, John.

JOHN: And by the way, what's in that bureau in our bedroom?

ETHEL: Why, clothes, of course.

JOHN: Well, I wouldn't remember. I haven't been able to get the drawers open for weeks.

ETHEL: Nonsense, you just don't appreciate fine things. Now, I'm trying to think—this desk—I must look it up in my book —yes, I believe it's Colonial. Yes, I think it goes back—way back.

JOHN: It can go back to Charlie Williams as far as I'm concerned.

MARY: That's an idea, Mother. Maybe we had ought to give it back to them.

ETHEL: Mary, don't be ridiculous.

MARY: But we've got so many old things.

ETHEL: Not like this. I have a feeling about this desk. There's —there's something—well, almost romantic about it.

MARY: Oh, no, Mother—not romantic. I think you're mistaken. (*The doorbell rings.*)

JOHN: Now, what? I hope it's not any more furniture. (*He steps to the door and opens it to admit* GERALD.) Well, if it isn't—Junior Williams.

GERALD: Gerald, Mr. Rogers. Hello, Mrs. Rogers. Hello, Mary.

MARY: H-hello, Gerald.

JOHN: Well, what can we do for you, Gerald? (*Kiddingly*) Did you by any chance come after your old desk?

GERALD: Say-y, do you mean that, Mr. Rogers?

ETHEL: No, of course he doesn't, Gerald. He's just joking.

GERALD: Oh. But—well, as a matter of fact, that's what I did come after. You see, when my mother donated that desk to the bazaar, she made a mistake.

ETHEL: A mistake? See, what did I tell you, John?

GERALD: Yeah, it was a terrible mistake. I—I need that desk to do my studying on. You paid twenty-two fifty, Mrs. Rogers. I'd like to buy it back.

MARY: But Gerald, have you got twenty-two fifty?

GERALD: Well, no—but my allowance is a dollar a week and I thought in time—

JOHN: Hmm, you must really want that desk back. That's funny.

ETHEL: There's nothing funny about it, John. It's just as I told you, and it isn't Gerald that wants the desk back. It's his mother.

GERALD: Oh, no, it isn't, Mrs. Rogers, I'm the one. Mother and Dad didn't want me to ask you for it.

MARY: I'm sure it's Gerald who wants the desk, Mother.

ETHEL (*As though* MARY *didn't understand*): What do you know about it, Mary?

GERALD: You can ask my mother and father if you don't believe me, Mrs. Rogers. They're right out in the car. We were on our way home from the bazaar.

ETHEL: We don't need to ask anyone anything, Gerald. I bought the desk fair and square.

GERALD: And you mean—you mean you won't sell it back to me?

ETHEL: No. I'm sorry, but I can't part with it.

GERALD: Ohh. . . . Well, gee. (*Turning away sadly*) I—I guess that's the end. I mean I better be going. (*He starts out sadly.*)

MARY: Goodbye, Gerald. (*The door closes*) Mother, I think that's the most unfair thing I've ever seen, not giving Gerald back his desk.

ETHEL: Dear, it wasn't his desk. And there was nothing very fair about sending him in—

MARY: But how do you know it wasn't his desk?

ETHEL: Oh, Mary, you're too young to understand these things.

MARY (*Almost in tears*): Too young—too young! (*She runs out left.*)

JOHN: What's the matter with her?

ETHEL: I can't imagine. But now, John, what do you think of my desk?

JOHN: I don't know what to think, but I—I guess you were right, Ethel. The thing must be worth something.

ETHEL: Something? It's very valuable or they wouldn't be try-ing— (*The doorbell rings.*) There. I'll bet that's Dora and Charlie. They sent the boy in first and—

JOHN: Well, we'll soon see. This is going to be good. (MARY

re-enters and stands watching. JOHN *opens the door.*) Well, if it isn't the Williamses. Come on in. (CHARLIE *and* DORA WILLIAMS *enter followed by* GERALD.)

CHARLIE: Hello, John.

DORA: Hello, Ethel.

ETHEL: Won't you take off your things?

DORA: No, thank you.

CHARLIE: We don't like to disturb you but Junior—I mean Gerald—came out to the car feeling so upset about that desk.

ETHEL: Oh, he did?

DORA: And I know it seems silly to make such a fuss. We don't care at all—

CHARLIE: No, but Dora had told the boy he could use it, and then when she was looking for stuff to give to the bazaar she forgot.

JOHN: Yes, he told us all that, Charlie.

ETHEL: And about paying out of his allowance but—well, we just can't do it.

CHARLIE: Sure, Ethel, we can understand how you wouldn't want to wait weeks and weeks for your money so I've agreed to advance his allowance. (*He pulls out his wallet.*)

JOHN: Oh, no, you don't. Look, Charlie, there's no need for you to beat around the bush. We know you want this desk and you want it bad.

CHARLIE: What's that? Why, I wouldn't give ten cents for it but the boy—well, for some reason he seems to have gotten fond of it.

DORA: Why should *we* want it?

ETHEL: I'll tell you why. You realize now that it's a valuable desk and you're sorry you sold it.

DORA: But it isn't valuable, Ethel.

MARY: Of course it isn't, Mother. It's of no value except to Gerald.

JOHN: How do you know so much about Gerald?

MARY (*Embarrassed*): Well, didn't he say—

DORA: It's sheer nonsense to insist that desk is valuable, Ethel. It's just an old desk that belonged to my grandmother.

ETHEL: Ah ha, I knew it was old, Dora. And you realized it was valuable just as soon as you found out I'd bought it. You know I'm always looking for antiques.

CHARLIE: Always looking, Ethel, but I guess you wouldn't know one if you saw it.

ETHEL: Well, of all the—

DORA: Now, Ethel, Charlie needn't have put it so bluntly but it's true. You know you're always picking up old junk.

ETHEL: Dora Williams, that's too much. You're always criticizing me—you criticized my cherry pies.

DORA: You criticized my raspberry cakes!

JOHN: I don't blame her, Dora. I don't see that raspberry cakes have anything to do with Washington's Birthday. It seems a little impolite. Raspberries. Why, it's like giving the Bronx cheer to the Father of our Country.

CHARLIE: You should talk about being polite. My wife makes the best Washington cakes in town and everybody knows it.

ETHEL: Everybody knows it all right. Maybe that's why you bought the last four after my pies were all sold.

DORA: Did you, Charlie?

CHARLIE: Well—uh—yes. I've got them out in the car.

JOHN: Ha, ha, everybody likes them including the Williams family.

MARY: Well, I guess *we* better like your cherry pies, Mother. Dad bought all that was left of them.

ETHEL: He didn't?

MARY: Yes, they're out on the kitchen table.

ETHEL: John Rogers!

GERALD: Excuse me, but I don't see where all this arguing about cakes and pies is getting us. What about my desk?

ETHEL: It's my desk. I bought it fair and square and I'm not going to sell it back to you.

MARY: But Mother, is it really fair and square when Gerald needs the desk?

ETHEL: Now, Mary, you keep out of this.

CHARLIE: I think you're being very stubborn, Ethel, when the desk is of no value except to the boy.

ETHEL: No value—no value. You know it's of value. Maybe you'll admit it if I show you in my book. (*She crosses upstage, picks up book from table and shows cover.*) Look— *Why Are Antiques Old?* (*She opens book and thumbs through as she returns downstage.*) Here we are—desks— Colonial—Early Colonial—and here it is. This sounds just like it. Circa 1776.

DORA: Circa? What in the world is that?

ETHEL: You wouldn't know. It means "about." They don't know the exact date of these old things so they put circa in instead. About 1776. Now, listen—the desks of this period had four legs— (*Indicating desk*) see, four legs— (*Reading again*) And the tops were usually either flat or slanting— well, this one's flat— (*Reading*) And a drawer or drawers —(*She breaks off*) There, if that doesn't describe this one—

CHARLIE: That could describe any desk.

DORA: It doesn't mean a thing.

JOHN: It does seem a little general, Ethel.

ETHEL: (*Who has been reading further*): All right—all right— then how about this? Desks of this period usually have a secret compartment behind one of the drawers. A secret compartment—how wonderful! I haven't looked yet but there must be one. (*Looking at book again*) It says here they're usually covered by a small sliding panel.

DORA: That desk hasn't got any secret compartment, Ethel. That's just silly.

GERALD: I—I wouldn't even bother to look for it if I were you, Mrs. Rogers.

MARY (*Nervously*): Mother, they ought to know if there's a secret compartment or not.

ETHEL: Well, I'm going to look anyhow. It must be there. The book says so. (*She kneels down in front of desk and pulls the drawer out, placing it on top of desk. She reaches in space where drawer came from and feels around.*)

GERALD (*To* MARY): Oh-oh. (MARY *and* GERALD *edge toward each other and stand upstage center looking frightened.*)

ETHEL: Here's something—no, that's not it.

CHARLIE: You won't find—

ETHEL: Oh, yes, I will. Here it is—it slides—it's the secret panel!

DORA: What's that? (*They all come close to desk except* MARY *and* GERALD *who still stand upstage.*)

ETHEL: Yes and I—I've got it open.

JOHN (*Peering*): Well, can you beat that!

ETHEL: And my goodness, there's something in it. I feel something. It's a piece of paper. (*She takes her hand out holding a folded piece of paper. Then rising, she blows some dust off the paper.*) My, just think, this could have been put in there a hundred years ago!

DORA: Well, what is it? Is there anything written on it, Ethel?

GERALD: Oh, boy. (*He reaches for* MARY'S *hand and she takes his. The others are too interested in the paper to notice.*)

ETHEL: I don't know. (*She unfolds it.*) Yes, it's a note. Oh, isn't this exciting? We're apt to find out almost anything.

JOHN: Well, don't keep us in suspense, Ethel. What does it say?

ETHEL (*Spreading it out*): Now, I'll read it. "Dear M." Oh, my, I wonder who M was.

DORA: What's the rest of it? Is there any date?

ETHEL: No, there's no date. Now, let me see. "Dear M: I am thinking of you. It seems a long time since I have seen you." Oh, I said this desk was romantic!

CHARLIE: Go on.

ETHEL: "I hope that if I am made president it won't take so much of my time that I won't be able to see you often."

JOHN: President?

ETHEL: Of course. Some great man owned this desk. There's one more line. (*Reading on*) "Yours, until we meet again." Signed "G.W." G.W., G.W. Now, let me think—who—

CHARLIE (*Turning to his wife*): I don't have to think who it is.

GERALD: Oh, boy!

CHARLIE: G.W. Dora, do you realize what you've sold these people?

DORA: What do you mean?

CHARLIE: G.W.—George Washington.

DORA: But it can't be.

CHARLIE: Of course it can. Dear M. Martha Washington.

ETHEL: Why, isn't that wonderful? George Washington's desk —I can't believe—but here it is—right in this room. (GERALD *and* MARY *heave sighs of relief, smile at each other and relax.*)

JOHN: It gives you a funny feeling—kind of an awed feeling.

MARY: It's—it's wonderful the way things have turned out, isn't it, Mother?

GERALD: Yeah—I'll say.

MARY: May I—may I see the note?

ETHEL: Of course, dear. It's such nice handwriting. (MARY *takes the note and looks at it. During next few lines she puts it in her pocket.*)

CHARLIE: Ah, yes, Washington did everything well. He was a great man. One of the greatest men this country's ever had.

JOHN: You're absolutely right, Charlie. Makes me feel small just to think of him.

CHARLIE: Me, too. You know the ideas Washington had for this country are still serving us well. Freedom, democracy—all of us working together for the good of all.

ETHEL: Oh dear. . . .

DORA: Ethel, what's the matter?

ETHEL: We haven't been working well together—even at the bazaar. We argued about the cakes and pies—

DORA: I know, Ethel. I feel awful now just to think of it.

CHARLIE: I don't feel so good myself. I tell you, John, when you think of what Washington wanted this country to be—and then you look around—even good neighbors like us quarreling over nothing.

JOHN: Yeah, when I think of the times I've picked on your bad qualities, Charlie, instead of thinking about your good ones—

CHARLIE: I guess we're like a lot of folks in this country. We don't realize what we've got. We ought to be working together—all of us.

DORA: We will work together. Just wait and see, Ethel. Next year at the bazaar—and not only at the bazaar but in everything. Why, you folks are the best neighbors we've got.

CHARLIE: Sure they are, and you know, there isn't anyone I'd rather see have that desk than you, Ethel. Gerald, now that you know how valuable it is, you don't want it up in the attic any more, do you?

GERALD: No, as far as I'm concerned, everything's all right. I'd like Mrs. Rogers to have it.

ETHEL: Well, that's very sweet of you, Gerald, but I couldn't think of keeping it now that we know it belonged to George Washington.

DORA: But Ethel, you bought it fair and square—you've got to keep it.

ETHEL: No. It was your desk in the first place, Dora. You've got to take it back.

CHARLIE: But you're the one who discovered it. If it hadn't been for your book—

JOHN: No, Charlie, that would be taking an unfair advantage. Twenty-two fifty for a desk like that—it's probably worth thousands of dollars.

GERALD: Oh, it's still an old desk. I—I don't think it would be worth that much.

CHARLIE: Why, certainly it would. If you'd take it to a museum—

ETHEL: A museum? Why, that's exactly what we'll do with it. The money I paid for it has gone to a good cause. And in a way, the desk doesn't belong to any of us. (*Dramatically*) It belongs to posterity.

DORA: Posterity—I think you're right, Ethel.

JOHN: That historical museum in the city—that's the place. There's a Professor someone in charge there. He's an authority.

CHARLIE: Better call him right up.

GERALD: Oh, I—I wouldn't do that.

DORA: But why not?

MARY (*Quickly*): It's Washington's Birthday. They're probably not open.

ETHEL: Oh, that's just when they would be. Everybody looks at all the historical exhibits. And just think, next year they'll be able to see this desk, and it'll say presented by Charlie and Dora Williams and John and Ethel Rogers. We must call them right up and have the professor come out. (*She starts left.*) Now, let me see, the note from Washington, where is it? I gave it to you, Mary.

MARY: Yes, Mother, but—but do you have to show that to the man?

ETHEL: Of course, and I want to read it to him now over the phone. It's the proof. Give it to me quickly. Where is it?

MARY: In my pocket but—but—all right, Mother. (*She fishes a note out of her pocket and hands it to her mother.*)

ETHEL: Your pocket. Well, you must be more careful, dear. This is a valuable document. (*She spreads it out and looks at it again.*) My, isn't it wonderful? I—I still can't realize— "Dear M." (*Reading on dreamily*) "I'll phone you from the drugstore after dinner." The drug—my goodness, this is a different note—there must have been two folded together. Mary, where's the other one? Oh, but a telephone. Did they have telephones in Washington's day? Why, that will be something even the Professor doesn't know.

JOHN: Don't be silly, Ethel. Of course they didn't have telephones and if they had drugstores they called them apothecaries.

CHARLIE: What's going on here?

MARY (*Almost crying*): Oh, Gerald, I handed her the wrong note—the one you gave me yesterday. I had that in my pocket too.

GERALD: It's all right, Mary. You didn't mean to. I guess it's all over but the shouting.

CHARLIE: Gerald Williams—

GERALD: Yes, Father.

CHARLIE: Hmm, Gerald Williams— G.W. Gerald, did you write those notes?

GERALD: Yes, Father, there's no use lying. I did write them.

CHARLIE: Spoken in the true spirit of George Washington. But what's the idea—and who's this Martha?

MARY: It isn't Martha. It just says dear M. M for Mary.

ETHEL: You, Mary? Then this isn't George Washington's desk at all.

GERALD: We were rather relieved when you thought it was but

I guess we shouldn't have been. It wasn't very nice of us to let you think—

DORA: But what's it all about? What's all this secrecy and why in the world were you writing Mary notes?

MARY: Well, Mrs. Williams, why do you think any boy writes a girl notes?

GERALD: Yeah, why do you think? But we knew none of you would like it.

JOHN: Why not? All kids write notes when they're in school.

GERALD: But these aren't kids' notes. After all, you've read two of 'em. Does a fellow have to bare his soul?

CHARLIE (*Laughing*): Oh, so that's it, Junior—I mean Gerald. You two—well, kind of like each other.

DORA: Well, for goodness' sakes.

JOHN: So our little Mary has a boy friend.

MARY: What's so funny about that?

JOHN: Now—now, I didn't mean anything. It's all right—it's all right. And you couldn't have a nicer one than Gerald Williams.

GERALD: You mean you don't care, Mr. Rogers? You don't any of you care?

CHARLIE: Of course not, Gerald. Why, I guess every boy has a girl he kind of likes while he's going to school.

MARY: But you're always calling us children, as though we weren't grown up at all. We thought you'd think we were too young.

ETHEL: My land, imagine these kids!

MARY: See what I mean? Kids.

ETHEL (*Laughing*): All right, Mary. Young folks then. But imagine you young folks getting us all excited like this. Thinking we had a desk that belonged to George Washington.

DORA: And now it's just an old desk that came out of our attic.

ETHEL: But from the description in my book, it did sound like a Colonial piece—and that secret compartment—

JOHN: No, Ethel, they've been making copies of these old desks for years. You might as well give it back to Gerald.

GERALD: Oh, no, I don't want it back any more. It was just the note. And you bought it, Mrs. Rogers.

ETHEL: All right. Maybe you'd like to have it in your room, Mary.

MARY: Why, yes. And Gerald, I can use the secret compartment to keep your notes in.

JOHN: Well, that settles the business of the desk. But you know, Charlie, all this has strangely stirred my conscience. There's a lawn mower of yours in our basement. I borrowed it last summer.

CHARLIE: Say, that's right and you know, John, I've got your garden hose. I'd forgotten all about it. Look, John, I've always wanted to do something for you, so you just keep my lawn mower.

JOHN: Say, Charlie, I couldn't do that, unless, well, you keep my garden hose.

CHARLIE: Why, thanks, that's white of you, John.

ETHEL: Well, listen to all that. Desk or no desk, Dora, the spirit of Washington must have got into our husbands.

DORA: It certainly must have. I've never heard them 'fessing up and telling whose garden tools were whose before.

GERALD: I guess it's all right, but the only difference I can see is that next summer I'll have to come over and borrow the lawn mower instead of the garden hose. (*They all laugh.*)

CHARLIE: Well, just the same, Washington made us realize a lot of things today.

GERALD: He certainly fixed things up for us, didn't he, Mary?

JOHN: There's one thing he can't fix. I'm just as hungry as I was an hour ago.

MARY: Well, Dad, Washington can fix that too. There are six cherry pies in the kitchen, remember?

ETHEL: Why, of course. Who wants pie?

THE WILLIAMS: We do!

DORA: And we've got some Washington cakes in the car. Who wants cake?

THE ROGERS: We do!

JOHN: What could be sweeter? You'll eat our pies—

CHARLIE (*Laughing*): And we'll give you the raspberry! (*They all laugh as the curtain falls.*)

THE END

The Easter Hop

Characters

MOTHER, *Alice Carter* MARIE CARTER
FATHER, *John Carter* DON RANDALL
SALLY CARTER SPIKE BENSON
BOB CARTER VOICE FROM RADIO

TIME: *Saturday afternoon before Easter.*
SETTING: *The Carter living room.*
AT RISE: MOTHER, *Alice Carter, is seated in large wing chair upstage right sewing on a blue party dress. The belt of the dress hangs over the back of the chair.* MARIE, *aged eight, is seated at card table working on fancy Easter eggs. On the table are several painted eggs, feathers, beads, crepe paper, paints, glass of water, brushes, etc.* MARIE *is busily painting a face on an Easter egg which has yellow crepe paper hair.*

MARIE (*Holding up egg*): Look at my Easter egg, Mom. I just finished painting the face.
MOTHER (*Looking up*): Very pretty, dear. Where did you learn to make such fancy ones?
MARIE: Miss Burgess showed us at school. You can make all kinds. This one's going to be a glamour girl. Her hair is crepe paper and her eyebrows are feathers and then for earrings I just stuck on two little beads.
MOTHER: My goodness!
MARIE: But to be a real glamour girl she should have something in her hair—jewels maybe.

MOTHER: Well, there are some sequins upstairs in the sewing table. I'd get them for you but I've just got to keep working on your sister's dress.

MARIE (*Rising*): I'll bet I could find them, Mom.

MOTHER: Very well. They're in the right-hand drawer. (MARIE *runs off left as* FATHER, *John Carter, enters right, carrying a newspaper.* MOTHER *looks up.*) Well, John, you're home early.

FATHER: Of course—tomorrow's Easter, isn't it? But a fine Easter from what the weatherman says. (*Indicating paper*) Listen to the forecast. Cloudy, cold and rain.

MOTHER: Hmm, I don't care if it snows.

FATHER: Why, Alice, you amaze me. (*He seats himself downstage left and puts paper on table next to him.*) Of course, I've never worried about Easter weather—I won't cut any figure in the Easter parade, but I thought you had a new hat.

MOTHER: I have, and once I felt excited about it, but now there are too many other things to worry about. Mainly, the Easter Hop.

FATHER: The what?

MOTHER: The Easter Hop, John. We've only been talking about it for weeks.

FATHER: I haven't heard a thing of it.

MOTHER: Then that's because you haven't listened. Spring vacation starts Monday and the high school crowd always has this big dance on Monday night—the Easter Hop.

FATHER: Hop, indeed. If it's a dance why don't they call it a dance, and what are you worried about that for?

MOTHER: Because Sally hasn't been invited.

FATHER: But I thought everyone was invited. I thought the whole school was invited.

MOTHER: Oh, I don't mean that. No boy has asked her. She has no date for the dance.

FATHER: I thought we decided she was too young for dates.

MOTHER: John, that was last year. This is different. Now, most of the girls in her crowd don't want to go unless they have dates, and I've been trying so hard to finish this dress for her.

FATHER: But if she doesn't want to go, why worry about finishing the dress?

MOTHER: But she *does* want to go, John. It'll break her heart if she doesn't go.

FATHER: Well, why look at me? Do you want me to take her?

MOTHER: Don't be ridiculous!

FATHER: Very well, then, I was just trying to be helpful. What about Bob?

MOTHER: Yes, I'd thought of him as a last resort, but it's an admission of failure, John, if your own brother has to take you to a dance. Oh, I don't know what to do.

FATHER: Well, things will probably work themselves out.

MOTHER: They don't always, John. Sometimes these things need a little help. Sally is shy. This is all new to her. She's so sweet and pretty you'd think any boy would be glad to take her. But she doesn't know how to play up to them yet.

FATHER: Play up to them? You wouldn't want her to do that, would you?

MOTHER: Oh, John, you know what I mean. And besides, you have no idea what I've been through. Every time the phone rings the poor child thinks it's someone calling for her, and when it's not, she's so disappointed I'm afraid she'll be getting a complex. They do, you know.

FATHER: Now, Alice, if anyone seems to be getting a complex, you do.

MOTHER: Well, no wonder. That isn't all I've got to worry about. We have a house guest coming for the weekend.

FATHER: House guest? Why haven't you told me before?

MOTHER: Because I didn't know before. A telegram came this morning. It's Mabel Randall's son—he's on his way home from college for spring vacation, and Mabel wanted him to stop and see us.

FATHER: Indeed? Who's Mabel?

MOTHER: You know, John, she used to be Mabel Krouse. We grew up together.

FATHER (*Laughing*): Oh, yes, that funny-looking, freckle-faced kid.

MOTHER: Well, she's not freckle-faced any longer. She married Donald Randall, and he's done very well. Their son, Don, is a junior at Amboy Tech, and he's arriving here today to stay over tomorrow.

FATHER: Well, there's nothing can be done about it. Bob will have to entertain him.

MOTHER: Dear, Bob's still in high school and he'll seem like a mere child to Don, and I suppose we'll seem like old dodos.

FATHER: Old dodos! Alice, I don't mean to be an old dodo for anyone. What time is he coming?

MOTHER: I don't know. The wire just said Saturday.

FATHER: Well, stop worrying about him. He'll get here when he arrives. Tomorrow we'll take him to church with us, fill him up on Easter ham, and in the afternoon take him for a walk—in the rain, presumably, if the weather forecast is right.

MOTHER: John, for goodness' sakes, stop fussing about the weather. I don't know why you should care anyhow—you never bother dressing up on Easter Sunday.

FATHER: Well—uh—a man does like a nice sunny day— (*Rising and crossing to her*) and I might add, a sunny wife. (*He touches her cheek trying to kid her a little.*) Come on, Alice, how about a smile? Aren't you even curious about your annual Easter present?

MOTHER (*Somewhat tartly*): Why should I be curious? You

always give me a white gardenia. And I must say I always feel silly all decked out in a corsage and a new Easter bonnet, and you stalking along beside me wearing that slouchy old hat of yours and looking like something out of a "whodunit."

FATHER: Now, Alice, it's the women who dress up for Easter. Nobody looks at the men. (MARIE *runs in left.*)

MARIE: Mom, I found the sequins. (*She seats herself at table again.*) Hello, Daddy. (*Holding up egg*) I'm making fancy Easter eggs. Look.

FATHER: Well, very fancy, I'd say. I hope you're using duck eggs.

MARIE: Don't be silly. Nobody uses duck eggs.

FATHER: No, I suppose not, but it would be a good idea this year with the weather that's been predicted. (*He sits down again.*)

MOTHER: John, please— (*The phone rings.* MOTHER *rises, putting* SALLY'S *dress on chair and crosses left to phone.*) Oh, maybe this is for Sally, maybe someone's asking her to the dance. (*She picks up phone.*) Hello? Oh, Mrs. Green . . . Oh, you've finished Jane's dress? Well, I've practically finished Sally's. Perhaps they can go to the dance together . . . Oh. I see. She's going with Ted Harvey. Well, isn't that nice? . . . Well—well, have a nice Easter, Mrs. Green. All right. Goodbye. (*She hangs up.*) John, all that woman really called up for was to let me know that her Jane had a date for the dance. (SALLY, *about fifteen, enters left. She is sweet and pretty, but somewhat shy.*)

SALLY: Mom, did I hear the phone?

MOTHER: Uh—yes, dear.

SALLY: It wasn't for me, though, was it?

MOTHER: No, Sally. It was Mrs. Green. She'd finished Jane's dress and—

SALLY: And what, Mom? Did she say if Jane was going with anyone?

MOTHER: Well—uh—yes, as a matter of fact she did. Jane's going with Ted Harvey.

SALLY: Oh, Mom, even Jane's got a date. What'll I do?

MOTHER: Now, Sally, there's plenty of time.

SALLY: Plenty of time?—when it's Saturday afternoon and the Hop is on Monday?

MOTHER (*Picking up dress from chair*): Look at your dress, dear, how beautifully it turned out.

SALLY: Mom, what good is a dress when—

MOTHER (*Going on*): I do want you to try it on to see if the skirt hangs right. (*Holding it in front of Sally*) Oh, it is lovely. You'll look like an angel in it.

SALLY (*Almost crying*): Who wants to look like an angel? I'd rather look like a glamour girl.

MARIE (*Holding up her egg. Sing-songy*): Glamour girl— glamour girl. I've got a glamour girl. Look, Sally.

SALLY: Oh, Marie, I don't feel like playing with Easter eggs! (BOB, *about sixteen years old, enters left.*)

BOB: Say, Mom—oh, hello, Dad. Say, Mom, isn't there anything cool to drink in the house? Spike and I have been playing ping pong downstairs and we got dry.

MOTHER: Did you look in the refrigerator, Bob?

BOB: Yes, but I couldn't see anything.

MOTHER: Well, look again. There are some Cokes behind the milk bottles.

BOB: O.K., Mom. (*He starts to turn, then stares at* SALLY.) Say, kid, what's the matter with you?

SALLY: Nothing.

MOTHER: Uh, Bob—what are you doing about the Hop Monday night?

BOB: What am I doing?

MOTHER: I mean, are you going?

BOB: Sure—going stag.

MOTHER: But isn't that rather selfish, dear? Your father and I—well, we think it would be nice if you took Sally.

BOB: Oh, for gosh sakes.

FATHER: Now, son—

BOB: Dad, you don't understand. Spike and I—well, we're playing the field.

FATHER: I see, but—

SALLY: Well, you can all just stop arguing about it. I wouldn't go with Bob anyhow.

MOTHER: But Sally—

SALLY (*Starting left*): If a girl hasn't anyone but her brother to go with, she might as well stay home! (*She rushes off crying.*)

BOB: See, she doesn't want to go with me anyhow.

MOTHER: Bob, I should think you'd have a little sympathy for your sister.

BOB: Sympathy? Gee, Mom, I got sympathy all right—

MOTHER: Then I should think you could do something.

BOB: But what can I do? Can I help it if all the fellows just think of Sally as a kid? Why, it was just last year she was still running around in pigtails. And then she's so quiet. She never does anything to make the fellows notice her.

MOTHER: Bob, whom did you say you had downstairs with you?

BOB: Who? Spike, Mom. Spike Benson.

MOTHER: Spike Benson. He's a very nice boy.

BOB: Sure, good old Spike—a swell fellow.

MOTHER: Bob, you've got to see what you can do. You've got to get Spike to ask Sally to go to the dance with him.

BOB: Huh? Gosh, Mom, I couldn't do a thing like that.

MOTHER: You could if you wanted to.

BOB (*Imploringly*): Dad—

FATHER: Yes, son, I think you'd better try, or I'm not going to be able to live with your mother.

BOB: But Dad, I can't push my own sister at a fellow.

MOTHER: You've got to try, Bob.

BOB: And besides it won't work. The more you push a girl at a guy, the faster he runs. Believe me, I know.

FATHER: You'd better see what you can do, Bob.

BOB: Oh, for gosh sakes. It's futile, I tell you. Just futile. (*He goes off left.*)

MOTHER (*Walking up and down with dress*): Oh, dear, I suppose it is futile but I didn't know what else to do. Oh, John.

FATHER (*Rising*): Alice, will you please stop stewing?

MOTHER: How can I? Well, I've got to go upstairs and get her to try on this dress. (*She starts left.*)

FATHER (*Starting left*): I'm coming, too. I need a rest.

MOTHER: But John, the young man may arrive—he may be here any minute.

FATHER: Yes, and he may not be here until midnight. I, for one, don't propose to worry about him. Besides, if I'm going to have company to entertain I need a nap. (*They both go off left.* MARIE *hums a little tune as she pastes sequins onto the hair of her Easter egg. Then holding egg up with one hand and holding the sequins on with the other, she says singsongy.*)

MARIE: Glamour girl—glamour girl. I've got a glamour girl. (*There is a buzzer off right, not too loud.* MARIE *frowns and looks worried for a moment.*) Dear me, if I let go now, they'll all fall off. (*She looks right and calls*) Come in. Come on in! (*After a moment,* DON RANDALL, *a young man about twenty, appears in doorway right. He wears no hat, carries a small bag in one hand and a cardboard flower box in the other.*)

DON: Excuse me, I thought I heard someone say come in.

MARIE: Yes, you did. I'm making Easter eggs and I couldn't let go for a minute until the paste gets dry.

DON: Oh. Well—uh—this is where the Carters live, isn't it?

MARIE: Yes, I'm Marie, and I'll bet I know who you are. You're Don Randall, from college.

DON: Right you are. Your mother's expecting me, I think. Are your mother and father at home?

MARIE: Yes, my mother's upstairs working on my sister's dress and my dad's taking a nap. This is dry now. (*She puts her egg down and starts to rise.*) I'll go get them.

DON: No, no, wait a minute, I don't want to disturb anyone. Why don't I just make myself at home?

MARIE (*Settling down again*): Well, all right.

DON: Sure, I'll just shove my stuff up the corner here. (*He goes upstage right and puts bag and box behind large chair.*) Fact is, I wouldn't mind a nap myself. (*He turns wing chair a little more upstage so that he will be out of sight from downstage when he sits in it. The belt of* SALLY'S *dress can be seen hanging over the back of the chair.*) Will it disturb you if I kind of settle down here?

MARIE: Oh, not at all. I'm making Easter eggs. Look.

DON (*Going to her and looking*): Say, I've never seen any like that. They look like dolls.

MARIE: Sure. (*Holding up egg*) This one is a glamour girl.

DON (*Laughing a little*): So I see.

MARIE: My sister wishes she was a glamour girl.

DON: Oh, and she isn't?

MARIE: No. No one's asked her to the dance—the Easter Hop, and my mother's just sick about it. She wants my brother to get a date for her but my brother says it's fu-tile.

DON: Oh—uh—well, I can see it would create somewhat of a problem. How old are your brother and sister?

MARIE: Sally's fifteen and Bob's sixteen. They both think they're terribly grown up but of course they're not—not really grown up, like you, I mean.

DON (*Laughing a little*): Thank you very much.

MARIE (*Picking up a fresh egg and a paint brush*): Well, I guess I'd better start on another egg. Oh dear, my paint water is so full of paint I guess I'll have to get some fresh. (*She rises with her glass.*)

DON: O.K. (*Going toward chair*) And I think I'll just kind of sprawl out here and take my nap. (MARIE *goes out left.* DON *sits in wing chair upstage. He is out of sight from downstage left. After a moment,* BOB *enters left followed by* SPIKE BENSON, *who is about* BOB'S *age.*)

SPIKE: Well, three games out of five. I guess that makes me champ.

BOB: Yeah, for the time being. But say, Spike, what is your honest opinion of my sister, Sally?

SPIKE: Gee, what do you keep harping on her for? And why so formal all of a sudden? "My sister, Sally." We always just called her "the kid" before. She's a good kid, all right.

BOB: Well, Spike, she's not exactly a kid any more. She's—well, she's growing up.

SPIKE: She is? Yeah, I suppose it happens to everyone eventually. Well, guess I'd better be running along.

BOB: Aw, no, stick around, Spike. What's your hurry? There was something I wanted to—well, about this dance Monday night—the Easter Hop.

SPIKE: Yeah? What about it?

BOB: Well, we both said we were going stag. But I thought maybe you'd kind of—well, changed your mind.

SPIKE: What would I do that for?

BOB: I don't know. I just thought—well, maybe you'd like to take some girl.

SPIKE: Who? Me? And disappoint all the rest of them? I should say not. (SALLY *enters left wearing the new dress except for belt. She looks lovely. She stops when she sees* SPIKE *and* BOB.)

SALLY: Oh. I didn't know you two were in here.

BOB: Why, Sis, hello. . . . Here's Sally, Spike. See, here's Sally.

SPIKE: Yeah . . . Hi ya, kid.

BOB (*Staring at her*): Gee, Sis, you look different somehow. What's that you got on?

SALLY: What does it look like? The new dress Mother made. And she left the belt down here somewhere. (*Looking about and seeing belt on wing chair upstage*) Oh, there it is. (*She starts toward chair.*)

SPIKE (*Starting right*): Well, I guess I'd really better be going—

BOB (*Desperately*): No—wait a minute, Spike. (SALLY *takes hold of belt and tugs at it. She is surprised when it doesn't move. Then looking over back of chair, she lets go of belt and backs away.*)

SALLY: Oh—ohhh, there's someone here! (*She backs away farther toward left, a little upstage.* DON *rises slowly from chair, looking at* SALLY *and smiling.*)

DON (*To* SALLY): My goodness, how you *have* grown up!

SALLY: What do you mean?

DON: Why, a moment ago you were a little girl—sitting there painting Easter eggs.

SALLY: Oh, no, that was my sister.

DON: Ah, that explains it. I was about to—that is, I was taking a nap.

BOB: But gee, who are you? What are you doing here?

DON: Why, I live here—temporarily, that is—over the weekend. I'm your mother's house guest. I'm sure she's expecting me.

My name is Don Randall. (SALLY *backs farther upstage left.*)

BOB: Oh, sure. I remember. Mom said some fellow from Amboy Tech was coming.

SPIKE: Amboy Tech? Don Randall? Is that what you said your name was?

DON: Why, yes.

SPIKE: Then you're Don Randall, the All-American halfback!

DON: That's right.

BOB: For gosh sakes, isn't that just like Mom? Why didn't she say you were the big football star?

DON: Perhaps your mother doesn't read the sport pages.

BOB: Well, gee, we're sure glad to see you. I'm Bob, and this is my friend, Spike Benson.

SPIKE: I'm certainly glad to know you. (DON *steps downstage and shakes hands with both boys.*)

DON: Glad to know both of you. But the young lady. I don't know her name yet.

BOB: Young lady? Oh, that's my kid sis—I mean, that's Sally.

DON: Sally? Well! (*Going toward her*) A beautiful name for a beautiful lady. (*He takes her hand.*)

SPIKE: Lady? Huh?

DON: You know, Sally, you remind me of someone.

SALLY: Do I?

DON: Yes. Who is it? (*Half closing his eyes*) I know—that new movie star that everyone's talking about. The one with the come-hither eyes.

SALLY: You—you mean Sheila Lawrence?

DON: That's it.

BOB (*Somewhat awed*): You—you know, Spike, she does look a little bit like her.

SPIKE: Yeah, I—I guess she does.

SALLY (*Pulling her hand away from* DON *embarrassed*) : Well, I—I've got to get my belt.

DON : Oh, that's what you were after. (*He steps quickly over and takes belt from back of chair.*) I'm sorry I was leaning on it. Here, allow me. (*He puts the belt around her waist and steps back.*) That's a beautiful dress.

SALLY : Thank you. Mother made it especially for the Easter Hop on Monday.

DON : Monday? That's just my luck. I'm only staying for Sunday, but I did bring something you can remember me by. (*He goes upstage and brings back cardboard box, opening it as he goes toward her, taking out an orchid corsage.*) For you, Sally.

SALLY (*Thrilled*) : An orchid! (*He hands it to her and she holds it up to her dress.*)

DON : Yes. I knew it would be perfect on a blue dress. (*He places box on table at left.*)

BOB : But how did you know Sally was going to have a blue dress?

DON : Why—uh, perhaps I'm getting psychic. I just had a feeling that I was going to meet a beautiful girl in a blue dress. And at Amboy we have a theory that it's always well to be prepared.

SPIKE : Well, for gosh sakes!

SALLY : An orchid! It—it's wonderful. Oh, if you'll excuse me, I've just got to show my mother! (*She runs out left excitedly.*)

DON (*Coming back to boys*) : Delightful girl, your sister.

BOB : Yeah, yeah. That's what I've been telling Spike.

SPIKE : You don't need to tell me. I—I guess I know a pretty girl when I see one.

DON : Yes, I'm sure you must. You look to me like a young man of discernment.

SPIKE (*Pleased*): Huh? Well, gosh. (MARIE *runs in left with glass of water and a dish with more eggs in it.*)

MARIE: Say, what happened to Sally? She walked right past me holding a big flower in front of her and she didn't even see me.

BOB: Mr. Randall gave it to her.

MARIE (*Going to table*): Oh, Mr. Randall, I forgot all about you. I had to boil some more eggs.

DON: That's quite all right, Marie.

MARIE (*Settling down again and motioning at* SPIKE *and* BOB): Well, you couldn't have had much of a nap with them in here.

DON: Not much, perhaps, but enough. (MOTHER *rushes in left toward* DON, *followed by* SALLY, *who is still walking on air and still carrying her orchid.*)

MOTHER: Don—Don Randall—my dear boy. I didn't know you were here until Sally told me. Welcome.

DON: Thank you, Mrs. Carter.

MOTHER: My, I feel as though I knew you already. You do look like your mother. And to think of your bringing flowers for the child—

DON: Child?

MOTHER: I mean Sally. I keep forgetting that she's growing up. She's simply thrilled. Now you're just to make yourself at home—

DON: I've been doing that, Mrs. Carter.

MOTHER: Well, I am sorry to have been so long welcoming you. I do hope Sally and the boys have been entertaining you all right.

DON: Mrs. Carter, I've been having a wonderful time. (FATHER *enters left, looking somewhat grumpy.*)

FATHER: Alice, I just dozed off when you called me.

MOTHER: John, Don Randall is here.

FATHER: Randall? Oh, yes, yes, of course. (*Trying to be more pleasant and going to* DON *and shaking hands.*) How do you do, my boy? Glad to know you.

DON: Thank you, Mr. Carter, it's nice to be here.

FATHER: Well, sit down, won't you? Sit down.

DON: Thanks. (*He sits down downstage right.* SALLY *sits downstage left, still admiring her orchid.* SPIKE *and* BOB *have moved upstage center and sit down.*)

FATHER: Yes, yes, glad to know you—

MOTHER: John, you said that.

FATHER: Why—uh—of course I did and I mean it. It's nice to have a guest for Easter. How long can you stay, my boy?

DON: Why, I'd planned just over tomorrow—they're expecting me home on Monday. But now that I've met your daughter— (*He nods smilingly toward* SALLY) and heard about the Easter Hop, well, I wish there was some way I could manage to stay over.

MOTHER: Why, that would be wonderful. Don gave Sally an orchid to wear on her dress, John.

FATHER: Hmmm. So I see. An orchid, huh?

SPIKE (*Rising suddenly and stepping downstage a little*): Say, excuse me, I just thought of something. Sally, all this talking about the Easter Hop, it reminded me—well, I've been meaning to ask you—

SALLY (*Rising*): Ask me?

SPIKE: Yeah, ask you to go with me. Will you be my date for the Easter Hop?

SALLY: Will I? Oh, Spike, of course I will.

MOTHER: Well, isn't that nice.

SALLY: And Mr. Randall—I mean, Don—do you mind if I wear your orchid?

DON: Of course not, Sally. I'd be honored.

SALLY: Well, then I want to be sure it will keep. I'd better put it in the refrigerator right away. (*She picks up flower box from table and starts left.*)

SPIKE (*Gazing admiringly at* SALLY): I'll go with you, Sally. (*They go off left.* BOB *has stepped downstage and is looking worried.*)

BOB (*Suddenly*): Say, where does this leave me? (*He starts left and as he exits calls*) Sally, do you know if Gertie Simpson has got a date for the dance? (*He goes off left.*)

MOTHER (*Laughing*): Well, it seems to be contagious. Even Bob is going to ask a girl.

FATHER: Amazing—amazing.

MOTHER: Oh, John, you don't know how relieved I am that Spike asked Sally. Now that she has a date for the Hop, I can relax and enjoy Easter.

FATHER: And so can I, Alice—if you're going to be in a sunny mood, though of course it's still going to rain.

MOTHER: Oh, John, who cares about the weather? If the children are happy— (*Remembering their guest and turning to him*) Oh, Don, you'll have to excuse us. Here we've been discussing family affairs and forgetting we had a guest.

DON: Oh, that's all right, Mrs. Carter. I'm interested in this particular family affair.

MOTHER: You are? You mean about Sally? But how did you know?

DON (*Laughing and motioning toward* MARIE *who is busy with her painting*): Well, our artistic friend let me in on some of it.

MOTHER: Goodness, that little one. She's such a talker.

DON: I enjoyed it, and then I must admit that when the boys came in I played possum behind the big chair. I overheard Bob trying to inspire Spike to ask Sally to the dance.

FATHER: Oh, then Bob did try.

DON: Yes, but that wasn't enough to bring Spike around. I think I helped a little by showing appreciation of your daughter's charms.

MOTHER: Well, my goodness.

DON: Yes, I hope you don't mind my butting in.

FATHER: I should say not, my boy. We've been trying to butt in all day.

DON: You see, I know how these things work. It's not so long ago that I was in high school. I made Spike realize what a really pretty girl Sally is, just by putting in my two cents' worth.

FATHER: Two cents' worth? It seems to me that orchid was a little more expensive than that. In fact, I'm not quite sure it's appropriate for a fifteen-year-old girl.

DON: Well, Mr. Carter, the fact is the orchid wasn't really meant for Sally.

MOTHER: What? (*The door buzzer sounds off right.*) Oh dear, there's someone at the door. Will you go, Marie?

MARIE (*Rising*): O.K., Mom. (*She runs out right.*)

DON: Yes, Mrs. Carter, I'm afraid I must apologize for not having any flowers for my hostess. You see, the orchid was really meant for you. It was to be your Easter corsage.

MOTHER: Well, you dear boy. That was so thoughtful of you. But now don't you worry about it a minute. I'll have an Easter corsage. John always gives me one white gardenia.

FATHER: Now, Alice— (MARIE *runs in right carrying a white cardboard box.*)

MARIE: It was flowers, Mom. For you.

MOTHER: There, you see— (*Taking box*) Here it is—one white gardenia. (*She opens box and takes out an orchid.*) Why, no, no, it isn't. It's an orchid. John, they must have made a mistake.

FATHER: It's no mistake. I ordered an orchid and they sent one. You talk as though I didn't have any originality.

MOTHER (*Holding it up*): My, I'm just as thrilled as Sally was with hers.

DON: It's beautiful, Mrs. Carter.

MOTHER (*Looking into box again*): And why, what's this? (*She takes out a single white carnation.*) A white carnation!

FATHER: That, my dear, is for me to wear in my buttonhole. You say I never get dressed up for Easter. And you wonder why I don't want it to rain. Well, let me show you something else. (*He goes off right.*)

MARIE: Mom, it's almost time for my program. The Kiddies' Kut-up. May I turn the radio on?

MOTHER: Yes, dear, but don't turn it on too loud. (MARIE *runs to radio and turns it on. Some music comes on after a minute.* MOTHER *turns to* DON *and nods toward door right.*) Now what is he up to? (FATHER *reënters with a round box from which he is taking a light gray hat.*)

FATHER: Here, my dear. I left this in the hall because I wanted to surprise you. (*He puts box down and sets hat rakishly on his head.*)

MOTHER: John, a new hat for Easter. Why, John, you look wonderful—just wonderful!

DON: It's very smart indeed, Mr. Carter.

FATHER: I thought so. I thought it suited me very well, but now what's going to happen? Rain. It'll get spotted, wrinkled, out of shape. By the time we get to church it'll look exactly like my old one.

MOTHER: Oh, John, no wonder you've been so upset. (*The radio blares a little.*)

FATHER (*Noticing radio*): Must we have the radio on?

MOTHER: Marie's waiting for a program.

VOICE FROM RADIO: The Kiddies' Kut-up program will not be

heard today. Instead we have some Easter music for you. But first the weather announcement.

FATHER: Oh, no! Not that.

VOICE FROM RADIO: The weatherman has been promising us rain, rain, rain. But listen to this, folks. He's changed his mind.

MOTHER: John!

VOICE FROM RADIO: Now he promises us sunshine and lots of it for the Easter parade. Yes, sir, folks, it's going to be fair weather for Easter! (*Low music continues from radio.*)

FATHER (*Joyously*): Fair weather for Easter! (*He takes* MOTHER's *arm and does a few dance steps as he marches her around a little.*) Alice, we'll wear our Easter bonnets—we'll be the smartest couple in the Easter parade.

DON (*Taking* MARIE's *arm*): And we'll be the next smartest. How about it, Marie? Will you walk with me?

MARIE: Oh, I'd love to, but I thought maybe you'd want to walk with Sally.

DON: Oh, she'll probably be with Spike.

MARIE: Yes, I suppose she will. My, it's too bad I'm not a glamour girl—not yet, that is.

DON: Be patient, Marie, be patient.

MARIE (*Running to table*): I know—I'm going to give you my fanciest egg for an Easter present. (*Handing him glamour girl egg*) She's a glamour girl.

DON: Why, thank you, Marie. I'll take her home with me. (*Then holding egg up and laughing as the others look on.*) A hard-boiled glamour girl for Easter. I'm sure my mother will be pleased. (*They all laugh as the curtain falls.*)

THE END

The Life for Mother

Characters

LOUISE NEUHAUSER   BILLY NEUHAUSER
JANE NEUHAUSER   JOHN NEUHAUSER, *father*
DAN NEUHAUSER   MARGARET NEUHAUSER, *mother*

SETTING: *The living room of the Neuhauser home.*

AT RISE: LOUISE NEUHAUSER, *sixteen years old, stands stage center looking at a newspaper.* DAN, *about fifteen, and* JANE, *twelve, stand near her.* BILLY, *about eight, is sprawled in chair left. He bounces a ball now and then.*

LOUISE: I simply can't believe it.

DAN: Neither can I— (*Taking newspaper from* LOUISE) until I look at this newspaper.

JANE (*Looking over his shoulder*): Mother's picture right on the front page!

BILLY: What does it say about her, Jane?

JANE: It says "Attractive author of new book—published this week."

BILLY: Gosh, is Mom famous?

DAN: It looks like it. (*He shakes his head and puts the newspaper on desk.*)

LOUISE (*Walking about*): It all seems like a dream—everything that happened this morning. People calling up—reporters and—

DAN: Well, you girls were here when she left for the luncheon. How did she act?

360

JANE: Oh, excited, of course—and kind of dressed up for Mom.

LOUISE (*Somewhat sadly*) : Yes, I lent her my new hat.

DAN: Don't sound so sad about it, Louise. I guess Mom hasn't had a new hat in ages.

LOUISE: Oh, I was glad to. It just seemed funny, that's all. Mother's always the one who's lending *me* things—why, just yesterday I spilled ink on my white blouse and had to borrow one of hers.

JANE: She looked nice in the hat, didn't she, Louise? Those flowers at the side just seemed to suit her—why, I never knew Mom could look so young and pretty.

DAN: I guess we never half appreciated Mom.

LOUISE: Well, she's getting plenty of appreciation now—being guest of honor at that newspaper club luncheon.

JANE: I guess everybody's hanging on her every word.

DAN: Gee, I'm going to do that more often. Sometimes I don't even listen when she tells me to pick up my clothes. But after this—

LOUISE: You may not get another chance, Dan.

DAN: Huh? What do you mean?

LOUISE: Well, I guess authors never stay at home very much. Besides, home will seem pretty tame to Mother after all the adulation she's receiving.

DAN: Adul-what?

LOUISE: Adulation, addle brain. Don't you ever learn any new words? After all, if you're the son of a famous author—

JANE: What I say is, we've got to make things just as nice as possible for Mom when she gets home. Treat her the way they're treating her at the luncheon. Have some surprises for her—

LOUISE: Yes, Jane, we *are* going to, but I doubt if it will help. (BILLY *stops bouncing his ball and looks up worried.*)

BILLY: You mean Mom won't be at home any more? (*He looks as though he's going to cry.*)

JANE: Now, Billy, don't cry—

BILLY (*His face puckering*): I want my mother!

FATHER (*Off right, calling*): Margaret! Margaret! Where are you, I say?

DAN: It's Dad! (JOHN NEUHAUSER, *father, enters looking harassed. He carries a newspaper.*)

FATHER: Margaret— (*He breaks off.*) Children, where's your mother?

JANE: She isn't here.

DAN: Dad, what are you doing home in the middle of the day?

FATHER: One of the men at the office brought me this paper and I rushed right out. I just couldn't believe your mother had written a book. Why isn't she at home? (BILLY *begins to cry*) What's the matter with everyone? Billy, what are you crying about?

BILLY: I want Mother.

FATHER: Well, so do I. But it seems she isn't here. (*He takes out his handkerchief and mops at his brow.*)

LOUISE: No, Dad, she's guest of honor at a luncheon because of the book.

JANE: But Dad, you knew Mother was writing, didn't you?

FATHER: Yes—yes—I knew she was writing something—in the evenings when I read my paper she sometimes pecked away at the typewriter, but I thought it was something for her club or—

LOUISE: And to think she kept it a secret when her book was accepted for publication!

FATHER (*Sitting down in chair right heavily and staring at paper again*): Look at this paper—"Margaret Dale, author." What I can't understand is why it says Margaret *Dale*. Her name's Neuhauser.

LOUISE: But Dale was her maiden name.

FATHER: Of course, but she changed that to Neuhauser when she married me.

JANE: But the publishers thought Neuhauser was kind of a funny name, I guess.

FATHER: What's that? Neuhauser wasn't good enough for them?

LOUISE: They thought Dale sounded better, Mother said. More euphonious.

DAN: If you'd stop using those dollar words, Louise—

FATHER: Never mind. Your mother certainly can't go around having people call her Mrs. Dale.

DAN: Sure she can, Dad—and they'll probably call you *Mr.* Dale.

FATHER: What's that?

LOUISE: I wouldn't be surprised. Everyone knows that the husband of a famous woman is just more or less background.

FATHER: Background?

JANE (*Almost crying*): That's all any of us will be from now on—just a background to Mother's life. But I'd even be glad to be background if only she'd be at home.

FATHER: At home? What are you talking about? Your mother's not going away. What would we do? Why, even now when I get home like this and she isn't here, it doesn't seem right—

JANE: When she went to the luncheon she smiled at us and then she said, "I'll be seeing you sometime."

FATHER: She did?

LOUISE: Now, Jane, don't exaggerate. She'll be home today all right—she may even be home a week or two before she goes to Hollywood or somewhere.

FATHER: Hollywood?

LOUISE: Authors often go to Hollywood, Father.

FATHER: Louise, are you out of your mind? What would your mother do in Hollywood?

JANE: Maybe she'll meet Bing Crosby or someone. That's what I'd do if I were going.

BILLY (*Crying again*): I want my mother.

FATHER: Now—now, son, don't cry. Maybe it isn't as bad as we think and if it is we'll—well, we'll just have to face it.

JANE: How can we? When I think of living without Mother—why, just this morning Mother sewed up a run in my stocking, as busy as she was.

DAN (*Sadly*): Yeah, and yesterday she sewed a button on my pants.

LOUISE: Yes—and she's forever doing things for me.

BILLY: Me, too. (*He has stopped crying and starts toward the others.*) Why, look at my finger—she bandaged it up where I cut it. (*He is examining the fingers on both hands.*)

DAN: You and your cuts. It was probably only a scratch. Why, look, you can't even find it.

BILLY: I can too. (*He is still searching.*)

FATHER: Now, boys. Of course you can't find the cut, Billy. It has already healed. That just shows how well your mother does things. We can all think of a thousand things she's done for us—I'm thinking of the way she fries my egg in the morning—not too hard, not too soft—just right. Children, we haven't appreciated your mother enough.

LOUISE: Of course not—and now it's too late.

FATHER: Why, when I think of how I've made mountains out of molehills. Your mother often makes little mistakes when she fills out her check stubs, and I've criticized her for that, not realizing how unimportant check stubs could be to a brilliant woman.

DAN: Brilliant?

FATHER: Certainly, brilliant. (*He is looking at paper again.*)

It says right here in the paper she's brilliant. It says critics acclaim new book.

LOUISE: What do you make of that title, Dad?

FATHER: Title? I don't even know what it is.

LOUISE (*Crossing to* FATHER *and pointing at newspaper*): The title is *What a Life*. It's right at the head of the column here.

FATHER: Oh, yes, so it is.

JANE: *What a Life*—you can't tell anything from that. Is it about love or romance—

DAN: All books don't have to be about love.

FATHER: No, that title *What a Life* has somewhat tragic overtones. It's probably about— (*He looks at paper again.*) Good gracious, it's about us!

LOUISE: About us?

DAN: What?

JANE: You don't mean—

FATHER: It says right here—"Mrs. Dale has written a book about her own family . . . the characters are her husband, her two sons, her two daughters—"

LOUISE: Oh, my goodness!

DAN: And the title is *What a Life?*

FATHER: Yes, son. I'm thinking of that. Why would your mother write a book about us and call it such a thing as that?

LOUISE: It's obvious what she means. What a *hard* life. Why, haven't we just been saying all the things she's done for us— how hard she's worked and that we haven't appreciated her. Now, she's put it all into a book.

FATHER: Louise, your mother wouldn't do anything like that.

LOUISE: Oh, yes she would. She probably couldn't help herself. When people have as hard a time as Mother's had, they have to tell someone.

FATHER: But did she have to tell the whole world?

LOUISE (*Dramatically*): Dad, she had to bare her soul to somebody or she couldn't have gone on, and that was probably the only way she knew. She had to get it out of her system.

FATHER: Louise, where did you get such ideas?

LOUISE: Well, after all, I've studied a little psychology—I ought to know.

DAN: Oh, you and your psychology.

LOUISE: Laugh if you like but I know I'm right. Mother's mental reflexes have become active.

FATHER: What can we do? This is terrible.

DAN: Why didn't any of us realize we were giving Mother such a hard time?

JANE: Well, we realize it now. We've got to change *our* mental reflexes—make Mother know we appreciate her, do everything we can for her.

LOUISE: You're quite right, Jane—and even though I'm afraid it's too late, I've already started. I've baked a cake.

FATHER: Baked a cake?

LOUISE: Yes, Dad, don't you see? Right this minute Mother's receiving lots of attention from everyone. When she gets home she won't want to face the same old situation—Mother, do this, do that.

FATHER: Yes, I see your point. We've got to create a new atmosphere—have everything just right.

LOUISE: Exactly—be thinking—and I'd better get to frosting my cake. I might even decorate it.

JANE: Go ahead, Louise, and I'll plan the rest of the supper. (LOUISE *goes out left.*)

DAN: Ho, what can you cook?

JANE: Well, I can make waffles. You just stir up the batter and the waffle iron does the rest.

FATHER: Fine, Jane. Now, let's see, what else can we do? (*He puts his paper on table and rises.*) This room—doesn't it look a little upset?

Jane: Yes, Dad, Mother was in such a rush this morning, she didn't have time to do a thing.

Father: Well, then, boys, that's where we come in. Get some brooms—get some dustcloths.

Billy: O.K., Dad. (*He runs out left.*)

Father: We'll clean up.

Dan: But Dad, I'm not very good at that sort of thing.

Father: You'll have to learn.

Jane (*Pointing toward window*): If someone could fix the bracket on that curtain rod it would help. I've heard Mother say several times that it was loose.

Dan: Oh, I can do that. All I need is a screw driver and something to stand on. (*He exits left quickly.*)

Jane: Well, I'm going to start supper. (*She exits left as* Billy *re-enters carrying a broom and a dustcloth.*)

Billy: Here you are, Dad. Shall I dust?

Father: Fine, Billy, and I'll sweep. (*He takes the broom and starts dabbing about at the floor with it. He leans over, pushing the broom underneath a chair, and pulls broom back and forth a couple of times, then dabs at the floor some more.*) Always get under things, son, not just around them. If a job's worth doing, it's worth doing right.

Billy: O.K., where shall I start?

Father: Well, let me see—you might start— (*He looks around.*) On second thought, you'd better take over with the broom. (*He hands the broom to* Billy *and wipes his brow.*) I've just thought of an errand.

Billy: You mean I've got to dust and sweep too?

Father: Well, perhaps Dan will help you when he finishes fixing the curtain rod. I'm just going down to the drugstore— I'll be back in a minute. Now, just kind of pick up—fix things nicely. (Father *exits right.* Billy *puts down his dustcloth and starts sweeping briskly.* DAN *re-enters carrying a small stepladder and a screw driver.*)

DAN: Gosh, Billy, do you have to raise such a dust?

BILLY: Well, I'm sweeping.

DAN: Yeah, but the more dirt you raise, the more you'll have to dust.

BILLY: I never thought of that. Maybe I've swept enough. (*He leans the broom against table at right and looks about.* DAN *put stepladder near window, climbs up on it and starts working at the bracket with his screw driver.*) I wonder what I ought to do next. Dad went out for a minute but he said to kind of pick up and fix things nice.

DAN (*Looking down and around room*): Well, there's that coat to pick up and—say, I've got an idea. You know how Mom always fixes Dad's chair up before he comes home?

BILLY: Sure, but it's Mom we're fixing for.

DAN: Exactly. Fix *her* chair up. Light the lamp by it, and let's see—she always puts out Dad's newspaper—we'll get her knitting ready.

BILLY: O.K. (*He lights the lamp on table near chair left, and then looks around the room.*) Where's her knitting?

DAN (*Looking down and around*): In her knitting bag—on the desk there. (*He turns to his work again.*)

BILLY: I see it. (BILLY *crosses upstage, opens knitting bag on desk and takes out some knitting. He returns toward Mother's chair and table. As he does so a needle drops out. He picks it up, stands looking at it for a moment, the needle in one hand, the knitting in the other, then shoves needle back, weaving it back and forth through the knitting. Just as he does so the other needle drops out. He looks surprised, then quickly picks second needle up and shoves it through, and then places the knitting on the table next the chair. He stands off and surveys the whole set up.*) Say, Dan, I've got an idea.

DAN: Yeah, what is it?

BILLY: You know how Mom always puts out Dad's slippers for him. Well, why don't I get her bedroom slippers and set them right by the chair?

DAN: Gee, I don't know, Billy. Maybe you'd better ask Louise.

BILLY (*Going left, calling*): Louise! Louise!

LOUISE (*Off*): Yes, what is it?

BILLY: Come here a minute.

LOUISE (*Appearing in doorway left*): What do you want, Billy? I'm just going to frost the cake.

BILLY: I was getting Mom's chair all comfortable for her. Do you think she'd like her bedroom slippers?

LOUISE (*Laughing a little as she comes into the room*): Why, I don't know. Maybe that's a nice idea. (*Calling*) Jane!

JANE (*Appearing in doorway left*): What's the matter, Louise? The waffle batter's all mixed.

LOUISE: Good. Billy's got a cute idea. He wants to put Mom's slippers by her chair here. What do you think?

JANE: Oh, I think that would be grand. Go ahead, Billy, get them.

BILLY (*Happily*): I will. (*He runs out left.*)

LOUISE: And we'd all better hurry. You, too, Dan, with those curtains. Mom will be home any minute now. (LOUISE *and* JANE *go off left.* FATHER *enters right looking pleased with himself. He holds a small package.*)

FATHER: Well, I made it. She's not home yet, is she?

DAN: No.

FATHER: Good. Haven't you got that thing fixed?

DAN: I'm having a little trouble. The more I turn this screw the bigger the hole gets.

FATHER: Well, I—I thought everything would be out of the way.

DAN: Gee, Dad, we're going as fast as we can. (BILLY *runs in*

*left carrying a pair of bedroom slippers. He runs to chair left
and puts slippers down in front of it.*)

BILLY: See, Dad? How's that? Mom's slippers set out just the
way she always does yours.

FATHER: Hmm, that's a nice touch—a very nice touch—and
wait until you see what I've got. (*He takes paper off package
and then takes a bottle from a cardboard carton.*) I bought
a little present for your mother—to kind of top things off—
something she'll like.

DAN (*Turning*): What is it, Dad?

FATHER: Perfume—expensive perfume—the best. You know
I often give her something practical for the house like an ironing board or a coffee pot—but this is different. (*He holds it
up to show* DAN.)

DAN: Boy, that's all right, Dad. That's something a fellow
would give his best girl.

FATHER: That's what I thought.

BILLY (*Coming to* FATHER): Let me see. (*He looks at bottle.*)
But what does it do?

FATHER: It doesn't do anything, son, except smell.

BILLY (*Sniffing*): I don't smell anything.

FATHER: Here—here—I'll show you. (*He takes off the stopper.*)
There—take a sniff. The clerk said it was a haunting fra-
grance.

BILLY: Phew-w—I wouldn't want it to haunt me. It smells
awful.

FATHER: Now—now, I wouldn't expect you to be too enthusiastic, but your mother will love it. (LOUISE *and* JANE *enter
left.*)

LOUISE: Well, the cake's all frosted. It's a little runny, but I
put it in the refrigerator. They say that's a sure way to make
frosting set.

JANE: And I've started the first waffle, so there'll be a good stack of 'em when Mom gets here.

FATHER: You're just in time, girls. What do you think of this for a present for your mother? (*He waves the bottle under their noses.*)

LOUISE: Oh, Dad, how marvelous!

JANE: It's just what she'll like!

FATHER: Fine—I thought you'd approve. (*He puts stopper on bottle quickly, shoves bottle in his coat pocket and sits down in chair right.*)

JANE: Well, I guess we're just about all set.

LOUISE: Yes, hurry up and finish, Dan.

DAN: O.K., don't rush me. (DAN *starts puffing away, working harder than ever with his screw driver.*)

LOUISE: And we've got to get this broom out of here—

JANE (*Surveying the room. She walks near chair left*): I think that's nice having Mom's chair all ready and her slippers— but do you think we ought to have her knitting?

BILLY: Sure—that's like Dad's newspaper—all ready for her.

JANE: But doesn't it look as though we're trying to make her work? What do you think, Louise?

LOUISE (*Coming over and looking at table*): I don't know—of course she does relax when she knits— (*She stops and stares at knitting, then grabs it up.*) What on earth's happened to Mom's knitting? Billy, you've pulled the needles out!

BILLY: I did not.

LOUISE: Who did, then?

BILLY: Nobody did. They fell out.

LOUISE: Billy, how could you be so careless?

DAN (*Turning from his work*): What's he done now?

JANE: Dropped the needles out of Mom's knitting.

DAN: Can you imagine anyone being so dumb? (*He turns and*

gives a couple of hard twists on the screw driver, something gives way and the curtain rod and curtains fall with a crash.)

LOUISE: Oh-h—Dan Neuhauser, now what have *you* done?

DAN: I—I don't know. I don't know what happened. The bracket broke right off.

BILLY: Now, who's dumb?

DAN: Quiet, you.

FATHER (*Rising*): Well, this is a fine how-do-you-do. We wanted to have things extra nice for your mother and—

DAN (*Climbing down off ladder*): Well, I couldn't help it, Dad.

FATHER: You couldn't help it—that's no excuse— (*He stops.*) Oh-h—oh, dear me. (*He puts his hand in pocket and then turns around and stares at chair.*) The perfume—

JANE: What's the matter, Dad?

FATHER: The perfume— (*He takes the bottle out of his pocket.*) The stopper came out. It's all over me—it's all over the chair—

LOUISE (*Coming to look at chair*): Oh, my goodness. That big stain. Dad, don't you realize Mother just put a new slip cover on this chair last week? She paid two dollars a yard for the material.

FATHER: I can't help it. I paid ten dollars for the perfume.

BILLY: It smells awful in here.

DAN: And it isn't only perfume. I smell something else. Something's burning.

JANE: Oh—my waffles! (*She rushes out left.*)

DAN: It doesn't smell like waffles to me. It smells like sugar burning or—

LOUISE: No, it's just Jane's waffles. (JANE *rushes back in looking angry.*)

JANE: It wasn't waffles at all, Louise. It was your cake frosting that was burning up.

LOUISE: You're crazy, Jane. My frosting is on the cake.

JANE: That's what you think. My waffle batter is on the cake. You mixed the bowls up!

LOUISE: *I* mixed them up? Nothing of the kind. You must have.

JANE: I don't know *who* mixed them up—all I know is that we have no cake and no waffles and the kitchen's a mess. The waffle batter is running all over the refrigerator and burnt frosting has dripped all over the floor.

FATHER: Well, this is a fine mess. A fine mess. Your mother will be here any minute now and I wouldn't blame her if she turned right around and *went* to Hollywood. And maybe I'll go with her.

BILLY: Gee, Dad—maybe she wouldn't want you—not the way *you* smell.

MOTHER (*Off right, calling*): Hello, everyone—hello! Here I am.

ALL: It's Mother! (MOTHER *enters all smiles.*)

MOTHER: Hello, family, I'm home at last— (*She stops and stares.*) My—oh, my! I thought *I'd* had a big day—but what's happened here?

JANE: Everything—we wanted to fix things up nice and—

DAN: And the curtains fell down.

BILLY: And your knitting came undone.

MOTHER: And what do I smell? What on earth do I smell? (*Crossing to* FATHER *and sniffing*) John, you smell like a cosmetic counter.

FATHER: Yes, my dear. I bought you a present. Now it's on me—and—er—your new slip cover.

MOTHER: Well! And is something burning?

JANE: Yes, Mother—cake frosting—on the waffle iron.

MOTHER: But what in the world is it doing on the waffle iron?

LOUISE: Because I put the waffle batter on a cake I made.

MOTHER: Well—well—well! (*She starts to laugh.*) You wouldn't think so many things could happen in one afternoon. Do you see now why I had to write a book about you?

LOUISE: Yes, Mother, we certainly do, and we don't blame you. We're such a mess—we do everything wrong—

MOTHER: Now, now, you mustn't feel sorry for yourselves— we'll get everything straightened out. (*Walking about*) Those curtains needed to be fixed over again anyhow—and as for that slip cover—I made it too big. We can send it to the cleaners now and maybe they'll shrink it.

BILLY: But your knitting, Mom.

MOTHER: Never mind, Billy. It was to be a sweater for you. You'll just have to wait a little longer for it. And we can get this living room picked up—the broom and—my goodness, here are my bedroom slippers. I'm going to put them right on. (*She sits down in chair left and takes off a pair of high-heeled shoes.*) I was all dressed up so on the way to the luncheon I foolishly thought I'd buy a new pair of shoes—extra high heels. (*She holds them up, then sets them on the floor.*) My feet are killing me! (*She slips her feet into her bedroom slippers.*) I don't know how my slippers found their way down here, but they feel wonderful.

JANE: Don't tell me we did one thing right.

MOTHER: Of course you did. (*She takes off her hat, puts it on table next to chair and rises.*) There, now I can really get to work.

LOUISE: But Mother, we wanted you to take things easy.

MOTHER: That's all I've been doing all afternoon.

DAN: But you've had such a hard life, Mom.

MOTHER: What?

JANE: You had to become a famous author, Mom, to make us see—

MOTHER: Famous, nonsense. Of course the critics seem to like the book, but I don't know if most people will enjoy reading about my day or not.

DAN: Your day, Mom?

MOTHER: Yes, dear. You know, famous women are always writing about their days, what they do, etc., so one morning after breakfast after you'd all gone, I had an extra cup of coffee before I did the dishes, and I thought: I wonder if anyone would be interested in *my* day, and I started to make notes. Well, now the critics seem to think my day is the typical American day.

LOUISE: My goodness, you mean all mothers have as hard a time as you do, Mom?

MOTHER: Hard? What on earth are you talking about?

FATHER: Well, my dear, you called the book *What a Life.*

MOTHER: Of course. What a *wonderful* life. I wrote about all the funny things that happen in a family, the fun we have together—the affection—

FATHER: Margaret, my dear.

CHILDREN: Oh, Mother!

MOTHER: I told about the time you forgot our anniversary, John, and then got up in the middle of the night to try and buy me a present—and about the time you climbed out on the roof, Billy, hoping to see Santa Claus—

BILLY: Boy, wait till I tell the kids at school I'm in a book!

MOTHER: Well, I'm glad you all approve. You know, John, if I make any money on the book I thought we could use it to finish paying on the house.

FATHER: Margaret. (*He kisses her.*)

LOUISE: Oh, Mom, I'm so relieved. Even if you have to go away.

MOTHER: Away? Away where?

JANE: Well, authors sometimes go to Hollywood.

MOTHER: Land sakes—as though I'd ever do anything like that. I told the publishers that if I ever wrote anything else, I'd have to do it right here where I'd have some inspiration.

DAN: Inspiration, Mom?

MOTHER: Why, of course—all of you—my family. I couldn't write a word anywhere but at home. This is the life for me. (*She starts bustling about again, picks up the broom.*) Besides, I don't suppose I ever *will* write another book—that is— (*She stops and then starts laughing.*) But just the same, maybe I ought to make a few notes about this afternoon.

DAN (*Taking the broom from her and leaning on it*): Sure, Mom, why don't you?

LOUISE (*Running to desk*): Here's a pencil, Mother.

JANE (*Getting some paper*): And some paper.

FATHER (*Leading* MOTHER *to chair left*): Sit down, Margaret.

BILLY: We'll help you, Mom.

MOTHER (*Holding pencil and looking off into space for a moment*): Let's see—my day started out calmly enough— (*She writes a little, then looks up smiling.*) But by the time the cake had been frosted with the waffle batter—

CHILDREN (*All laughing*): That was the end of a perfect day!

THE END

Mom's a Grandma Now

Characters

FATHER, *Henry*   MARIE
MOTHER, *Elizabeth*   VICTOR
BETTY   GRANDPA TERWILIGER
JACK

TIME: *The Saturday before Mother's Day. Late afternoon.*
SETTING: *A living room.*
AT RISE: *The stage is empty and the phone is ringing.* BETTY, *sixteen, and* MARIE, *twelve, enter right wearing jackets. Each one carries a small paper bag.*

BETTY: Oh, the phone. I'll get it. (*She runs toward phone throwing off her jacket as she goes. Picking up phone*) Hello? No, this is Betty. You want Mother? Just a minute. Call Mom, Marie.

MARIE (*Calling as she goes to doorway left*): Mom—oh, Mom! Mom! I guess she isn't here. (*She takes off her jacket, throws it over a chair and sits down in easy chair left, taking a small box out of her paper bag.*)

BETTY (*Into phone*): I guess Mother isn't here right now. . . . I don't know. We've been shopping all afternoon and just got in . . . Oh . . . Oh . . . Sure, we'll be here. Goodbye. (*She hangs up.*)

MARIE: Who was it?

BETTY: Old Mr. Terwiliger's daughter. She's sending him over with a shawl Mom wanted to borrow.

MARIE: What's Mom want a shawl for?

BETTY: How should I know? Anyhow, I'm glad she's not here. It gives us a chance to look at our presents again. I wish the boys would come. (*She sits down at right and opens paper bag.*)

MARIE: So do I. I can hardly wait to see what they bought for Mom.

BETTY: I just hope they didn't get anything too practical.

MARIE: They wouldn't dare. Didn't we all agree that this Mother's Day was going to be different?

BETTY: Yes, but I still don't quite trust the boys. They've got one track minds and think Mom always has to have pots and pans or something.

MARIE: Well, my present's certainly glamorous enough. (*Lifting lid of small box and showing perfume bottle*) Wait until Mom gets a sniff of this.

BETTY: She'll love your perfume, Marie— (*Holding up flat box*) and she'll love these nylons too. (*Slipping box back into bag*) Here comes someone.

MARIE: It's not Mom—it's the boys. (JACK, *fourteen, and* VICTOR, *eight, enter right, wearing jackets.*)

JACK: Hi, there.

BETTY: Hi—we've been wondering where you were. (*The boys take their jackets off and throw them over chairs.*)

JACK: Well, the stores are so crowded—everybody's buying presents for mothers.

MARIE: You're telling us?

VICTOR: Wait until you see what we've got. I bought some—

JACK: Quiet, Victor. Where's Mom?

BETTY: It's all right. She's not around. Let's see your presents. (BETTY *and* MARIE *go to the boys and they are all at stage center.*)

VICTOR: Show them mine, Jack. (*To girls*) He wouldn't let me carry it because he was afraid I'd lose it.

JACK: He almost did lose it on the way home. He's got a hole in his pocket and it dropped out.

MARIE: Honestly! Mom's always mending his pockets but he carries so much junk around.

VICTOR: Well, hurry up and show my present.

JACK (*Taking small card with earrings attached from his pocket*): Here it is—a pair of earrings.

VICTOR: They cost a dollar twenty.

JACK: But they look more expensive than that . . . see? (BETTY *and* MARIE *both look.* BETTY *takes card and holds it up.*)

BETTY: Oh, they're beautiful!

MARIE: Look at the way they sparkle.

VICTOR: Well, let me have them. I can keep them now. I'll put them in my other pocket. (BETTY *hands card with earrings to* VICTOR *and he shoves it in his pocket.*)

BETTY: But what did you get, Jack? Where's your package?

JACK: I haven't got a package—

MARIE: What?

JACK (*Takes small envelope from inside coat pocket*): All I've got is this little envelope— (*He takes card from envelope.*) And it cost five bucks.

BETTY: Jack, what in the world? That's not a down payment on a vacuum cleaner or something, is it?

JACK: Vacuum cleaner, huh! It's reservations. (*Showing card*) Look—

MARIE (*Reading*): Reserved: A table for two in the Palm Room for Saturday evening, May—

BETTY: Jack! That smart new room in the Plaza Hotel. How perfectly wonderful.

JACK: Sure, dinner and dancing in the Palm Room for tonight.

And it's all paid for. That is, except for tips and extras maybe. Dad can take care of that, I guess.

BETTY: Of course he can. Oh, Jack, I don't know how you ever thought of it.

JACK: Well, we wanted something different—but I was kind of worried just at first.

MARIE: Worried? Why?

JACK: Because Mom and Dad haven't done anything like that for a long time. But I got to thinking maybe we ought to push them into it.

BETTY: You're absolutely right. Mom will have a big evening for a change—and everything fits in perfectly. I've got nylons for her to wear. (*Showing box*) Look, as sheer as a morning mist.

JACK (*Laughing*): Yeah? What's a morning mist?

BETTY: I don't know—but that's what it says on the box. And Marie's got perfume.

MARIE (*Showing box*): Yes—and look what it's called—Evening Enchantment.

JACK: Gosh, for an enchanted evening at the Palm Room. That's all right.

VICTOR: And don't forget my earrings.

BETTY: Of course not, Victor. Mom can wear them too. They'll add the final touch.

MARIE: If only Dad doesn't let us down, and come home with an orange squeezer.

BETTY: Oh, he won't. I told Dad a dozen times he had to get something frivolous this year.

JACK: So did I.

BETTY: Poor Dad. I'll bet he's having a time. He hates shopping anyhow and with all those crowds—

JACK: Say, hadn't we better get these things out of the way before Mom shows up? Where did you say she was?

BETTY: We didn't say. We don't know where she is.

JACK: Maybe she's upstairs resting.

MARIE: Oh, you know Mom never rests. Besides, we called up-stairs—someone wanted her on the phone.

VICTOR: Well, wherever she is, I wish she'd come. Isn't it almost suppertime?

BETTY: Oh—not yet, Victor.

VICTOR: But I'm hungry.

BETTY: As usual. Go get yourself a cookie then. (VICTOR *goes out left.*)

JACK: Say, what about supper? If Mom and Dad are going to dine at the Palm Room, when do *we* eat?

MARIE: Oh, they won't dine until later. Mom will have time to fix something for us before she leaves.

BETTY: Not on your life. We'll fix hamburgers for ourselves—I know—hamburgers and hot chocolate and maybe we can invite some of the gang in if Mom says it's all right.

JACK: Say, that would be swell. I know Mom won't care. (VIC-TOR *re-enters chewing on a cookie, with another in his hand. He also carries a piece of paper with writing on it.*)

VICTOR: Look what was propped up against the cookie jar—a note from Mom.

MARIE: A note from Mom? What does it say?

VICTOR: I don't know.

BETTY: Well, let me have it, Victor. (*Laughing*) If that isn't just like Mom. She knew that sooner or later one of us would go to the cookie jar.

JACK: What's it all about? Where is Mom?

BETTY: Let's see. (*Reading*) Dear Children: I have wonderful news for you—

JACK: Huh?

BETTY (*Going on*): Your sister's baby arrived this morning—a six-pound boy.

MARIE: A boy!

JACK: Well, isn't that something!

VICTOR: Gee . . .

BETTY (*Still reading*): I've gone to Plain City to see her, and I called your father at the office and told him the news.

JACK: Gosh, is Dad going to be excited.

BETTY: Who isn't excited? And I'll bet Mom is relieved. I know she's been worrying a little.

MARIE: Sis with a baby—I still can hardly imagine it.

BETTY: I wonder when we'll get to see the baby! Oh, isn't it perfectly thrilling?

JACK: I'll say.

VICTOR: Gosh, a baby. I thought Mom was going to go out tonight and wear my earrings.

MARIE: That's right. The reservations and everything.

JACK: Do you suppose this means she'll stay over? Does she say when she'll be back, Betty?

BETTY (*Reading to herself*): It's all right. Let me read the rest of the note. (*Reading*) Visiting hours at the hospital are from two to four so I'll be home on the five o'clock bus.

JACK: Well, that's good.

BETTY (*Still reading*): Take care of yourselves—love, Mother. P.S. Betty, if you have a minute, run the iron over that dress laid out on my bed. I have to wear it tomorrow. I was just going to do it when the call came from Bill.

JACK: I'd like to see Bill now. I'll bet he's the proud papa.

MARIE: Yes and— (*Breaking off*) Oh, my goodness, I just thought of something—I'm an aunt.

BETTY: And so am I.

JACK: And I'm an uncle. Why, we all are. We're aunts and uncles now.

VICTOR: Me, too?

JACK: Sure, you're Uncle Victor.

VICTOR (*Grinning a little and straightening up*): Uncle Victor.

JACK (*Laughing*): I guess babies are all right, huh, kid?

VICTOR: Yeah—and now I don't have to run all the errands maybe—if I'm an uncle.

MARIE: You're still the youngest in the family. In fact, you're about the youngest uncle I ever heard of.

VICTOR (*Not quite so happy*): Well, I'm still an uncle.

BETTY: Of course you are, and Dad's a grandfather and Mom's —why, Mom is a grandmother!

MARIE: So she is—a grandmother. I can hardly believe it.

VICTOR: Do grandmas wear earrings?

JACK: Sure they do—or—I guess they do. Say, it is kind of funny, isn't it? For once we get Mom all these frivolous things and then right away she turns into a grandmother.

BETTY: Well, what difference does that make?

JACK: Oh, I don't know—but grandmother—it sounds so kind of dignified or something.

MARIE (*A little worried and holding up her perfume*): Do you thing she'll still like Evening Enchantment?

JACK: And what about dancing in the Palm Room?

BETTY: Oh, you kids, stop worrying. I don't think Mom's going to be any different just because she's a grandma. That's an old-fashioned idea. Grandmothers nowadays aren't any different from anyone else. (*Going to table and picking up magazine and looking through it*) I saw something in this magazine just the other day.

JACK: Well, I don't know.

BETTY: Yes, here it is. "Glamorous Grandmas in Hollywood."

MARIE: You mean movie stars?

BETTY: Of course. Look at this one. (*Showing picture*) She has the lead in a new musical show. And here's another at one of the night spots. Look, Jack.

JACK (*Looking at picture in magazine*): Wow, some grandma.

BETTY: So what are you worrying about? I guess Mom can still go dancing if she wants to.

JACK: Sure, she can.

BETTY: Why, it's perfectly ridiculous to think that just because Mom is a grandmother she'll want to settle back and act as though she's a hundred.

MARIE: Can you picture Mom doing that? Why, she'll love all the things we've got for her.

BETTY: And Jack, your idea of their going out tonight is better than ever. Now they've really got something to celebrate.

JACK: Say, that's right—their first grandson.

FATHER (*Off right. Calling*): Anybody home?

VICTOR: Gee, here's Pop.

JACK (*Laughing*): You mean *Grand*pop. (*Calling*) We're all in the living room, Dad. (FATHER *enters right with a package under his arm.*)

ALL: Hi, Grandpa! Welcome home, Grandfather.

FATHER (*Putting package on side table. Then rather solemnly*): So you've heard the news. What do you think of it, Victor?

VICTOR: *Uncle* Victor.

FATHER: Why, so you are. I hadn't thought of that angle. It seems incredible. Children, ever since your mother called me at the office—of course we didn't have much time to talk—but I've thought of nothing but this—this important thing that's happened to us.

BETTY: It's wonderful, isn't it, Dad?

FATHER: Wonderful and amazing. To think of your sister, Helen, being a mother. My, I don't know where the years have gone. It seems only yesterday that she was a little girl, no bigger than Victor.

VICTOR: *Uncle* Victor.

JACK: Victor's certainly taking this business of being an uncle seriously.

FATHER: Son, it is serious. I suppose you children can't realize it. But it makes a man stop and think. Your mother and I are grandparents now. It's made a change in me already.

JACK: But you don't look any different, Dad.

FATHER: It's more than a matter of appearance, son. It goes deeper. It's something inside. (*Pounding his chest*) It's like a millstone.

BETTY: A millstone?

FATHER: No—no, I mean a milestone—a milestone in my life. Why, do you realize, children—once I was a baby like that little fellow in the hospital?

JACK: So you were, Dad. Mom showed us your baby picture once. You certainly looked funny.

FATHER: Jack, this is nothing to laugh about. My point is that I grew into a young man—then I was a husband, then a father. I thought nothing more could happen to me, but now —now I'm a grandfather. Soon I'll be a great grandfather.

BETTY: Now, wait a minute, Dad—

JACK: Aren't you getting carried away?

FATHER: No—no, it will happen. That dear little fellow in the hospital that we haven't seen will grow into a man.

MARIE: I guess he will but not for quite a while.

FATHER: The years fly by, Marie. We must be thinking of that little fellow and what we can do for him. And we must be thinking of your mother. This—this will mean a great deal to her. We must be extra nice to her when she gets home.

BETTY: Of course, Dad. We've got all kinds of surprises for her.

MARIE: Wonderful presents—we'll show them to you. But what did you get, Dad?

JACK: Yeah, what's in your package?

BETTY: Let's see it, Dad. I hope it's something Mom's going to like.

FATHER: No, I'm afraid there's no use even looking at it, children.

MARIE: But why not?

FATHER: Because it's wrong, all wrong. I bought it and then as soon as I walked out of the shop I had a feeling that I'd made a mistake.

BETTY: Dad, you didn't buy an electric iron or a mixer—not after all we'd said?

FATHER: No, I bought a bed jacket. I went into this shop and I saw just the thing—an old fashioned sort of jacket—lavender wool—knitted.

MARIE: But it—it sounds awful. You didn't buy *that?*

FATHER: No, that's just the trouble. I remembered what you children had said so I picked out another one—pink and frilly with ribbons.

BETTY: But Dad, that's wonderful. It sounds just right. (*She runs to table and takes cover off box.*) Oh-h! (*Holding box up*) Look at this, everyone.

JACK: Say, that's sharp.

MARIE: Pink chiffon! It's beautiful—perfectly beautiful.

VICTOR: Gee, is Mom going to wear that in bed?

FATHER (*Taking box from* BETTY): No, son, she is not. Now that I see it again I am sure that it is not the sort of thing a grandmother should wear.

JACK: But Dad, that's silly.

BETTY: Why, Mom would love it.

FATHER: No, the young lady at the shop was right.

JACK: What do you mean?

FATHER: I asked her for something for a grandmother and she knew immediately—her woman's instinct told her to bring me the lavender knitted one.

BETTY: Oh, Dad, I'll bet she thought you meant for *your* grandmother.

FATHER: Betty, a grandmother is a grandmother and if my mind hadn't been confused by all your talk about frivolous things I should have known. I should never have asked to see anything else.

BETTY: Well, it's a good thing you did ask. This frilly one is perfect with all the things we've got— (*Holding up her box*) Look—nylons—

VICTOR (*Fishing card with earrings from his pocket*): And earrings, see?

MARIE (*Taking lid of box from perfume*): And exotic perfume —smell it, Dad.

FATHER (*Shaking his head*): Tsk, tsk, tsk!

JACK (*Taking envelope from pocket*): And to top it all off, Dad, look what I've got. Reservations for the Palm Room. You and Mom are stepping out tonight.

FATHER: Stepping out? Jack, have you lost your mind?

JACK: Of course not, Dad.

FATHER: But how could you imagine that your mother and I would want to go out tonight now—now that this has happened. We'll want to sit at home quietly and—and "reminisce."

MARIE: But I'll bet Mom would love to go out.

BETTY: She can wear all the things we've got her and sleep late tomorrow morning and we'll serve her breakfast in bed and she can wear her new bed jacket then.

FATHER (*Putting cover on box*): Your mother will never wear this bed jacket. I am going to put it away in the hall closet and Monday morning I shall return it and get the lavender knitted one.

CHILDREN: Oh, Dad. No!

FATHER: And as for those reservations, Jack, perhaps you could return them and get your money back.

JACK: But Dad—

FATHER: As for the other presents, I don't know. Of course none of you knew this was going to happen today but now that it has, well, perhaps you could return them and get something more appropriate. (*He starts right with box.*) I'll just take this into the hall. (*He goes out.*)

VICTOR: Gee, does Pop mean I have to return these earrings? (*He looks at them sorrowfully and shoves them back into his pocket.*)

JACK: I guess I never should have got these reservations. (*He puts them back into his pocket.*)

BETTY: Our beautiful presents. We just can't return them. (BETTY *and* MARIE *place packages on side table near chair at left.*) What on earth is the matter with Dad?

JACK: I don't know. I guess it's just being a grandfather. He— he seems to have changed all of a sudden. . . . Gosh, you don't think Mom will have changed too, do you, the way Dad says?

MARIE: Of course not. Betty, why don't you show Dad the magazine? Maybe that will make him see the light.

BETTY: That's a good idea. (FATHER *re-enters without package.* BETTY *picks up magazine and shows it to him.*) Look, Dad—you seem to think grandmothers have to be so stodgy and settled down. Why, look at these Hollywood grandmothers.

FATHER: Hollywood?

BETTY: Yes, look at this picture of one of them all dressed up. See her cute little hat.

FATHER: Ridiculous. Can you picture your mother wearing a hat like that?

MARIE: Well, she's never had one but there's no reason why she shouldn't have. (*The doorbell rings off right.*)

BETTY: Oh dear, the doorbell. Victor answer it.

VICTOR (*Frowning*): *Uncle* Victor. And I don't see why I always have to do everything. (*But he goes off right.*)

BETTY: That's probably old Grandpa Terwiliger.

FATHER: Oh . . . Did you know he was coming?

BETTY: Yes, he's bringing something that Mom wanted to borrow.

FATHER: Grandpa Terwiliger. Just think. And I'm a grandfather too now. Why, he and I are cronies.

JACK: But Dad, he's seventy-six and lives with his daughter.

MARIE: And why, she's older than you are.

FATHER: Age doesn't seem to enter into it. (VICTOR *enters right with* GRANDPA TERWILIGER, *a talkative old gentleman carrying a dark old-fashioned shawl folded over one arm.*)

VICTOR (*As they enter*): Here's Grandpa Terwiliger.

CHILDREN: Hello, Mr. Terwiliger. Hello, Grandpa.

BETTY: Won't you sit down, Mr. Terwiliger?

TERWILIGER: No, nope, can't stay but a minute, but I have to congratulate the new grandpa. (*He walks over to* FATHER *and shakes hands.*) Well—well, Henry, how does it feel to be one of us?

FATHER: Why, fine, Grandpa, fine. I guess I haven't quite got used to it.

TERWILIGER: Oh, you will—you will. Kind of grows on you. Pretty soon you'll never know you've been anything else. And say, you know you're eligible for our club now.

FATHER: Club?

TERWILIGER: Sure—the Grandfather's Club. We meet once a month and show snapshots of our grandchildren.

FATHER: Oh? Well, we haven't got any snapshots yet.

TERWILIGER: 'Course not, but you will have—lots of 'em. Yep, we have lots of fun at our get-togethers. Course when you get as old as I am you don't feel like dancing a jig but we have fun all right. Sit back and chew the fat and look at the snap-shots. It's kind of restful.

BETTY: But Mr. Terwiliger, Dad doesn't need to rest. He isn't so very old.

TERWILIGER: He's old enough to be a grandfather, isn't he? Yes, sir. (*Laughing*) Ha! Ha! Well, guess I ought to be getting back. Don't walk as fast as I used to and my supper'll be most ready. (*Starting right*) Oh, I most forgot. Here's that shawl your mother wanted to borrow. (*He deposits shawl on table right near easy chair.*) Belonged to my wife when she was alive and she always said there was nothing like it for keeping drafts away from her shoulders and knees. Well, goodbye, everyone.

CHILDREN: Goodbye, Mr. Terwiliger. And thanks a lot.

FATHER: I'll just go to the door with you, Grandpa.

TERWILIGER (*Slapping* FATHER *on shoulder*): Fine, Gramp.

FATHER: What? Oh, yes—yes, of course. (*They go out right.*)

JACK (*Flopping into chair at right*): Well, it looks as though Dad's a full-fledged member of the Grandfather's Club.

VICTOR: Do they have a club just to look at baby pictures?

BETTY (*Sitting left*): Well, I like to look at baby pictures, too, but to meet regularly once a month to do it—why, it's like the second edition of the family album. Imagine Mr. Terwiliger talking to Dad as though he were an old man.

MARIE (*Doubtfully*): Well, as Mr. Terwiliger said, Dad *is* old enough to be a grandfather.

JACK: Yeah, and I suppose that makes Mom old enough to be a grandmother. (*He picks up shawl from table.*)

BETTY: Jack, what do you mean by that?

JACK (*Unfolding shawl a little*): Look at this shawl. Did you ever see anything so old-fashioned?

BETTY: No, I never did, and I can't believe Mom would ever wear a thing like that.

MARIE: Then why did she borrow it?

JACK: Search me. (FATHER *enters right.*) Say, Dad, what do you suppose Mom wants with this old shawl?

FATHER: Why, to wear it, I expect. Didn't Mr. Terwiliger say his wife liked it to keep drafts from her shoulders?

BETTY: But Dad, Mom never complains about drafts. She's always moving around so much. You always say she never sits still for a minute.

FATHER: Well, maybe she will from now on. It's as I've been trying to tell you. Things are going to be different.

BETTY: Well, I still don't believe that Mom's going to wear that shawl. (*Rising*) And that reminds me—she mentioned a dress she wanted pressed for tomorrow. I'd better run up and get it. (*She goes off left.*)

FATHER: Yes, children, your mother will be here soon. She will be tired from her journey. We've got to get ready for her.

JACK (*Rising*): O.K., Dad. I'll pick up some of this stuff. (*He starts picking up coats and hats.*) Maybe Uncle Victor would help.

VICTOR: Sure, I'll help, Jack.

JACK: *Uncle* Jack to you. (JACK *and* VICTOR *go off right with coats and hats.*)

MARIE: And I'll put these packages out of sight. (*She picks up perfume and nylons from table at left and goes to desk and puts them in drawer.* JACK *and* VICTOR *re-enter.*)

FATHER: That's better, children, but there is more. (*He picks up shawl.*) I think we should drape this shawl cosily around your mother's chair. (*He drops shawl on seat of chair at right.*) Well, you children take care of that. I'd better go upstairs and get her knitting. (*He starts left.*)

MARIE: Her knitting?

FATHER: Certainly—she'll probably want to knit tonight while we talk. Knitting is very restful. And I think I'll just get my house slippers on.

JACK: But Dad, Mom still might want to go out.

FATHER (*As he goes off left*): Nonsense, Jack—just forget that foolishness.

JACK: Oh, for gosh sakes. I don't know what I'm going to do about the reservations—and they cost me five bucks.

MARIE: And what about our other presents? If Mom doesn't like them—

JACK: It looks as though everything's going to be one big bust—everything we planned. (*Jerking at shawl*) Do we have to put this old shawl over Mom's chair?

MARIE: I guess so. (*She spreads shawl over back of chair.*)

VICTOR (*Sadly*): Gee, what's the matter? Aren't we going to have fun any more?

MARIE: I don't know. I suppose it will make a big change in our lives too—if Mom is different.

JACK: Yeah—like tonight. Betty suggested we have the gang in for hamburgers and now we won't be able to.

MARIE: Mom always let us have our friends in whenever we wanted to and she enjoyed it as much as we did. (*Starting to cry*) Oh, I can't bear it. I just can't bear it if Mom is changed the way Dad says.

JACK: Oh, look, Marie—now, don't cry. Maybe she won't be. Maybe we're making too much of this. Betty still doesn't believe it. (BETTY *enters left looking distressed.*)

BETTY: Jack, Marie—I don't know what to do. I don't know what to think.

JACK: What's happened, Betty?

BETTY: That dress Mom wanted me to press—it was on her bed just as she said. And it's a funny-looking, old black thing.

MARIE: It—it is?

BETTY: Perfectly plain—with a high neck and long sleeves. I just can't imagine Mom wearing it.

JACK: But she said she was going to in the note, didn't she? That she was going to wear it tomorrow?

BETTY: That's just it. If Mom's going to wear a dress like that, then it must be true. (FATHER *enters left carrying a small old-fashioned rocking chair. Under one arm he holds* MOTHER'S *knitting bag.*)

FATHER: Well, children, look what I've found.

BETTY: Dad, where did you get that?

FATHER: I found it in the upstairs hall. It's been in the attic for years—belonged to my grandmother.

VICTOR: Sure. I remember seeing that old rocking chair in the attic.

MARIE: But who brought it down?

FATHER: Why, your mother must have, don't you see? She evidently planned to bring it downstairs and then didn't have time.

BETTY: But what does Mom want with a rocking chair?

FATHER: Why, to sit in, of course. They're wonderful things— wonderful to rest the back. Yes, I guess she's arrived at the time of life when she feels she'd like a rocking chair. (*He places it upstage center.*) This will really be her chair. We'll get it all set up for her. This will be her place. Jack, just move that side table over. (JACK *brings table from chair at left and places it next to rocking chair.*)

MARIE (*Sadly bringing shawl*): And I suppose you want the shawl, Dad?

FATHER (*Draping shawl over chair*): Yes—yes, and I've brought her knitting too. (*He places knitting on table.*) We'll just put that on the table. Now, that looks nice, doesn't it? Your mother's worked hard all her life, and now that she's a grandmother she can just sit back and take things easy.

MARIE (*Giving up*) : Dad, the presents we got—I guess they *are* all wrong.

BETTY: Yes. I've been trying to think what we could do—if there was some way to get some other presents.

JACK: But what could we get that would be—kind of—well, dignified?

FATHER: Do you know what I think? If you could return all your things you'd have enough for a nice footstool.

VICTOR: Would Mom like a footstool?

FATHER: Yes, to go with the rocking chair. It's the very thing she needs.

BETTY: But it's so late now.

FATHER: Yes, you can't do it until next week. I think you'll just have to explain to your mother. (MOTHER *enters right wearing hat and coat. She carries a purse and a large paper bag.*)

MOTHER: Well, family, here I am!

BETTY: Mom, you're home!

OTHER CHILDREN: Oh, Mom!

MOTHER: How are all my little uncles and aunts? (*Turning and smiling at* FATHER) And how's Grandpa?

FATHER (*Going toward her*) : I'm fine, my dear—just fine.

MOTHER: The baby's beautiful—simply beautiful—a beautiful baby boy. Oh, Henry, you'll be so proud of him.

FATHER: I'm proud already—just bursting with pride.

BETTY: And how's Sis?

MOTHER: Feeling wonderful. She sent her love, and we're all to go down next weekend and see the baby. (*She starts to take off coat and hat and puts her purse and bag down on table at right.*)

FATHER: Elizabeth, my dear, let me take your things. (*He takes her hat and coat and puts them on chair right.*) You must be tired.

MOTHER: Well, a little. It has been kind of a rush.

FATHER: You'd better sit down right away—sit down and rest. (*He takes her by the arm and leads her toward rocking chair.*) We've got everything ready.

MOTHER (*Staring*): Why, so you have. . . . The old rocking chair and Mrs. Terwiliger's shawl. I'd started to bring the chair down and then I spent so long dusting it that I didn't have time. (*She breaks off and sits down.*) It's perfect—just perfect. (*The children are watching her gloomily.*)

BETTY: Do you—do you really think it is, Mom?

MOTHER: Why, certainly. Just wait until I get this shawl on. (*She pulls it around her shoulders.*) Well, how do I look?

FATHER (*Nodding his head and smiling*): Exactly like a grandmother, my dear.

MOTHER: Good. That's what I should look like.

BETTY: But you don't look like a very old grandmother.

MOTHER: Never you mind, Betty. I'll look older when I get that black dress on. Did you have a chance to press it?

BETTY: Not yet, but I've got the ironing board out. Mom, are you really going to wear that dress tomorrow?

MOTHER: Why, of course I am. (*There is a pause.* FATHER *nods his head, still smiling. The children all stare at* MOTHER.) Children, what's the matter? Why are you all staring at me?

JACK: Well, gee, Mom. Dad told us how it was going to be—

MARIE: But we couldn't believe it. We just couldn't believe it.

MOTHER: Couldn't believe what? Victor, what's the matter with you? Why do you look so solemn?

VICTOR (*Suddenly*): I don't want to be an uncle.

MOTHER: You don't? But Victor, you ought to be happy.

VICTOR: At first I thought it was going to be fun but it isn't. Nothing's going to be any fun. (*He turns away almost crying.*)

MOTHER (*Rising and dropping shawl on chair*): Victor dear,

tell me what's bothering you. (*She puts her hand on his shoulder.*)

VICTOR: No! (*He jerks away and as he does so, the card with the earrings drops out of his pocket. Note:* VICTOR *can have earrings in hand upstage from audience and drop them as he jerks away.*)

MOTHER: Victor, you've dropped something. (*She leans over and picks card up.*) Why, they're earrings.

JACK: Oh, for gosh sakes. Now you've done it, Victor.

VICTOR: Can I help it? There must be a hole in my other pocket too.

MOTHER: What is all this? Why, these earrings are lovely. Where did you get them, Victor?

VICTOR: I bought them. They *were* to be for Mother's Day.

MOTHER: For me? Why, they're beautiful. (*She takes earrings off card. They are the clip-on variety. She goes to mirror and puts them on. Then turning*) Look, children, aren't they stunning? And why, they'll be perfect with my new hat. (*She goes to table and picks up paper bag.*)

BETTY: New hat?

FATHER: Elizabeth, you—you've bought a new hat?

MOTHER: Yes. I suppose it was silly but when I left the hospital I passed this little hat shop and there was this hat in the window—and I felt so happy I just went in and bought it. It's a little different from anything I've had.

MARIE: Mom, you—you mean it's a hat for a grandmother?

MOTHER: Well, I don't know. I'll let you judge for yourselves. (*She takes a very perky hat from bag and puts it on. It has a feather.*)

BETTY: Mom, it's just as cute as can be!

MARIE: And why, it's like the one in the magazine.

JACK: Sure, the one the movie star was wearing.

MOTHER: Yes, I saw that picture. In fact, it gave me the idea. I thought to myself, there's no reason why I can't be—well—sort of a glamorous grandma.

JACK: Hooray for Mom!

FATHER: Elizabeth, are you really going to wear that hat?

MOTHER: Of course I am. Don't you like it?

FATHER: Well, it isn't just what I'd pictured for a grandmother —it doesn't seem to go with—well—knitting. (*He points to the knitting on table.*)

MOTHER: Knitting? My goodness, what's that doing out here? I thought I'd put it away.

FATHER: You had. But I got it out. I thought it would be restful.

MOTHER: Restful? Henry, I've just finished a jacket and a blanket and three pairs of booties and I don't think I want to do any more knitting until my next grandchild comes along. (*The children are all smiles.* FATHER *looks worried.*)

FATHER: Well, if that is the case, will you please explain all this? (*He points to the rocking chair and shawl.*) The shawl —the chair—they seem incongruous with your present attitude.

MOTHER: But they are for the tableau.

ALL: Tableau?

MOTHER (*Laughing*): Why, yes. My, my, I've been so rushed I forgot you didn't know. The ladies are having tableaux at the Mother's Day tea tomorrow afternoon, and Mrs. Nelson got sick at the last minute so they called me. They're having four generations of pioneer women. I'm to be a great-great grandmother.

BETTY: A great-great grandmother—so that's it. (*The children all start to laugh.*)

VICTOR: So that's what the shawl and rocking chair were for.

MARIE: And the dress too.

JACK: There, you see, Dad? Stuff like that is all right for a great-*great* grandmother. I guess the joke's on you.

MOTHER: Henry, what is all this?

FATHER: Well—er—it really isn't a joke. I just thought—

BETTY: Dad just thought you'd be changed, Mom. Oh, you'll like our presents after all.

MOTHER: Presents?

MARIE: Yes, Mom, and as long as Victor's let the cat out of the bag we might as well show them to you now. (*She runs to desk and takes presents from drawer.*)

JACK: Dad thought you wouldn't like what we've got.

MOTHER: Why not?

FATHER: Well, they—the things seemed rather frivolous.

MOTHER: Frivolous indeed. (*Going to him and smiling*) Henry, are you sure you haven't been dramatizing this business of being a grandfather?

FATHER: Well—uh—it seemed to me an important thing.

MOTHER: Of course it's important, but we don't need to be so solemn about it. (MARIE *has the presents and hands* BETTY's *package to her and the children stand listening.*) My lands, they say women are sentimental but men are as bad or worse once they get started. Children, I went through this when each one of you was born. Your father came in to me looking so serious and he always said, "Elizabeth, this is going to be a big responsibility."

VICTOR: Gee, did you say that, Dad?

FATHER: Why, I—I guess I did. (*Then smiling*) But do you know what your mother always answered? She said, "What if it is a responsibility, Henry? We're going to enjoy it."

MARIE (*To* FATHER): And she's going to enjoy her grandson. (*Then to* MOTHER, *handing her the perfume*) Well—here's my present, Mom.

MOTHER (*Lifting lid of box*): A bottle of perfume. It's just wonderful, dear.

BETTY: And here's what I got, Mom. (FATHER *starts right. He tiptoes out and no one notices.*)

MOTHER (*Opening box*): Nylons. They're so lovely. Why, with my earrings and perfume and new hose, I—I'll feel like stepping out.

JACK: Will you, Mom? Well, that's just what you're going to do. (*He hands her envelope.*)

MOTHER: What's this? (*Taking out card*) Reservations for the Palm Room—you mean your father and I are going out tonight? (*Looking for* FATHER) Why, where is he? Where is your father?

BETTY: I don't know.

JACK: Maybe he went upstairs.

MOTHER: Dear me, I do hope I didn't hurt his feelings. Your father's so sensitive. (FATHER *re-enters carrying his box and looking a little sheepish. He coughs to attract their attention and* MOTHER *turns.*) Why, Henry, there you are.

FATHER: Yes, I just went to get— (*Handing her box*) Well, here's my present, Elizabeth.

MOTHER: Your present? (*Taking lid off box*) Henry, a bed jacket—and so beautiful. It's the kind I've always dreamed of.

FATHER: Yes. I thought—that is, the children and I thought you might like to have breakfast in bed tomorrow morning. There was some talk of our going out tonight. That is, if you're not too tired.

MOTHER: Tired? Nonsense. I may be a grandmother but I still like to go out with my best beau. You're still my best beau, Henry—even if you're a grandfather.

FATHER (*All smiles*): Am I, my dear? Well, in that case—

(*He takes her arm.*) Grandpa and Grandma are stepping out tonight and they're going to have a grand time! (*The children all smile happily as the curtain falls.*)

THE END

See the Parade

Characters

MOTHER

FATHER

RALPH CARROLL

JOHNNIE CARROLL

DORIS CARROLL

GRANDPA

CHARLIE SCOTT

TIME: *Memorial Day.*

SETTING: *An American living room.*

AT RISE: MOTHER *is seated on the sofa while* JOHNNIE, *a boy of twelve dressed in a Boy Scout uniform, stands near her.* MOTHER *is brushing the back of* JOHNNIE'S *coat. He holds his Boy Scout hat in his hand.*

JOHNNIE: Mom, I brushed my hat before. Does it look all right?

MOTHER: Of course, Johnnie.

JOHNNIE: And I shined my shoes.

MOTHER: A lot of good that will do after you've paraded for an hour or so.

JOHNNIE: But Mom, your whole uniform has got to be perfect for a parade and that includes your shoes, too. The Scoutmaster said so.

MOTHER: Yes, dear, I know. (*She rises, puts brush on small table near sofa.*) Well, I'm just glad that this parade happens only once a year. I've spent all morning getting the members of this family ready.

JOHNNIE: Then where are they? Where are Dad and Ralph? And Grandpa was going to meet us here. Doris is out on the porch practicing with her baton—and everyone's starting to line up at the corner now, Mom—see? (*He runs to window.*) The parade will be starting—

MOTHER (*Walking over to window, too*): Nonsense, there's plenty of time. . . . (FATHER *enters left wearing World War I uniform. He puts his hat on table left. He is rubbing his sleeves over the brass buttons on his coat.* MOTHER *turns as he comes in.*)

FATHER: Alice, do these buttons look shined up enough to you?

MOTHER: Yes, Henry. If I tried, I could see myself in them.

FATHER: Well, they ought to look nice—I've spent all morning on them.

JOHNNIE: Say, Dad, we'd better hurry!

FATHER: Oh—lots of time yet. Alice, this place here at the side where you let my coat out—

MOTHER: What's the matter with that?

FATHER: Nothing, but I wondered if it showed.

MOTHER: Of course it doesn't show. Henry Carroll, I never knew men could be so vain.

JOHNNIE: It's because of the parade, Mom—and if you think we're vain, you ought to see Doris strutting around.

FATHER (*Still fussing with coat*): Alice, a man doesn't like to feel he's gained so much weight he can't wear his uniform.

MOTHER (*Laughing a little*): Well, what do you expect after all these years? (GRANDPA *enters right, wearing uniform of Spanish American War.*)

GRANDPA (*Very chipper*): Howdy, folks, how are you?

JOHNNIE: Gramp—you look super!

MOTHER (*Smiling at him*): Hello, Father.

JOHNNIE: Didn't you bring Grandma?

GRANDPA: Grandma's sitting on the porch waiting for the parade to start.

MOTHER: Oh, fine—I'll go down and sit with her if I ever get this family of mine ready. Henry's feeling bad because I had to let out his coat. (*She sits on sofa again.*)

FATHER: Now, Alice—

MOTHER: Yes, you are, Henry.

GRANDPA: Say, I remember Grandma had to let mine out when I was about your age, Henry. Now, I'm so old I'm getting thin again.

JOHNNIE: See, Dad, all you have to do is wait till you're as old as Gramp.

GRANDPA: Sure—another twenty-five years and you can have Alice take that coat in again. (ALICE *laughs.* GRANDPA *sits in easy chair right.*) Say, where's Ralph?

FATHER: Getting his uniform on, I suppose. I tell you, I'm going to be mighty proud having my son marching beside me today.

GRANDPA: Yep—there'll be three generations of us, Henry. I remember how proud I felt when you got back from World War I and could march beside me. Now you feel the same way about Ralph. So do I. After all, he's my grandson.

JOHNNIE: I'm your grandson, too, I guess. What about Doris and me? Aren't you proud to be marching with us?

GRANDPA: Of course I am. I saw Doris out on the porch just now. She looks mighty pretty.

JOHNNIE: Yeah, now that she's a drum majorette— (DORIS, *a girl of fifteen, runs in right. She is swinging a baton.*)

DORIS: Mother—Mother, I've been practicing again. How do I look?

MOTHER: Like something out of an operetta, dear. Very nice, indeed.

DORIS: Do you want to see me throw my baton?

MOTHER: Oh, not in here, dear, the ceiling's not very high—you might break something.

DORIS: Break something? You don't think I'm going to drop it, do you? (*She throws baton lightly into air and catches it.*)

FATHER: Look out for the lamps. (*He sits left.*)

JOHNNIE: It is kind of crowded in here, Doris.

DORIS: Oh, I'm good, I am. (*She throws baton higher this time and drops it. She looks crestfallen.*)

JOHNNIE: Hey, you dropped it. You're not going to do that in the parade, are you?

DORIS: Of course not. The ceiling *is* too low—that's what's the matter. But look at the way I'm going to strut. (*She marches right and left swinging her baton back and forth in front of her in style of drum major and now and then twirling it.*)

GRANDPA (*Stamping feet and clapping hands*): Best I've ever seen in all my years of parades!

DORIS: Do I twirl my baton gracefully, do you think?

JOHNNIE: Gracefully. Listen to her. You talk about us men folks being vain, Mom—

DORIS: I'm not vain. I just want to do it well. After all, when I'm going to lead—

JOHNNIE: You're not leading the parade.

DORIS: I didn't say I was. But I'm leading one part of it.

JOHNNIE: Grandpa and the old fellows are leading the parade.

GRANDPA: Old fellows, humph! (*He rises jauntily.*) Be careful whom you're calling old. You're as young as you feel and today I feel sixteen—yes, siree. Sixteen! (*He grabs DORIS and dances her around.*)

MOTHER: My goodness, you'd all better save your energy for the parade. It's a good thing I'm not marching. At least someone will have pep enough left to fix our picnic lunch.

JOHNNIE: Gee, Mom, I'm hungry already. Are we going to have hamburgers?

MOTHER: Yes, dear, and potato salad and pickles and—

FATHER (*Looking at watch*): Where *is* Ralph? Johnnie, you'd

better run up to his room and tell him we're all waiting for
him.

JOHNNIE: O.K., Dad. (*He runs out left.*)

DORIS (*Still twirling baton*): Ralph's probably busy pinning on
all his medals. After all, this is the first parade he's been in
since he got home. (*You hear a band playing off.* DORIS *runs
to window.*) Look—there's the Legion band—they're all lined
up at the corner. Oh, parades are such fun.

GRANDPA: They're not all fun—at least for us grown-ups.
They make us remember things that we ought to remember.
(JOHNNIE *runs back in.*)

JOHNNIE: Ralph's not in his room, Dad.

FATHER (*Rising*): Not in his room? What on earth—have you
seen him, Alice?

MOTHER: Why, I—not since early this morning, I guess. I've
been so busy—

DORIS: Maybe he got ready early and went on down to meet
some of the other fellows. Come on, Johnnie. Let's run down
to the corner and see.

JOHNNIE: All right. (DORIS *and* JOHNNIE *rush out right.*)

FATHER (*Walking about*): I just can't understand this. I'm
sure Ralph knew what time we were to be ready and that you
were going to meet us here, Father.

GRANDPA: Well, maybe he went down already, the way Doris
said. Young fellow like that wants to talk to his own buddies.

FATHER: I don't think so. His best friend can't march at all,
you know. Charlie's always been his buddy.

GRANDPA: Charlie? Charlie who?

MOTHER: You know, Father—Charlie Scott next door. The
boy who came home blind.

GRANDPA: Sure—sure, I do—getting so old I forget names.
That was an awful thing—Charlie losing his sight.

MOTHER: Ralph still isn't over it. I think he minds Charlie

being blind more than Charlie does. They went all through the war together and then when that mine blew up in Charlie's face—oh, it seems terrible. (RALPH, *a tall young man in his twenties, enters left. He is not wearing a uniform. He stops as he sees everyone in the room.*)

RALPH: Oh—Mom, Dad—and Gramp, too. I—I thought you'd be gone.

MOTHER (*Rising and going to him*): Ralph, where have you been? We've been worried.

RALPH: I just took a walk, Mom, and I came in the back way. Didn't want to run into the parade.

FATHER: But son, it's late—and your uniform—you're not ready.

RALPH: My uniform?

GRANDPA: Yes, boy, it's almost time to start. We've been waiting for you.

RALPH: But you—you didn't think I was going to march in that parade?

FATHER: Didn't think—of course we thought. Why, I've been looking forward to it for weeks—having you march beside me—

RALPH: I—I'm sorry, Dad. I thought you knew how I felt. Parades seem silly to me.

GRANDPA: Silly?

RALPH: What good does all that marching up and down the street do the boys who died? And bands playing—they can't hear the bands. And how about Charlie Scott? He can't even see your parade.

GRANDPA: I know, Ralph, but it's in honor of all those boys—not only of your buddies but of all the men who have fought for our country. It makes us remember—

RALPH: I don't want to remember. (*He turns away.*)

FATHER: Ralph, the children—Doris and Johnnie—they'll be disappointed, too. The children love the parade.

RALPH: Well, I'm not a child, Dad. I'm sorry—really—to disappoint you all, but I just can't see it. Making a big splash and show about something as serious as war—

MOTHER (*Going to him and putting her hand on his shoulder*): Ralph, dear, please, everyone's been looking forward to this day. Won't you forget the way you feel? Won't you put on your uniform and—

RALPH: I wish I could, Mom, but I can't. I've had enough of my uniform. No, you go along, Dad—I'm not going to march. (DORIS *and* JOHNNIE *run in right.*)

DORIS: We didn't see Ralph— (*She stops*) Oh, here he is, Johnnie.

JOHNNIE: Hi, Ralph. You'd better hurry.

FATHER: Your brother is not going to march, children.

JOHNNIE: Not going to—Ralph, you—

FATHER: Never mind, Johnnie. (*Picking up his hat and starting right*) Come along, we'd better go down and get in line.

DORIS: But Dad, what's the matter with Ralph?

FATHER: I said never mind. Now, come along—come along, Father.

GRANDPA: Yep, all right—expect that's the best thing to do. (*He looks back at* RALPH *once more and then marches out.*)

FATHER: Goodbye, Alice. We'll see you later.

MOTHER: Goodbye, dear. (FATHER *and* DORIS *and* JOHNNIE *go out. There is a pause.* RALPH *looks at his mother.*)

RALPH: You—you think I'm selfish, don't you, Mom?

MOTHER: I—I don't know, dear. I just don't understand.

RALPH: I did my job while I was needed.

MOTHER: As if we didn't know that. We only have to look at your medals—

RALPH : Medals—they're shoved away in a drawer. I never look at them. And what good do you suppose Charlie's medals do him? He's got lots of medals, too.

MOTHER : Ralph, you—you seem so bitter about Charlie. You shouldn't be. I don't think he is.

RALPH : Mom, I don't see why you can't understand how I feel. War is a grim business. We all want to forget the fighting and the bloodshed, but we don't want people to forget that it *is* grim. And lots of people already have forgotten that. Are we really working for peace—all of us? I don't think so—we're quarreling among ourselves about petty, unimportant things—

MOTHER : But that's just the point, dear. The parade—

RALPH : The parade! Bands blaring—men marching—playing at war—what good will that do?

CHARLIE (*Off right. Calling*) : Ralph—Ralph—are you there? Mrs. Carroll—

RALPH : It's Charlie.

MOTHER (*Moving right*) : I'll go, dear. Charlie—I'm coming, Charlie. (CHARLIE *appears at door, wearing uniform of World War II. He feels his way with his cane but must not give the impression of a sorry figure. He stands very straight and is smiling.*)

CHARLIE : Is it you, Mrs. Carroll?

MOTHER (*Taking his arm*) : Yes, Charlie. (RALPH *stands still, staring at* CHARLIE *because of his uniform.*)

CHARLIE : I'm really getting very expert at finding my way around. Mother helped me across the yard, but I managed your front porch just with the cane here. I was hoping Ralph hadn't gone.

RALPH (*Moving forward to* CHARLIE. MOTHER *steps back*) : Here I am, Charlie, old boy, right here. Charlie, you're— you're wearing your uniform.

CHARLIE : Certainly I'm wearing my uniform. Isn't there a

parade? All my medals, too—really showing off today . . . (*Feeling* RALPH's *shoulders*) Why—why, Ralph, old boy, where's yours?

RALPH: I'm not wearing my uniform.

CHARLIE: Then you'd better hurry—time to start. I thought maybe you could find me a good spot on the sidelines somewhere before you started to march.

RALPH: You—you want to go to the parade?

CHARLIE: Certainly I want to.

RALPH: But you can't even see it. I—I'm sorry, Charlie, I didn't mean to say it like that.

CHARLIE: It's all right, Ralph. We know I'm blind. But that's not going to stop me from really seeing—from doing some of the things I want to do in the world—and what I want to do right now is see that parade. I can see it in my mind and I can hear it. Get into your uniform, come on.

RALPH: I—I wasn't going to march, Charlie. I wasn't going.

CHARLIE: What's that?

RALPH: Dad and Grandpa waited for me, but I couldn't. The whole thing seems stupid to me.

CHARLIE: The parade?

RALPH: Bands playing, men marching—for what? What does it mean?

CHARLIE: It doesn't mean anything, I guess, if you don't look beneath the surface—if you don't really see. If you don't see that it's a sign that we haven't forgotten—that we're going to try and make peace work.

RALPH: A sign? I never thought of it like that.

CHARLIE: A sign—a symbol—whatever you want to call it. There are lots of things we do in this world, just simple things perhaps, that remind us of deeper things.

RALPH: That's true.

CHARLIE: And of course it is stupid to have parades if folks aren't going to see why we have them. If they're just going to see them with their eyes and not with their minds—if they're not going to understand. Why, blind as I am, I can see.

RALPH: Yes, you do see, Charlie—so much more than I do. (FATHER *re-enters right, his shoulders sagging a little.*)

MOTHER: Why, Henry.

FATHER: I—I came back, Alice. Let Grandpa and the young ones march. I guess the parade's for them.

RALPH: No—no, it isn't, Dad. It's for all of us. I'm going to put my uniform on—wait for me.

FATHER: Ralph! You're going to march?

RALPH: You bet I am. Charlie's made me see what a parade really means. He's made me see the light. (*He rushes out left.*)

FATHER: Charlie—you look fine in your uniform, boy.

CHARLIE: Thank you, sir. You do too, I know.

FATHER: Charlie, what did you say to Ralph?

CHARLIE: Why, only that a parade isn't just a parade. It's a symbol of something bigger, sir.

FATHER: Ah, that's what I had in mind, but I couldn't express myself.

CHARLIE: The way I feel, sir, if the people watching that parade today—and the ones marching too—can just remember why all the men who *aren't* there were willing to die for their country—well, it will be worthwhile, sir. Those men wanted to make a better world. It's up to us to keep faith with them.

THE END

The Moon Keeps Shining

Characters

HENRY RICHARDS   JOHNNIE RICHARDS
ALICE RICHARDS   JIM BENSON
MARY RICHARDS

TIME: *Early evening in June.*
SETTING: *The living room of the Richards home.*
AT RISE: ALICE RICHARDS *is talking on the phone. She looks worried.*

ALICE: Hello—hello? Operator, I was talking to Gordon's Department Store—was I cut off? . . . Oh, hello, Gordon's. This is Mrs. Richards—I was calling about the dress—the formal— Oh, very well—I'll wait. (HENRY RICHARDS *enters right, carrying his newspaper. He looks cheerful and glad to be home.*)
HENRY: Hello, Alice. Is supper ready? I'm starved.
ALICE (*Turning from phone*): Henry, it's terrible. Her dress hasn't come.
HENRY: Whose dress? (*He sits down on sofa and opens his paper.*)
ALICE: Mary's, of course. She's going to the Senior Reception and— (*Into phone again*) Hello? Hello? What's that? You're sure it's on the delivery truck? But it's getting so late, and she's got to wear it tonight . . . Very well, if you're sure. (*She hangs up.* HENRY *has been looking at the paper. Now he glances up.*)

411

HENRY: When did you say supper would be ready, Alice?

ALICE: Henry Richards, how you can talk about supper at a time like this?

HENRY: But what's happened?

ALICE: I've told you. Mary's dress hasn't come. She picked it out several days ago, and it was to be altered.

HENRY: But where's she going? Can't she wear something else?

ALICE: Henry, I've told you a dozen times. The Senior Reception is formal. Commencement dances come only once in a lifetime—and Mary is going with Jim Benson.

HENRY: Oh, he's on the baseball team.

ALICE: Yes, and Mary's so excited. Oh, if anything happens to spoil this for her—

HENRY: Now, Alice.

ALICE: We've been in an uproar all afternoon.

HENRY: But that's silly. Just because Mary's going to a dance—

ALICE: Henry Richards, do you realize what this means to Mary? Why, it's like a milestone in her life—something she'll never forget. It's all romance and moonlight and—and honeysuckles.

HENRY: Honeysuckles? Now, Alice, you know we don't have any honeysuckles around here. And what do you mean romance? At Mary's age?

ALICE: Oh, Henry, your're so literal.

HENRY (*Grinning at her*): I'm hungry too, Alice.

ALICE: I don't mean romance the way you mean it. It's just that for Commencement, everything ought to be perfect. The moon ought to look twice as big as it is—

HENRY: The moon?

ALICE: Yes. I do hope there'll be a nice one tonight. And the boy you're with ought to seem like—well, a knight on a white horse.

HENRY: Hmm—Jim Benson will come in that old second-hand jalopy he runs around in.

ALICE: Never mind. It can still seem romantic. I remember the dance when I graduated.

HENRY: Did I take you, Alice?

ALICE: Certainly not. I didn't even know you then. I went with—I went with—let me see, whom did I go with?

HENRY: Ha-ha, I thought a girl never forgot.

ALICE: It's just his name that I've forgotten, Henry. Let me see—he was tall and blonde.

HENRY: Well, I'm getting blonde myself—around the temples here.

ALICE: Humph—never mind. I found a couple of gray hairs, too, the other day.

HENRY (*Rising and crossing to her*): Alice, you don't mind? The—the gray hairs, I mean?

ALICE: No, dear.

HENRY: But you—you sound so nostalgic or something.

ALICE: It's just Mary, dear. If that dress isn't delivered, it'll be terrible.

HENRY: Hmmm. Think of Mary growing up—graduating— worrying about a formal dress. Getting ready to go out into the wide world.

ALICE: Oh, it isn't that bad, Henry. She still has college.

HENRY: Of course, but it seems only yesterday she was playing with dolls.

ALICE: I know what you mean. It's happened so suddenly, and if anything happens to spoil this evening—why—why—her whole life may be ruined.

HENRY: Well, I know mine's going to be ruined if I don't get some supper.

ALICE: Stop talking about supper, Henry. We're not going to have any.

HENRY: What's that?

ALICE: I mean, not a regular one. I'll be busy helping Mary dress. I've laid out some sandwiches and milk on the dining room table. I thought we could all help ourselves. (*As* ALICE *is speaking,* JOHNNIE, *a boy about fourteen, enters left chewing on a sandwich and carrying a glass of milk.*)

JOHNNIE: That's what I'm doing, Mom. Hi, Dad.

HENRY: Hello, Johnnie. (HENRY *sits on sofa again.*)

ALICE: Johnnie Richards, you weren't to start on those sandwiches until later. How many have you had?

JOHNNIE: Oh, two, I guess. (JOHNNIE *slouches down in chair left. He finishes his milk and sets glass on table near chair.* MARY, *about seventeen, rushes in left. She is clad in a flannel wrapper, wears scuffies on her feet and her hair is long and loose and falls about her face.*)

MARY (*Excitedly*): Mother—Mother, did it come yet?

ALICE: No, dear, but—

MARY (*Wailing*): Oh, Mother!

ALICE: But I've called the store and they say it will be here any minute.

HENRY: No greeting for your poor old Dad, Mary?

MARY: Oh, Dad, I didn't even see you. Everything's gone wrong!

ALICE: Now, dear—everything is going to be all right.

MARY: But if I don't have anything to wear—

JOHNNIE: You might wear that old wrapper, Mary. (*Looking at her in mock admiration*) Man, what glamor. You'd knock the fellas cold!

MARY: Johnnie Richards—you keep quiet! Mother, look at my hair. I can't do a thing with it!

ALICE: But it's lovely, dear.

HENRY: Your hair's very nice, Mary. Soft and pretty and—

MARY: And girlish, I know. I always wear it this way and it's

so terribly young. If I could just put it up or something so
I'd look older.

JOHNNIE: Why is it that girls always want to look older than
they are?

HENRY: They don't—for long. That phase lasts only a few
years. As soon as a girl is twenty-five she wants to look
young again.

JOHNNIE: Well, if you ask me, girls are goofy. And I'm never
going to have anything to do with them.

HENRY: That, too, is just a passing phase, I'm afraid, son. One
of these days you'll think of nothing else.

JOHNNIE: No, sir.

MARY (*Looking at watch on wrist*): Mother, look at the time.
If my dress doesn't come, I'll die—I'll simply die!

ALICE: Now, Mary—

MARY: Can't we do something?

ALICE (*Going to phone*): I can call the store again but it seems
silly. (JOHNNIE *has finished his sandwich. He rises and goes
out left as* ALICE *dials number and speaks into phone.*) Hello?
Hello?

MARY: Don't they answer?

ALICE: I'm afraid they're closed, dear. (*She hangs up.*)

MARY: Mother!

ALICE: But that doesn't matter. They told me the dress was on
the delivery truck.

MARY: But now if it doesn't come, we can't call or anything. Oh,
I knew something would happen. Now I won't be able to go
to the dance!

HENRY: Nonsense, Mary. You can wear something else—that
nice blue dress.

MARY: Dad, that's a street dress.

HENRY: Oh, pardon me.

MARY: Can't you understand that this is a formal dance?

(JOHNNIE *re-enters chewing on another sandwich just in time to hear this.*)

JOHNNIE: Who's taking you to the old dance, Sis?

MARY: Jim Benson.

JOHNNIE: Hey, he's all right. But I thought he was going with Butch Jones' sister.

MARY: Wherever did you get that idea?

JOHNNIE: Well, from something Butch said I thought—

MARY: Mary Ellen Jones may wish he were taking her, but he's taking me—that is, if I can go. (*Almost crying*) Oh, Mother!

ALICE: Now, Mary, stop your fussing. (*The doorbell rings off right.*) There, you see? Your dress. I knew it would come.

MARY (*Excitedly running right*): Oh, Mother—

ALICE: Wait, you can't go to the door like that. I'll get it. (ALICE *goes out right.*)

MARY: Oh, Dad, it's come! I was so worried.

JOHNNIE (*As he is about to exit left again*): Gee, I never heard so much ado about nothing.

HENRY: Johnnie, wait, bring me one of those sandw— (*But* JOHNNIE *has gone out again.*) I guess he didn't hear me. Well, I didn't want a sandwich much anyway. What I'd really like is a steak and some French fries and—

MARY: Oh, poor Dad. Are you hungry? I don't see how you can be. I couldn't eat a thing.

HENRY (*A bit annoyed*): Mary, after all, I've worked hard all day at the office. (ALICE *re-enters carrying a cardboard box.*)

ALICE: Here it is, dear.

MARY (*Rushing over to* ALICE): Oh, Mother! Wait till you see it, Dad. (*She is looking toward* HENRY *and taking cover off and removing tissue paper as she talks.*) It's the most gorgeous shade of pink.

ALICE: It *is* beautiful, Henry—all frothy and pink and—

(MARY *is holding up a dress which is black with gold sequins —quite sophisticated.*)

HENRY: Pink? It looks black to me, but maybe I'm seeing things. I'm so hungry.

MARY (*Looking at dress in horror*): Oh-h—oh-h! This isn't my dress.

ALICE (*Staring at dress in astonishment*): No—no, it isn't, is it?

MARY (*Still holding it up*): They—they've sent the wrong one! Oh, how *could* they get mixed up? (*Looking at cover of box*) It's addressed to you, Mother.

ALICE: To—to me?

MARY: But I suppose that's natural. My dress was on your charge. But why did they put this in the box? (*Holding it up to her*) Even if I wanted to, I couldn't wear it—it's miles too big. Why, it would fit you, Mother.

ALICE: Yes, I—I guess it would.

HENRY: Looks just your size, Alice. Very pretty, too. I'll bet it's expensive.

ALICE: Now, Henry, it isn't so expensive—I mean, I don't think—

MARY: Oh, Mother. (*Clutching dress and crying*)

ALICE: Wait, Mary, don't cry on it. (*She takes dress from MARY, folds it carefully, puts it back in box and places box on a chair.*) We'll have to take it back. That is—

MARY: But where's *my* dress?

ALICE: I don't know, dear. There's evidently been a mix-up.

MARY: Mix-up! My dress is locked up in the store—and we can't get it! (JOHNNIE *re-enters with a sandwich.*)

JOHNNIE: Say, what's going on?

HENRY: They sent the wrong dress.

ALICE (*With her arm around MARY*): Mary, don't cry. I'm trying to think. There must be some way—maybe we can borrow a formal.

MARY: How can we? All the girls bought formals for the dance tonight and they're wearing them!

ALICE: But I just thought—Aunt Sophie is about your size. She used to go out formal.

HENRY: That was years ago, Alice.

MARY: Yes—do you think I want to wear something that's been laid away in moth balls for ages?

ALICE: No, darling, of course you don't. Oh, there must be something we can do. I won't have your evening spoiled.

MARY: It's spoiled already!

JOHNNIE: And so is everybody else's! Gee, I don't see why a dance is so important.

ALICE: Johnnie! It's the Senior Reception.

MARY: Oh, Mother, I can't bear it. I simply can't bear it. It was going to be so wonderful.

ALICE: I know, darling.

MARY: Now, I'll have to call up Jim and tell him I can't go.

ALICE: Not yet, Mary. Maybe we can still think of— (*The phone rings.*)

HENRY: There. They've delivered your dress to the wrong place and the people are calling up to tell you—

MARY (*Happily*): Oh, Dad, do you think— (*She runs to phone and picks it up.*) Hello? Hello? (*Her voice changing*) Oh, Jim . . . I—I was going to call you . . . What? *You* can't go? But what's happened? I see. (*Somewhat coldly*) Well, that's very interesting. It—it seems you might have let me know sooner. It's practically time to go to the dance now. Goodbye. (*She hangs up, looking very unhappy and angry.*) Well, of all the—

ALICE: What on earth?

MARY: Jim says he can't go to the dance. He's sorry but he's got a terrible cold.

HENRY: A cold?

MARY: I—I guess he didn't want to take me very much if a little cold can keep him at home.

ALICE: But Mary—

MARY: In fact, I doubt if he has a cold at all. It's probably just an excuse.

JOHNNIE: Aw now, Mary, Jim Benson wouldn't—

MARY: He's probably even going to the dance. He's probably taking Mary Ellen Jones. You said so yourself, Johnnie.

JOHNNIE: I did not.

ALICE: Mary, please—

JOHNNIE: I only said I thought. Butch told me she was going with Jim—and there are two or three Jims in school. Jim Trent and Jim—

MARY: Never mind.

HENRY: Mary, I don't see why you're so upset. You're just imagining things. Why, this makes everything all right.

MARY: All right? (*Tragically*) When my whole evening is ruined?

HENRY: You couldn't go to the dance anyway. You didn't have your dress.

ALICE: Henry, you're just making things worse. Mary, my darling—

MARY (*Crying*): My whole *life* is ruined.

ALICE: What did I tell you, Henry?

MARY: Mother, Jim didn't want to take me—and that's the worst of all. The last straw. First my dress doesn't come from Gordon's and then—

JOHNNIE: Gordon's? Gordon's Department Store? Is that where it was to come from?

MARY: Yes, of course but—

JOHNNIE: Gee—I just remembered. (*He hurries off right.*)

HENRY: Where's Johnnie going?

ALICE: I don't know, Henry. But I do think we'd all feel better if we had something to eat!

HENRY: Alice—food, Alice? Do you really think we might have some food? (*He rises.*)

ALICE: But of course, Henry. I made all those sandwiches. (JOHNNIE *re-enters carrying a cardboard box.*)

JOHNNIE: Look, Mom—I feel terrible. This package came yesterday afternoon when you were out, and I left it behind the umbrella stand in the hall. I thought you'd see it. It—it's from Gordon's. It must be Mary's dress.

MARY (*Tearfully*): My dress? When I don't need it? (ALICE *quickly takes cover off box and removes tissue paper.* HENRY *comes closer to look, too.*)

ALICE: It *is* Mary's dress.

HENRY: My, that's a pretty color.

JOHNNIE: Yeah—like a—a strawberry soda or something. You'll look good enough to eat in that, Sis.

HENRY: I wish you wouldn't talk about food, son.

MARY: What does it matter *how* I'd look in it? You would bring my dress when I don't need it, Johnnie Richards. That's just like you. You always do everything wrong. (*She bursts into tears and starts to run left.*)

JOHNNIE: But Sis—wait—don't you want your dress?

MARY (*Coming back and snatching box*): Very well—but what would you suggest? That I sleep in it? (*She runs off still crying.*)

ALICE: Oh, Henry. (*He puts his arm around her.*)

JOHNNIE: Hey, Mom. I'm sorry. I didn't mean to hurt—

ALICE: I know you didn't, Johnnie. Henry, what can we do?

HENRY: I don't know. But the first thing I'm going to do is bring those sandwiches in. You need food, too. (*He goes out left.*)

JOHNNIE: Mom, it was my fault in a way. I should have remembered that package.

ALICE: Never mind, Johnnie. She couldn't have used it anyway.
(HENRY *re-enters.*)

HENRY: Alice, I thought you said you made some sandwiches.
There's nothing on the dining room table but an empty plate.

ALICE: What's that? Johnnie Richards, what—you ate them all
up!

JOHNNIE: Mom, I—I didn't realize. I was hungry and I just
kept taking one and then another.

ALICE: Well, you can go straight out to the kitchen and make
some more.

JOHNNIE: Make some more? All right, Mom. But what'll I
make 'em with?

ALICE: What does a person usually make sandwiches with?
Look in the icebox. There are a few leftovers.

JOHNNIE: O.K., Mom. (*He goes out left.*)

ALICE (*Walking back and forth*): Oh dear . . . I feel terrible
for Mary. (*At window*) And look, Henry—there's the moon.
It's beautiful.

HENRY: The moon? (*He looks.*) Oh, yes, the moon. Always
reminds me of cheese. Do you suppose there's any cheese in
the icebox, Alice?

ALICE: I don't know. It's a perfect night—her big night—and
Mary can't enjoy it. Oh, the poor child!

HENRY: Now, Alice, I'm sorry, too. I do understand, you
know. But it's not such a tragedy.

ALICE: It is—to her. The Commencement dance means so
much. It was bad enough about the dress but then to have Jim
Benson call up and say he was sick.

HENRY: But he can't help that.

ALICE: Henry, I don't know if he's sick or not but Mary doesn't
believe it, don't you see? She thinks he's changed his mind

and doesn't want to take her—and that's a terrible feeling. (*She starts left.*)

HENRY: Alice, where are you going?

ALICE: To Mary. There must be something I can do for her. Henry, it's a terrible thing for a woman to feel she isn't wanted.

HENRY (*Disturbed*): What's that? Alice, what do you mean by—Alice, wait. (*But she has gone out left. He shakes his head looking a little bewildered. The doorbell rings and* HENRY *goes off right. You hear his voice off.*) Why, Jim Benson—it *is* Jim Benson, isn't it? Come in. (JIM BENSON, *a boy about seventeen, attired in white flannels and a blue coat, enters followed by* HENRY. JIM *is carrying a small white box.*)

JIM (*Excitedly*): Is Mary here, sir?

HENRY: Why, yes, she is but— (*Breaking off*) I thought you were sick.

JIM: Yes, sir—I mean, no, sir. That is, I—Mary isn't going to the dance with anyone else, is she?

HENRY: Not that I know of. You mean you want to take her?

JIM: Yes, Mr. Richards. I certainly do. I wanted to all along but I—well, I—I had to call her up.

HENRY: And say you were sick. I—I must say you don't look exactly sick to me.

JIM: It wasn't a lie, Mr. Richards—not really. I do have kind of a summer cold. My nose has been running and I sniffle. But if you think a little thing like a cold would keep me from taking Mary to the dance—

HENRY: Ah, then there was something else.

JIM: Well—uh—something did come up that—well—but it's all right now. At least I hope it is.

HENRY: I hope so, too. I suppose you don't care to mention what happened.

JIM: I—I'd rather not. That is— (*Looking at* HENRY) Well, as a matter of fact, I guess I don't mind telling you—man to man like this.

HENRY: Man to man?

JIM: What really happened was—it was an accident you understand, sir—I—scorched my pants.

HENRY: Oh—well.

JIM: Yes, you see—I'd bought a new pair of white flannels for the dance and when they came from the store, I thought they looked a little wrinkled. Mother said they didn't but I'm kind of particular especially since I was going out with Mary. Mother said she'd press 'em but then it was getting late and in the excitement of getting ready—you know how it is.

HENRY: Yes, I surely do.

JIM: So I decided to do it myself, and I guess I was hurrying and the iron was too hot.

HENRY: I can see the whole picture.

JIM: I felt awful when I saw that scorch. It was so burned that even Mom couldn't do anything with it so then I called Mary.

HENRY: And mentioned your cold.

JIM: But after that I felt so bad that Mom said there must be something we could do so she found an old pair of flannels of Dad's—they were too big around the waist but she sewed the buttons over. I guess they'll stay up all right.

HENRY: I'm sure they will. You look fine, son—just fine. I'd just forget all about it if I were you.

JIM: Yeah, and please don't mention it to Mary, Mr. Richards.

HENRY: You have my word.

JIM: As I say, I don't mind telling another man but it might make me appear—well, kind of ordinary or something to a girl. I figure at a Commencement dance with the music and moonlight—well, a fella wouldn't want to mention a thing like scorched pants. It isn't very—well—

HENRY: Not very romantic.

JIM: No, sir, it isn't.

HENRY: Well, I won't say a thing. (*Crossing*) And now I'd better let Mary know. (ALICE *enters left.*)

ALICE: Henry, she's— (*She stops.*) Why, Jim—Jim Benson!

HENRY: Jim's decided he feels well enough to go after all, Alice. That is, if Mary—

ALICE: Oh, how wonderful! I mean I'll tell her—I'll tell her right away. (*She starts left, then turns.*) Henry, she's got her dress on. When I went upstairs she'd put it on and was just standing staring at herself in the mirror. (*She goes out calling*) Mary—Mary, my dear, there's someone here for you.

HENRY (*To* JIM): Mary will be glad you made it. She didn't want to miss that dance.

JIM: I didn't either, sir. I've been looking forward to it for weeks.

HENRY: Well, I know you're going to have a good time. (MARY *enters wearing her pink dress, followed by* ALICE. MARY *looks radiant. She has a light coat over her arm.*)

MARY (*Walking toward* JIM): Jim—oh, Jim. We're going to the dance.

JIM: You bet we are, Mary. Gee, you—you look wonderful, Mary. That color—it's pink, isn't it?

MARY: Yes. (*Laughing a little*) And I hope it doesn't clash with my eyes—I guess they're kind of red.

JIM: No, they're not, Mary. Anyhow, I guess my nose is kind of red too from my cold.

MARY: I felt so disappointed when you said we weren't going.

JIM: So did I—and I decided—well, that nothing was going to keep me from taking you.

MARY: You're sure you feel all right, Jim?

JIM: I feel fine. And here—well, here are some flowers. (*He hands her the box.*)

MARY: Oh, Jim. (*Opening box and taking out a little corsage of roses*) Roses—oh, they're beautiful!

JIM: They kind of remind me of—well, I thought they'd kind of suit you.

MARY: Here, pin them on, Jim. (*She hands him corsage.*) On my shoulder here. (*He tries to pin them on but is overcome with shyness.*)

JIM: I—I guess I'm kind of all thumbs.

ALICE: Here, I'll help. (*She fixes corsage.*) You look wonderful—both of you.

HENRY: You certainly do.

MARY: I—I guess we'd better go, Jim.

JIM: Yeah . . . My car's outside and I've got the top down. It's such a fine night—with the moon out.

MARY: The moon—oh, I simply love riding in the moonlight! (JIM *puts her coat around her shoulders.*) Good night, Mother and Dad.

JIM: Good night.

HENRY: Good night—have a good time. (MARY *and* JIM *go out right.*)

ALICE: Oh, Henry, they're simply walking on air.

HENRY: He'd scorched his pants, Alice—but we're not to tell Mary. Now he's wearing his father's with the buttons set over.

ALICE: Oh, for goodness' sakes. My, my—the troubles of the young.

HENRY: Alice, you—you mean you don't envy them?

ALICE: Why, of course I don't. I'm so glad we're over that stage, Henry. It's so hectic.

HENRY: And you like me just as I am—gray hair and all?

ALICE: Henry Richards, what are you getting at?

HENRY: I don't know. I just got the idea tonight that you found life in general and me in particular a bit dull or something. You kept talking about when you were young.

ALICE: Henry, you old goose. I was just worried about Mary. Why, I wouldn't go back to being that young for anything. You're up in the clouds one minute—and then—all of a sudden the moon falls from the sky. For us it doesn't do that, Henry. It just keeps right on shining.

HENRY: Alice. (*He kisses her.*) Just the same, perhaps we ought to go out more often, and you ought to get dolled up in something like that black dress.

ALICE: Oh, my—the dress. I forgot all about it. (*She goes to chair, takes dress out of box and holds it up to her.*)

HENRY: Alice, you couldn't have picked out anything that would suit you better.

ALICE: Picked out? Henry Richards, how did you know— (*Trying to cover up*) I mean—

HENRY: You *did* order it, didn't you?

ALICE: Nothing of the kind. That is—all I did was tell them to lay it away and I'd think about it. I saw it when we were buying Mary's dress, but I certainly didn't tell them to go ahead and send it out.

HENRY: Well, you just keep it, Alice.

ALICE: Keep? I was going to ask you about it, Henry—at some —well, opportune moment. It is rather expensive, you know—

HENRY: Never mind. (*He smiles at her.* JOHNNIE *enters left.*)

JOHNNIE: Well, I made some sandwiches but I don't know how good they'll be. All I could find was some jelly and a little cold salmon.

HENRY: Jelly? And cold salmon?

JOHNNIE: I guess they'll taste all right, if you're hungry.

HENRY: Alice, we're going out. Put on your new dress.

ALICE (*All smiles*): Henry.

HENRY: We'll go to that place on the Avenue where they have the soft lights and music.

ALICE: Henry, you old darling.

HENRY: I guess the younger generation aren't the only ones who can have Commencement. We'll commence with steak and onions and go on from there. Johnnie, back the car out of the garage for us.

JOHNNIE: O.K., Dad.

HENRY: And put the top down.

JOHNNIE: The top down? But Dad, you never—

HENRY: You heard me. Your mother and I want to look at the moon. (*Quick curtain*)

THE END

Production Notes

Characters: 4 male; 1 female.

Playing Time: 30 minutes.

Costumes: John, Anne, and Caretaker wear modern dress. Columbus wears a dark tunic with a cord at the waist and a cape thrown back from his shoulders, long tights, and low shoes with buckles. He has long white hair. Father Perez wears a dark brown robe and a small dark skull cap.

Properties: Large bunch of keys. See notes under "setting."

Setting: A room in a museum. It is a sixteenth-century interior done in the Spanish manner with stucco walls and beamed ceiling. There are entrances at right and left. In the center of the upstage wall is another opening with heavy oak doors opened wide. These doors are very old, scarred and cracked to indicate age. Through the doors can be seen an alcove with an old wooden cross placed standing in front of Spanish hangings, and wrought iron lanterns hanging above on either side. There is an entrance to the alcove from backstage, but it cannot be seen from the audience. At left of the alcove is a large painting of Columbus. At center of stage on a low table is a large, old-fashioned rusty anchor. Upstage from the entrance at left is a glass case containing historical relics which are mentioned in play, but need not be plainly seen from the audience. On the wall above the case hangs a picture of Columbus leaving the harbor at Palos. Downstage right against the wall is a low Spanish chest. On the walls there are old maps and other pictures depicting incidents in the life of Columbus.

Lighting: The play opens in full light. When John is left alone, the lights become very dim. The effect should be one of darkness, but enough light should remain to see the outline of the stage set. Just before Columbus and Father Perez appear dim lights appear in the Spanish lanterns in the alcove, and gradually the lights become brighter so that the two men may be seen clearly. When Anne returns calling John, the lantern lights become gradually dim and finally go out altogether. The lights go on full when Caretaker reappears.

Note: The anchor from the *Santa Maria*, the doors and the cross of La Rabida are to be found in the museum of the Chicago Historical Society, but for the purposes of this play it seemed best to make the setting any American museum.

HAPPY HAUNTS

Characters: 4 male; 3 female.
Playing Time: 30 minutes.
Costumes: Boy and Girl wear modern dress. The Ghosts wear long flowing costumes of grayish white. They have full sleeves, and hoods with holes cut out to see through. These hoods are attached at the back of the neck and may be put on and off easily.
Properties: Cigarette lighter, tank vacuum cleaner, jacket, bill, paper, cookbook, wallet, umbrella.
Setting: The living room of a new and modern house. There is an arched opening in the upstage wall at right leading to the hall and outside. Downstage at left is a door leading to the rest of the house. The walls are all plain gray, and jutting out from the right wall is a modern fireplace. The upstage end of the fireplace is an opening invisible to the audience and leading to offstage right. The wall extending from the arched doorway to the left wall has an invisible opening in it near stage center. This may be accomplished by making the wall in two sections, with the left portion set about a foot downstage from the right portion and overlapping about a foot. Against the left wall is a television set facing right, and upstage from

the television set a bookcase filled with books. At stage center is a sofa with small tables at either end of it. On the sofa is a newspaper and on the table at right a large cigarette lighter. Near the television set and fireplace are chairs to complete the furnishings. Over back of chair near fireplace is a brightly colored smoking jacket.
Lighting: The upstage lighting should not be too bright. If possible, the lighting should come from floor lamps which should be placed so that they do not obstruct the view of upstage center. In the wall near door left is an electrical outlet.

HOMETOWN HALLOWEEN

Characters: 2 male; 4 female.
Playing Time: 30 minutes.
Costumes: Modern dress. Sue and Mary wear jackets as they enter. Lucy wears skirt and blouse.
Properties: Tabloid-size school paper; paint brushes, man's hat, newspaper.
Setting: The Brown living room. There is an entrance in the rear wall at right leading to hall and front door, and an entrance at left leading to other parts of house. There is a sofa upstage center, and a telephone stand with a telephone on it upstage left. Easy chairs are placed at right and left with tables near them, and other articles of furniture, small chairs, lamps, bric-a-brac, etc. to make a comfortable living room.
Lighting: No special effects.

THE GREAT GIFT

Characters: 4 male; 1 female.

Playing Time: 35 minutes.

Costumes: Elsa wears a fine brocaded gown with a full skirt, tight at the wrists and the waist in the style of the time. Herr Gustav has a full beard and wears a dark velvet robe, girded at the waist, which hangs to the knees and is embroided in gold. He also wears buskins. Peter is dressed in a plain black robe. Herr Dietz wears a plain dark robe, buskins and a peaked hat. Hans is dressed in the plain doublet and buskins of the guildsman. He wears a peaked hat with a feather in it.

Properties: Leather bag for Hans, containing two large books, a piece of brass and a lead type, page of print.

Setting: The great hall. There are entrances at left and upstage in the rear wall at right. The one at left is a large massive door with a heavy bolt opening inward from the grounds and the garden. The one at right is smaller and leads to other parts of the house. In the right wall is a large fireplace with a stool and small table near it. There is a fur rug in front of the fireplace. On the upstage walls hangs a tapestry and below it are shelves containing a number of large old volumes which lie flat on the shelves. At stage center is a heavy trestle table with a bench in back of it. A pair of candlesticks with their candles are on the trestle table, and a single candlestick with candle on the small table near the fireplace.

Lighting: No special effects.

GHOSTS IN THE LIBRARY

Characters: 7 male; 6 female.

Playing Time: 30 minutes.

Costumes: Louise, Don, Mary, Freddie, Grandma and Grandpa wear everyday modern clothes. Sherlock Holmes wears a tweed suit and a cap and is smoking a calibash pipe. Becky Sharp is dressed in an attractive 19th-century costume. D'Artagnan wears a cloak, plumed hat, elaborate boots. From his waist hangs a jeweled scabbard and he holds a rapier in his right hand. David Copperfield wears tightly fitting trousers, a frock coat, and tall hat. Jo March wears a plain colored long dress, gathered at the waist. The Baseball Player wears a baseball suit, mask, chest protector, shin guards. The Career Girl wears a modern business suit.

Properties: Pad of paper, pencils, school books, sheet of paper, comic book, books, matches, candle snuffer.

Setting: The library of Grandpa and Grandma's house. There is a backdrop showing long rows of shelves filled with books. The walls right and left also have shelves of books. Near the left back wall there must be at least one real bookcase from which books may be taken. There is an entrance downstage right leading to other parts of the house and another entrance at left upstage which leads to an alcove off the library. This entrance has a pair of straight draperies hanging across it. There is a large table at center with chairs around it. A small portable radio is on the table. Two or three comfortable chairs are placed left and right. The one at the left has a small table near it. Hanging on the back wall above the bookcases are two brackets with candlesticks in which there are large, burnt-down old candles.

Lighting: No special effects except candle light for portion of play when book characters are on-stage.

A BOOK A DAY

Characters: 4 male; 4 female.
Playing Time: 30 minutes.
Costumes: Modern dress. Louise wears a short jacket when she enters. The professor wears glasses.
Properties: Electric trains, three books, folded note, magazine.
Setting: The Davis living room. There are exits at right and left, the one at right leading to the front door and the one at left to the dining room and kitchen. There are easy chairs at left and right, and a love seat upstage center. Other smaller chairs and small tables with lamps and knickknacks on them are placed around the room. Upstage left on the floor and only partially in view is an oval of train track with an electric train on it.
Lighting: No special effects.

VOICES OF AMERICA

Characters: 11 male; 3 female.
Playing Time: 30 minutes.
Costumes: Sue and Johnnie wear brightly-colored band uniforms. Jane wears the uniform of a Girl Scout, and Pete is dressed as a Boy Scout. Mary is dressed as a French girl. The soldier and Wave are dressed in regulation uniforms. The characters representing statues of historical figures are dressed appropriately to suggest the proper periods.
Properties: Sandwiches, fruit, cookies, hard-boiled eggs, and other food appropriate for a picnic. Paper plates.
Setting: A city park with a background of trees. There are entrances at left and right. There are eight statues in the park; George Washington at right, John Paul Jones at left, and between them across the stage are statues of General Custer, General Grant, General Lee, Captain James Lawrence, Admiral Dewey, and Commodore Perry.
Lighting: No special effects.

VOTE FOR UNCLE SAM

Characters: 6 male; 3 female; 10, both male and female.
Playing Time: 25 minutes.
Costumes: Uncle Sam wears the traditional red, white and blue costume. Mr. World may wear ordinary trousers and a shirt, but his head, arms and legs protrude from a sphere with a brightly outlined map of the world on it.

432 PRODUCTION NOTES

(The sphere may be made by stretching paper, cardboard or cloth over a wire frame.) Miss Liberty wears a flowing white dress, and a seven-point band on her head. Miss Justice wears the black robe of a judge and carries a gavel. The citizens wear everyday clothing.

Properties: Knitting and magazine for Mrs. Too Busy, gavel for Miss Justice.

Setting: Uncle Sam's office. In the rear wall at right and left are doors. On the door at right is a sign, "Office of Miss Justice," and on the door at left, a sign, "Office of Miss Liberty." Between the doors on the wall hangs a large map of the United States. In the right wall downstage is a door to the outside. Upstage center is a large desk facing downstage, and back of it a high-backed chair. On the desk is a sign, "Office of Uncle Sam." A telephone, books, papers, etc., are also on the desk. Along the left and right walls are rows of straight-backed chairs.

Lighting: No special effects.

OUR FAMOUS ANCESTORS

Characters: 2 male; 3 female.
Playing Time: 30 minutes.
Costumes: Modern dress. Amy wears an apron over her dress. Aunt Hattie wears a rather old-fashioned but queenly hat, a cape, and glasses hanging from a ribbon on her dress. She carries an umbrella. Dick wears slacks and a sports jacket. Jane wears a skirt and jacket.

Properties: Dish towel, glass, Pilgrim place cards, handkerchief, ornate silver candlesticks, plate, silverware, black bag, umbrella, wedding picture, jar of relish, medal.

Setting: George and Amy Peabody's combination living and dining room. There are entrances at right and left, the right entrance leading outside, and the left to the kitchen. Upstage from right entrance is a window looking onto the yard and street. There is a dinette table against the back wall at center, attractively set for two—a place at either end—for Thanksgiving dinner. There is a chair at each end of the table. Dishes of fruit and jelly are placed on table, along with plain glass candlesticks with candles, water glasses of milk glass, place cards, and flowers. Downstage left is an easy chair, next to a small table and lamp, and upstage right another easy chair. At extreme downstage right there is an arm chair, and a table near it with a telephone on it. Against the rear wall at right is a small table with a radio, and against the left wall a small chest with drawers. On the chest is a silver dish with fruit and a framed wedding picture.

Lighting: No special effects.

SURPRISE GUESTS

Characters: 5 male; 5 female.
Playing Time: 30 minutes.
Costumes: Modern clothes of the type worn on Sundays and holi-

days. Mother wears apron over her dress at first.

Properties: Place cards, pen, newspaper, small table, bottle of milk, cigars.

Setting: The living room of the Webster family. Downstage right a doorway leads to the hall and outside, and midway upstage in the left wall wide double doors lead to the dining room and the rest of the house. At center upstage is a sofa and upstage from door at right is a small table with a straight chair near it. There are comfortable chairs downstage right and left, and any other pieces which may be needed to furnish the stage suitably.

Lighting: No special effects.

TURKEY GOBBLERS

Characters: 3 male; 4 female; 1 male radio voice.

Playing Time: 30 minutes.

Costumes: Modern dress. Mother wears an apron over her dress at first.

Properties: Box of candy, dropleaf table, plates, silver, glasses, pitcher of milk, silver bowl with dry cereal, several straight chairs, bowl of grapes, cardboard box tied with ribbon, flowers, platter of grated cabbage, serving spoons.

Setting: The Baldwin living room. It is homey and comfortable. There are entrances at right and left, the one at right leading to the front door and the one at left to the dining room, kitchen and other parts of the house. There is a sofa upstage center with a small table at each end of it. On one small table is a telephone and on the other a radio. There are two or three easy chairs placed around the room with tables near them. On one of these tables is a large box of candy and on another a vase. There are a few lamps on the tables and some straight chairs against the wall.

Lighting: No special effects. Light may be provided by lamps near chairs or on the tables.

A QUIET CHRISTMAS

Characters: 4 male; 5 female; male voice.

Playing Time: 30 minutes.

Costumes: Modern dress. Bill and Johnnie wear warm jackets when they enter; underneath they have on slacks and T shirts. Phil, Ruth and Irene wear coats and hats when they enter. Marie wears a beret and coat. When Hetty returns from the movies, she wears a coat and a scarf around her head, and when she goes out again she has on a fancy hat.

Properties: Newspaper, magazine, Christmas cards, axe, two checks, two zipper bags, bundles of holly, packages (some wrapped in Christmas paper, some wrapped in brown paper with stamps, and six wrapped in the same kind of Christmas paper), doll wrapped in blanket for baby, three suitcases, several men's and women's stockings, thumb tacks, cardboard cartons containing tinsel, tree ornaments and angel, Christmas tree stand, Christmas tree, large paper wrapped package for Hetty, tin horn, small stepladder, mistletoe, Christmas tree lights, long sheet of paper, pencil.

Setting: The Evans living room. It is comfortably furnished, but looks somewhat formal at rise because everything is very much in its place. The exit at right leads to the front door, the one at left to the rest of the house. There is a fireplace in the rear wall at center, with a mantel above it and a large picture over the mantel. There are comfortable chairs at right and left of fireplace with small tables near them. On the small table at right is a radio. Upstage right is a desk with drawers. The bottom drawer is a double one with letter files in it. There is a telephone on the desk. Bookcases are on either side of the fireplace, and other chairs, tables and lamps complete the furnishings.

Lighting: No special effects.

THE STAR IN THE WINDOW

Characters: 4 male; 3 female.

Playing Time: 30 minutes.

Costumes: Modern dress. Otto wears trousers and shirt. Mama wears a large apron over her dress. Mrs. Flanagan and Mr. Baker are rather shabbily dressed, and the Woman is very well-dressed. Mr. Jones wears a black coat and a homberg hat, and carries gloves and a cane.

Properties: Spectacles for Otto, book, purse for Mrs. Flanagan, money (both coins and bills), wallet with money for Mr. Jones, cloth.

Setting: A small neighborhood shop in a large city. The shop is decorated for Christmas with strings of evergreen, holly, paper Christmas bells, etc. There is a door downstage right which opens from the street. It bumps into a small hanging bell each time it opens and closes. Along the right wall, upstage from the door, is the show window, but all that can be seen from the inside of the shop are neutral-colored curtains which hang all around it on rods which are about six feet from the floor. In the center of the left wall is a door leading into living quarters back of the store. In front of the door and parallel with the left wall is a counter short enough so that there is space to walk around it from either end. On the counter are a small old-fashioned cash register, some boxes of candy and other small items for sale, and at the upstage end, a telephone. At the downstage end is a small radio. The cord from the radio hangs down over the end of the counter. The upstage wall is covered by shelves stacked with books and other merchandise. At the right end on high shelves are mirrors, one of which is tilted so that it slants toward the window. Downstage from the shelves is a table loaded with lights, tinsel, stars, and other Christmas items. Small Christmas trees are stacked around the shop. At the upstage end of the counter near the books is an old rocking chair.

Lighting: Otto turns off all onstage lights as indicated in text. Light should come from offstage left and right. A spotlight used from offstage right would make the light look more like a ray of light from a street lamp. If possible, there should be a plug near the back of the counter where Otto can plug in the Christmas lights to test them.

CHRISTMAS SHOPPING EARLY

Characters: 3 male; 3 female; male and female extras.
Playing Time: 35 minutes.
Costumes: Everyday modern dress.
Properties: Paper and pencil for Bob; stack of wrapped presents; dress for Ruth; pile of presents with wrappings bedraggled and torn; bag containing wrapping paper, cords, seals, etc.; big cardboard box containing wrapped presents; dusty carton containing wrapped presents; packages for Bob; step-ladder; coins.
Setting: A modern American living room. A door at downstage right leads to the front hall and a door downstage left leads to other parts of the house. Upstage from the door at right is a window looking out on the street. There is a large, brightly decorated Christmas tree at upstage center. (There must be some gold balls used as tree decorations.) A sofa is placed diagonally at right with a table at its upstage end. On the table is a telephone. Upstage against the rear wall at left is a bookcase. On the second shelf is a set of books all having the same binding. Behind these books are hidden some flat packages, wrapped with Christmas paper. There are chairs at left and right. Tables and lamps complete the furnishings.
Lighting: No special effects.

LIVING UP TO LINCOLN

Characters: 4 male; 3 female.
Playing Time: 25 minutes.
Costumes: Everyday modern dress. The Young Man and his wife are wearing winter coats.
Properties: Newspaper, pail of water and a squeegee, two or three pairs of curtains, large book, bucket and mop, large baby doll to be used as a baby, two cups of coffee and a plate of rolls, bills, cloth, change and one penny.
Setting: The Carter dining room. There is an entrance to the living room at right and an entrance to kitchen and other parts of the house at left. There is a table at center stage with five chairs around it. A couple of other chairs stand upstage at left and right and there is a buffet with some silver or candlesticks on it centered against the back wall. The table is set for five—cups, saucers, silver, egg cups, etc., and there is some food in evidence.
Lighting: No special effects.

THE LINCOLN UMBRELLA

Characters: 4 male; 4 female.
Playing Time: 25 minutes.

Costumes: Modern dress.
Properties: Scene 1: Books, large black umbrella. Scene 2: Papers, photographs, speaker's stand, chairs.
Setting: Scene 1: The sidewalk in front of a public school. This may be played before a curtain depicting the front of the school with entrance at center. Scene 2: The stage of an assembly hall in a school. The stage faces towards the audience. At right center is a table with old papers and photographs on it.
Lighting: No special effects.

HAPPY HEARTS

Characters: 3 male; 3 female.
Playing Time: 30 minutes.
Costumes: Modern dress. Ruth and Professor Stafford wear hats and coats when they enter.
Properties: Magazine, red paper, hearts, paste, scissors, packages, handkerchief, brown paper bag, odd-shaped package, long white box, dark red tie with white design, paints, crayons, brief case, file cards, papers, tooth brush, heart-shaped box of candy, square box of candy, bill, greeting cards in paper bag, pen, gift wrapping, valentines.
Setting: The living room of Professor Stafford's home. There are entrances at right and left, the one at right leading to the front hall and the one at left to other parts of house. The room is comfortably furnished with easy chairs at left and right with small tables near them. There is a table or desk against the right wall with a drawer large enough to hold two boxes of candy. A card table is set upstage left with two straight chairs in back of it. On the card table is a box of materials with which to make valentines; scissors, paste, etc.; lamps; pictures; books.

A CHANGE OF HEARTS

Characters: 5 male; 5 female.
Playing Time: 30 minutes.
Costume: Modern dress. Mr. Jenkins may wear a white jacket.
Properties: Scene 1: Papers, pencil and wallet with bill for Mr. Bowman; textbooks and valentine in envelope for Johnnie. Scene 2: Valentine in envelope for Miss Travers; valentines for Sue and Dorothy; dust cloth and wrapping paper for Mr. Jenkins; money for Bill and Charlie; two sundaes and three glasses of Coca-Cola; large heart-shaped candy box with a five-dollar price tag on it.
Setting: Scene 1: The principal's office of Plainview High School. This scene may be played before the curtain. There is a desk at right facing left. On the desk are papers, books, and a telephone, and behind it is a chair. There are a couple of classroom chairs with one wide arm for writing space against the backdrop near the desk. Scene 2: Jenkins Sweet Shoppe. There is an entrance at right from the street. At left, parallel with the left wall, is a candy counter and soda fountain.

Downstage is a candy counter with a glass front. On top of the counter are several valentine boxes of candy, and one extra-large heart shaped box with a five dollar tag on it is displayed on a wire rack. Upstage from the candy counter is a plain counter with a few glasses on it behind which may be imagined a soda fountain. There is also a cash register on the counter. At stage center and at right are two or three tables with chairs around them.

Lighting: No special effects.

A DATE WITH WASHINGTON

Characters: 3 male; 2 female.
Playing Time: 30 minutes.
Costumes: Modern dress. Bruce and Junior wear jackets when they enter.
Properties: Party dress; newspaper; hockey stick and skates for Junior; textbook and magazine for Mary; hockey stick and three bills for Bruce.
Setting: The Henderson living room. There is an entrance at left that leads to the front door and an entrance at right that leads to other parts of the house. There is a sofa against the upstage wall at center, and downstage from the sofa at left and right are easy chairs with small tables beside them. On the small table at right are some magazines and a large textbook and on the small table at left is a newspaper. There are attractive lamps here and there and any other pieces

may be used that are needed to furnish the room comfortably.
Lighting: No special effects.

THANKS TO GEORGE WASHINGTON

Characters: 4 male; 3 female.
Playing Time: 30 minutes.
Costumes: Modern dress. When characters enter from outside, they wear hats and coats or jackets. Mary's dress should have a pocket.
Properties: Battered metal tackle box, large bakery package, small desk, bill, wallet, two pieces of paper.
Setting: The living room of the Rogers home. The entrance at right opens onto the front porch, the one at left to other parts of the house. There is a window in the right wall upstage from the door. Upstage center is a sofa with small tables at either end. On one of the tables is a large book. Downstage left and right are easy chairs, and near them are small tables with lamps. In the upstage corners of the room stand old, rickety, straight-backed chairs. There is a mirror on the left wall.
Lighting: No special effects.

THE EASTER HOP

Characters: 4 male; 3 female; male radio voice.
Playing Time: 30 minutes.
Costumes: Modern dress. Sally wears a skirt and sweater when she first enters, and blue evening gown later. Bob and Spike wear

slacks and jacket, and Don wears regular tweed suit.

Properties: Needle, thread, blue evening dress, eggs, paints, beads, feathers, paint brush, crepe paper, glass of water, newspaper, belt for blue dress, two real or artificial orchids and one white carnation, one Easter egg very fancily decorated, two cardboard flower boxes, small grip, new man's hat.

Setting: The Carter living room. There are entrances downstage right and left, the right one leading to the hall and front door and the left to other parts of the house. Downstage right and left there are easy chairs, and upstage right a large wing chair facing left. A card table is set upstage left with a chair in back of it. Near the rear wall at left is a radio, and near left entrance a small table with a telephone on it. Other small chairs, tables. and lamps complete the furnishings.

Lighting: No special effects.

THE LIFE FOR MOTHER

Characters: 3 male; 3 female.
Playing Time: 30 minutes.
Costumes: Modern dress.
Properties: Newspaper, ball, handkerchief, broom, dustcloth, small stepladder, screw driver, knitting, bedroom slippers, bottle of perfume wrapped in paper, pencil, paper.
Setting: The living room of the Neuhauser home. Upstage right is a large window with drapes hung on either side of it. One curtain rod supports the drapes.

Upstage center is a small desk with a knitting bag on it. Near the desk is a chair with a coat thrown on it. Downstage right is a large chair with a new slip cover, and near the chair is a small table with a lamp on it. Other chairs and tables are placed about the room. The exit at right leads to the front door, the exit at left to the rest of the house.

Lighting: No special effects.

MOM'S A GRANDMA NOW

Characters: 4 male; 3 female.
Playing Time: 30 minutes.
Costumes: Modern dress.
Properties: Paper bags with boxes inside them (one box has a bottle of perfume, the other, stockings), small card with clip-on earrings attached to it, envelope with card inside, cookies, note, magazine, package with a pink bed jacket, dark old-fashioned shawl, small old-fashioned rocking chair, knitting bag, large paper bag with perky hat in it.
Setting: A living room. There are exits down stage at right and left; the one at right leads to the front door and the one at left to the rest of the house. The room is comfortably furnished with easy chairs at right and left, and tables and lamps near them. On one table are a few magazines. There is a desk with drawers in it upstage at right, and a telephone is on the desk. A mirror hangs on the upstage center wall.
Lighting: No special effects.

See the Parade

Characters: 5 male; 2 female.
Playing Time: 20 minutes.
Costumes: Mother is dressed in modern street dress. Johnnie wears a Boy Scout uniform. Father wears the uniform of World War I, Grandpa, the uniform of the Spanish American War, Charlie, the uniform of World War II. Doris wears a white satin costume with a short ballet skirt, shiny boots and a high visored hat with a plume. Ralph wears a modern suit.
Properties: Small clothes brush, baton, cane for Charlie.
Setting: An American living room. There are entrances at right and left, the one at right leading onto the front porch, and the one at left to other parts of the house. There is a window in the right wall upstage from the door which looks out onto the yard and the street. The room is comfortably furnished. There is a sofa upstage center. There are a couple of easy chairs, some straight-backed ones, small tables with lamps and perhaps a bookcase or two.
Lighting: No special effects.

The Moon Keeps Shining

Characters: 3 male; 2 female.
Playing Time: 30 minutes.
Costumes: Modern dress. When Mary first enters she wears a flannel wrapper and scuffies. Later she enters in her pink evening dress, carrying a light coat. Jim has on white flannels and a blue coat.
Properties: Newspaper, sandwiches, glass of milk, two large cardboard boxes, one containing a black evening dress with gold sequins, the other a pink evening dress, a small white box with a corsage of roses in it.
Setting: A comfortable living room. There are entrances at right and left, the one at right leading to the reception hall and front door and the one at left to other parts of the house. In the right wall upstage from the entrance is a window. There is a sofa upstage center flanked by end tables, and a small table with a telephone on it against the left wall, upstage from the entrance. There are chairs at left and right and occasional tables and chairs as well as lamps and pictures complete the furnishings of the room.
Lighting: No special effects.